The Last Forest

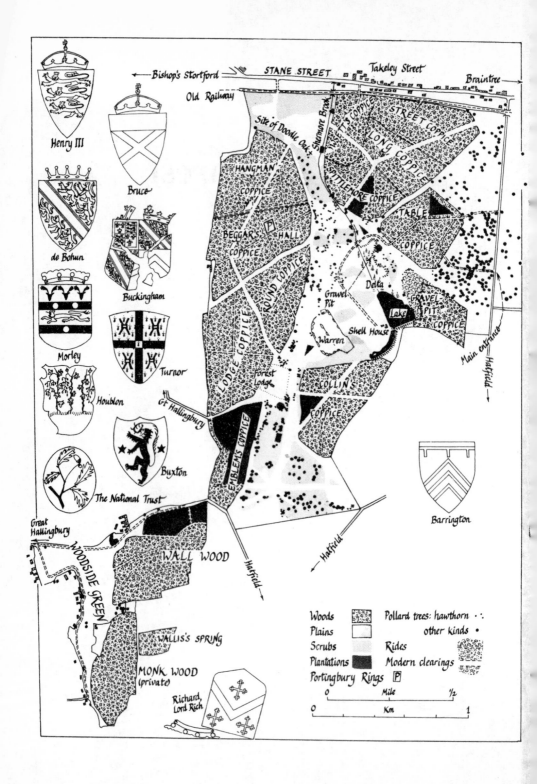

Henry III

Bruce

de Bohun

Buckingham

Morley

Turnor

Houblon

Buxton

The National Trust

Great Hallingbury

Bishop's Stortford ← → STANE STREET → Takeley Street → Braintree →

Old Railway

Site of Doodle Oak

Shermore Brook

HANGMAN COPPICE

BEGGAR'S HALL COPPICE

ROUND COPPICE

LODGE COPPICE

EMBLEM'S COPPICE

Gt Hallingbury

Forest Lodge

Warren

Shell House

Gravel Pit

Delta

Lake

COLLIN'S COPPICE

LONG COPPICE

STREET COPPICE

SPITTLEMORE COPPICE

TABLE COPPICE

GRAVEL PIT COPPICE

Main entrance

Hatfield →

Hatfield →

Hatfield →

Barrington

Great Hallingbury

WOODSIDE GREEN

WALL WOOD

WALLIS'S SPRING

MONK WOOD (private)

Richard, Lord Rich

Woods
Plains
Scrubs
Plantations
Portingbury Rings 🅿

Pollard trees: hawthorn
    other kinds
Rides
Modern clearings

0   Mile   ½
0   Km   1

The Last Forest

The Story of Hatfield Forest

Oliver Rackham

J. M. Dent
London

First published 1989
First paperback edition 1993
© Oliver Rackham 1989

This book is set in 11/13pt Linotron Times

Printed and bound in Great Britain at The Bath Press, Avon

for J. M. Dent Ltd
The Orion Publishing Group
Orion House, 5 Upper St. Martin's Lane, London WC2H 9EA

British Library Cataloguing in Publication Data

Rackham, Oliver
     The last forest : the story of Hatfield Forest.
     1. Essex. Hatfield Forest, to 1988
     I. Title
     942.6'712

ISBN 0-460-86089-5

Contents

List of Plates

List of Text-figures

Preface

Why write yet another book on Forests? There are, for a start, two versions of Forest history: one cannot be true, but the other may be. Forests are one of the most prolific fields of pseudo-history – a consistent, logical, accepted corpus of statements, copied from writer to writer down the centuries. We still read, for example, that Forests necessarily have to do with trees; that medieval England was very wooded; that the king's hunting was protected by savage laws and extreme punishments; that trees disappeared because people cut them down to build ships; that trees can only be regained by planting them; and that the Forestry Commission is heir to the ancient Forest administration. The story reads well and makes excellent sense, but has no connection with the real world; it cannot be sustained from the records of any actual Forest or wood.

If we leave aside this rival (and more popular) version, there remain many scholarly books and articles on English Forests in general, or on particular Forests. Most of these deal with only one or two aspects: legal history, common-rights, vegetation, grazing animals, etc. With few exceptions, they read like *Hamlet* with only the Prince of Denmark.

The English Forests were perhaps the most complex example in Europe of a 'cultural landscape' – formed by many-sided interactions, over the centuries, of human institutions and land management with the natural environment and with the behaviour of deer, domestic livestock, and wild plants and animals. Forests have been in decline for seven centuries, and most of what outlasted the middle ages was destroyed in the last century. Often the documents survive, though rarely enough to give a balanced picture of even the human interests in a Forest; but Forests themselves are destroyed, reduced to non-functioning fragments, or transformed so that little but the name survives. Disappointingly little remains in the Forest of Dean, or Alice Holt (Hants), or Salcey Forest (Northants). Except in Dartmoor Forest, Epping Forest and the New Forest, themselves altered from their medieval state, we can only conjecture in a general kind of way how the plants and animals interacted with each other and with the lords of creation.

If in this book I try to draw a more complete portrait of a Forest, it is luck rather than judgement that allows me to do so. Colin Ranson and George Peterken, of the Nature Conservancy, introduced me in November 1971 to the one Forest that is not fragmentary or altered, but is still almost complete and in working order. We can explore the *meaning* of Hatfield Forest, not as just a human interest, but also from the points of view of the plants, trees, deer and cattle. The written records also are particularly complete. In other Forests the story has often been told from the point of view of the king, less often from that of the 'peasants', but only with difficulty from that of the landowners. At Hatfield, exceptionally, all three human interests are documented, and the record runs almost throughout the nine centuries of the Forest's existence. The Forest was not in isolation: it was an unusual feature, set in an ordinary Essex landscape, and played some part in the lives of several hundred people. It still continues a tradition of land management which branches through European history right back to the ancient Cretans.

Hatfield and its surroundings turned out to be rich in archaeology. This extends the record back long before Hatfield was declared a Forest. It also fills out the written record from the eleventh century to the 1950s. Here, as in all landscapes I have known however well documented, fieldwork reveals complexities not apparent from the writings.

The Forest was an early acquisition of the National Trust. After 64 years it has much to tell us about the general problems of conserving complex ecosystems. The Trust (and their predecessors the Houblon family) have, in the main, done an excellent job of holding together the fabric of the Forest. If at times I am critical, I by no means disparage the long hours of service given by the Management Committee, the Trust's advisers and the Friends of Hatfield Forest. But knowledge and understanding change over the years, and it is hardly likely that everything done over seven decades will meet the standards of conservation of 1988. The Forest has always been a place of dispute, and continues to be so. Conservation in future depends on learning from the mistakes, even more than the successes, of the past. Hatfield warns us that in conservation, as in most human endeavours, changing fashions are easily confused with genuine advances in knowledge.

Hatfield Forest has now become a major place of public resort, which it was never intended to be. This places a great strain, not only on its management, but also on the National Trust's conservation philosophy. In principle, conservation must take precedence over public access; but how is that precedence to be sustained in face of a gradual increase that never gives rise to a decisive conflict? The writing of this book happens to coincide with the preparation of a new management plan, based on more complete knowledge of the Forest and what is worth conserving in it, but also on greater apprehension about developments outside.

Acknowledgements   This work forms part of studies of the woods of Eastern England, commissioned and financed by the Natural Environment Research Council and the Nature Conservancy Council, and done with the help of Cambridge University Botany School and Corpus Christi College, Cambridge.

In the Forest I am most grateful for the generous help given me by Lawrence Sisitka, the present Warden, and his predecessor Nigel Hester. Captain C.G.E.Barclay and Mr John Fielding, who have known and loved the Forest much longer than myself, put their accumulated knowledge at my disposal. I have had much help from John Workman and Mel Waterston of the National Trust. Rob Jarman and Keith Alexander, ecological advisers to the Trust, have spent many hours helping with the recent history of the Forest and its wildlife. The map of pollards (Frontispiece) is based on the work of Harry Lamb. My thanks are due to the Archivist and staff of Essex County Council for making the bulk of the Forest records available to me. Mrs Aline Puxley, of Welford Park, most kindly and hospitably allowed me the run of the Houblon family papers. Harold Whitehouse and Ken Adams let me have all the bryophyte records from the Forest, and Francis Rose and J.F.Skinner did so with the lichens. Mr and Mrs M.W.Oliver, Mr John Preen and Mrs K.R.Stanbrook welcomed me into their historic houses and encour-

aged me to measure and climb. Information about other buildings
and antiquities came from John Cherry (of the British Museum),
John Hunter, John McCann, Deborah Riddy and David Stenning.

Dr Keith Kirby, Mrs J.Evans, Dr Jarman and Messrs Fielding
and Sisitka kindly read and commented on the text.

Colin and Susan Ranson have made this book possible by their
continual encouragement and help with the fieldwork; Mrs Ranson
did much of the transcribing of documents.

The opinions expressed are mine, and are not necessarily those
of the National Trust or of any of the people mentioned. Translations
are mine unless otherwise stated.

English measures

1 inch	= 25 mm	
1 foot = 12 in.	= 0.30 m	
1 yard = 3 ft	= 0.91 m	
1 perch (unless otherwise stated)	= 16½ ft	= 5.0 m
1 mile = 1760 yards	= 1.6 km	
1 modern acre	= 4840 square yards	= 0.40 ha
1000 modern acres		= 4.0 km²
1 cubic foot		= 0.028 m²
1 load of timber	= 40 **or** 50 cu.ft (the arithmetic tells you which)	

1 penny (*d.*)		= £0.0042
1 shilling (*s.*)	= 12*d*.	= $\frac{1}{20}$ £
1 guinea	= 21*s*.	= £1.05

The acre is a rectangle of 40 by 4 perches. The modern acre is
measured with a perch of 16½ feet (5.0 m). In the past, acres have
often been measured with perches of other lengths. A 21-ft perch
gives an acre 62% bigger than the modern acre. 1 rood = ¼ acre;
1 (square) perch = $\frac{1}{160}$ acre.

The medieval penny must be thought of as something like sixpence
in the money of the seventeenth century, a shilling in the mid-nineteenth, and well over £1 in 1988.

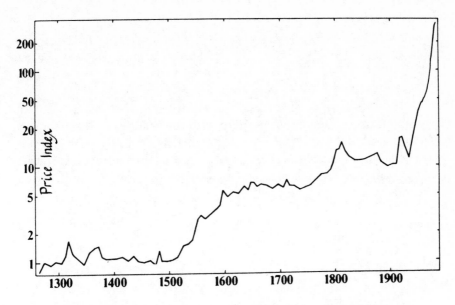

Fig. 1 The value of money, 1264–1984. Index of retail prices, on a logarithmic scale; the base year (index = 1.00) is 1450. Mainly after E. H. Brown and S. V. Hopkins.[1]

1 Introduction

Hatfield is of supreme interest in that *all* the elements of a medieval Forest
survive: deer, cattle, coppice woods, pollards, scrub, timber trees, grassland
and fen, plus a seventeenth-century lodge and rabbit warren. As such it
is almost certainly unique in England and possibly in the world. ... The
Forest owes very little to the last 250 years. ... Hatfield is the only place
where one can step back into the Middle Ages to see, with only a small
effort of the imagination, what a Forest looked like in use.

O. Rackham, *Trees and woodland in the British landscape*, 1976
[The warren and lodge turn out to have meanings which I did not then suspect]

Hatfield Forest lies three miles east of Bishop's Stortford and a mile
south of Stansted Airport, in the parish of Hatfield Broad-oak, Essex
(Fig. 2). It has nothing to do with Hatfield (Hertfordshire) or with
Hatfield Chase (West Riding). It belongs to the National Trust and
may normally be visited at any time.

The Forest (Frontispiece) is one-and-a-half square miles of wild
landscape, part woodland, part grassland with scattered great trees
and thickets. It is best seen from the east, rising above the Pincey
Brook. It covers high ground, with flat wooded hilltops and shallow
marshy valleys. It is bisected by the Shermore Brook, dammed to
form a lake.

This part of Essex has a harsh climate, with frosty winters and
hot summers; its storms are ferocious. The Forest lies on clayey
soils, and is very wet despite the low rainfall.

What is a Forest?

The modern meaning of *forest* is a place of trees, and especially
a place of *planted* trees. Hatfield Forest, like Epping Forest and

1

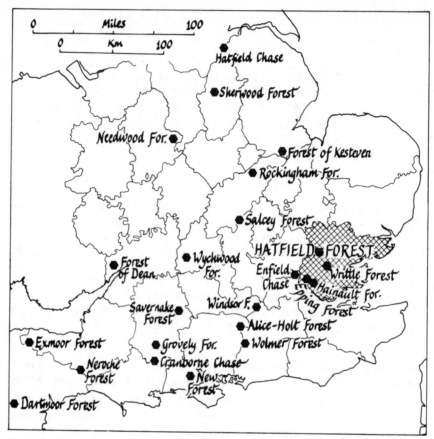

Fig. 2 The location of Hatfield Forest, and of other Forests mentioned in this book. The hatched area is the county of Essex. There were many other medieval Forests besides those shown.

Dartmoor Forest, was so called long before the word had this connection. It then implied not trees but deer. *A Forest was an area of roughland on which the king or some other magnate had the right to keep deer and to kill and eat them.* Throughout this book I use the word in this sense of a royal Forest, and spell it with a capital F to avoid confusion with the modern meaning.

The idea of Forests is not aboriginal but was brought to England by William the Conqueror; the New Forest was one of his earliest. The making of each Forest was a definite action – it usually involved introducing deer – which at Hatfield can be dated to within ten years of 1100. It did not normally disturb people's existing uses of the land, to which the king's deer were merely added. Most Forests were not the absolute property of the king, but also had landowners and people with common-rights.

Some Forests, like Epping Forest, were wooded; others, like Dartmoor Forest, were something else such as moorland. The system grew until the time of King John. By 1215 Hatfield was one of about 143 Forests in England, about eighty of which were wooded (that is, more wooded than their surroundings).[2]

In this book I explore the ways in which woods in Forests differed from those woods (the majority) which lay outside the Forest system.

Coppices and Plains

Hatfield was a wooded Forest, but it was not *all* woodland. It was, and still is, divided into *coppices* and *plains** (Frontispiece, Fig. 3). The coppices are definite woods of between 26 and 60 acres, each surrounded by an earthwork called a *woodbank*. There were seventeen coppices, of which eleven survive; they now comprise a little over half the area of the Forest (Table 1).

The plains are grassland; they are grazed by cattle and deer, and formerly by sheep, goats, horses and geese. They are set with ancient oaks, maples, hornbeams, ashes and hawthorns. Tongues of plain penetrate between some of the coppices. Here and there in the plains, and forming part of them, are *scrubs*, thickets of hawthorn and young trees with ancient trees embedded in them. Although there have long been scrubs in the Forest, they are not individually ancient, nor are they defined by woodbanks.

Also in the plains are the Warren – a term which implies the husbandry of rabbits as Forest does that of deer – and two buildings, Forest Lodge and Warren Cottage.

The shape of the Forest and its boundary houses   A Forest (like any large common) should have a distinctive shape – a complex,

---

* Some modern writers call the plains *chases*. This usage dates back about a hundred years, and is probably a misunderstanding of the Essex word 'chase', a lane between woods. The tongues of plain between, say, Lodge and Emblem's Coppices might properly be termed chases, although I have never found them so called.

Table 1 Area of Hatfield Forest, its coppices and plains, and of Woodside Green and its woods

	Acres in 1988	Acres before enclosure in 1857	Acres in 1720
Coppices:			
1. Dowsett's (Hampton's)	26.5	27.0	27.0
2. Street (Parsley's)	45.0	45.0	45.0
3. Long	29.8	29.8	29.8
4. Spittlemore	30.5	30.5	30.5
5. Table (Elgin's)	40.5	40.5	40.5
6. Gravel-pit	18.7	29.1	29.1
7. Warren (Cottage)	—	34.8	35.5
8. Collin's (Gray's)	51.9	51.9	51.9
9. Emblem's	34.7[a]	34.7	34.7
10. Lodge	59.9	59.9	59.9
11. Round	40.7	40.7	40.7
12. Beggar's Hall	58.1	58.1	58.1
13. Hangman's (Northwood)	50.9	50.9	50.9
14. Doodle-Oak	—	24.7	24.7
15. Low-Street	—	—	39.7
16. Middle	—	—	34.7
17. Bush-End	—	—	46.8
Total coppices	**487.1**	**557.6**	**680**
Plains	**422.3**	**541.1**	**435**
Lake	**8.0**	**10.0**	**—**
Total area of Forest	**917.5**	**1108.7**	**1115**
Wall Wood	62.4	62.4	62.4
Monk Wood[b]	35.3	35.3	35.3
Wallis's Spring[b]	7.9	7.9	7.9
Woodside Green[c]	65.7	65.7	65.7
Total National Trust area	**1045.6**		

[a] Now mostly plantation.
[b] Not National Trust; private woodland traditionally associated with the Forest.
[c] 45.6 acres in Great Hallingbury, 20.1 acres in Little Hallingbury.

All areas are given in terms of the modern acreage of the plots, derived where possible from the second edition 25-inch Ordnance Survey, or, failing this, from the Hatfield Tithe Map of 1838.

concave outline, funnelling out into 'horns' where roads enter it. At intervals round the perimeter there should be *boundary houses*, farmsteads which front on to the Forest (on which their occupiers had the right to graze livestock) and back on to their own private fields. Hatfield was like this (Fig. 3) until the Enclosure Act of 1857 which abolished the social order of the Forest. The Forest then lost most of its fringes and was reduced to an un-Forest-like shape. To the east and south it is bounded by straight roads of that date, and to the north by an old railway.

The boundary houses still stand as ghosts of the former outline of the Forest. Many of the buildings or their sites date from the middle ages. They disprove popular theories that the Forest was once much larger than it is now and joined up to Epping Forest.

Purlieu woods and Woodside Green   Wall Wood and Monk Wood, to the south-west of the Forest, are not part of it, but were anciently associated with it and in theory came under some of the Forest regulations. They adjoin Woodside Green, which looks like an extension of the Forest plains. Like other Essex greens, this is very irregular in shape and has houses abutting on it like the boundary-houses of a Forest. It once had pollard trees on it, a few of which still survive. Wall Wood and Woodside Green belong to the National Trust; Monk Wood (with its satellite Wallis's Spring) is private.

Trees, Woods, Beasts and Men

Native and introduced animals and plants   Some species of wildlife are *native*: they arrived in England by natural processes in prehistoric times. These include most of the familiar animals and plants of the Forest: for instance hornbeam, maple, oak, cowslip, fox, hare.

Other creatures were originally brought by human agency from overseas, but have become wildlife and maintain themselves without further intervention. These are termed *naturalized*. The Normans introduced the pheasant, rabbit and fallow deer, all of which have influenced the Forest. Later the sycamore became naturalized, and recently the grey squirrel and Canada goose.

Exotic species are those introduced from overseas (or from a distant part of Britain) which do not maintain themselves. In Hatfield

5

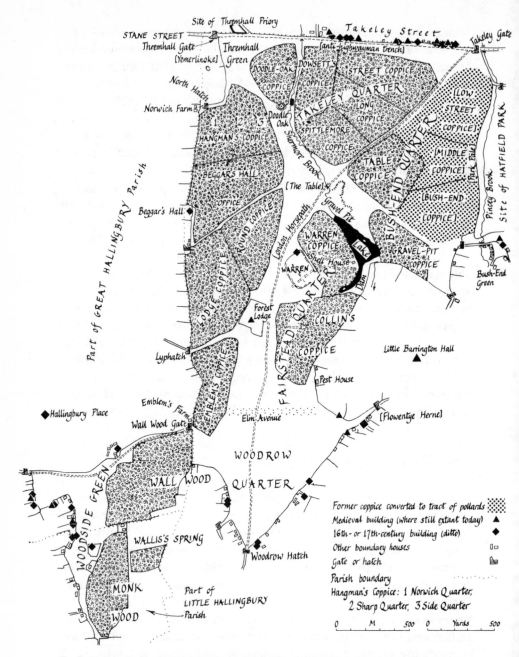

Fig. 3 Topography of Hatfield Forest as it was up to 1857, with the traditional names of quarters, coppices and other features. Scrubs existed but their extent is not known. Woodside Green and the purlieu woods are included.

6

Forest these are all trees: for example horsechestnut, black pine, and London plane, all of which were put here by the Victorians and will eventually die out unless deliberately replaced. Sweet-chestnut is in this category here, although elsewhere in Essex it is an ancient introduction and is naturalized.

Trees and men Throughout history, and long before written history, trees have been part of our cultural landscape and have been used and managed. There are five traditional ways (apart from orchards) in which trees interact with human activities:

1. *Woodland* Woods are land on which trees have arisen naturally. They are managed by the art of *woodmanship* to yield crops of produce in a perpetual succession. When cut down the trees replace themselves by natural regrowth. This has been the normal practice, from at least the middle ages onwards, in thousands of woods all over England; I have described Essex examples in my book on South-East Essex. Wall and Monk Woods belong to this tradition.

2. *Wood-pasture* This land-use involves grazing animals as well as trees. There is a conflict, in that the shade of the trees spoils the pasture and the livestock eat the regrowth of the trees. This book is concerned with the special techniques for reconciling them in places such as Hatfield Forest, where trees and livestock could not be separated.

3. *Non-woodland:* trees in hedgerow and field. They do not concern us directly, although the tradition of such trees is particularly strong and long-standing in the lands outside the Forest (p. 68).

4. *Plantations* Here the trees are not natural vegetation: somebody has planted them. Plantations are usually of just one or two species, often conifers or other exotic trees, and are not expected to maintain themselves. They are felled for timber, die, and are replaced by a new planted crop. This is the practice of *forestry* as the British understand it. With rare and unimportant exceptions, the tradition of plantations is no older than 1600, and the practice of 'restocking' – destroying a wood and making a plantation on the site – is younger still. Plantations are a recent, and only minor, feature of the Forest.

5. *Garden trees* People have grown exotic ornamental trees in gardens at least since Roman times. These came to Hatfield Forest only through the recent, especially Victorian, fashion of using such 'specimen' trees as features of the landscape at large.

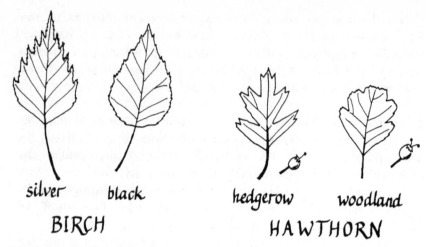

Fig. 4 The two birches and the two hawthorns.

The trees of Hatfield Forest   The Forest is an excellent example of *semi-natural* vegetation. It is natural in that the trees and plants are wild and have not been sown or planted. It is artificial in that the particular plant communities have been influenced by many centuries of woodcutting, grazing etc. For example, without grazing by farm animals there would be almost no grassland.

The great majority of the trees of the Forest are the native species of woodland and wood-pasture: they include ash, maple, hazel, hornbeam, alder, two species of sallow, spindle, crab, elder, and probably beech. The Forest oak is the pedunculate species, *Quercus robur*. Birch – we have both the 'silver' birch and the 'black' birch – is native to Essex, but may be a recent arrival here (p. 222–3). We have several kinds of elm, which are of special interest (p. 199ff).

There are two species of birch, and two of hawthorn, and both pairs hybridize, producing intermediates (Fig. 4). The *silver birch*, *Betula pendula*, can be recognized by its somewhat weeping habit, very white bark breaking up into black fissures when old, twigs with little warts, and leaves with little teeth on big teeth. *'Black' birch*, *B. pubescens*, does not weep, has reddish bark, hairy twigs without warts, and leaves with only small teeth. Silver birch is generally the less common species, and in Hatfield Forest is less common than black except in Hangman's and Beggar's Hall Coppices, where the two are about equal.

The ordinary *'hedgerow' hawthorn*, *Crataegus monogyna*, is often a single-stemmed tree with fibrous bark when large; it has small sharp thorns, leaves with deep narrow sharp-pointed lobes, one style to the flower and one pip to the fruit. The *'woodland' hawthorn*, *C. laevigata*, is a straggling bush with several stems; it has big blunt thorns, shiny leaves with several rounded lobes, two styles and two pips. The woodland species is rare except in ancient woods, but in some of those on clay (e.g. the Leaden Roding woods) is the commoner of the two. The hedgerow species is the familiar one in all other situations where hawthorn grows. In Hatfield, as in other Forests, unusually among ancient woods, hedgerow hawthorn is by far the commoner; the woodland species, though present in all the coppices, is rare except in the extreme north.

Planted trees are few but prominent. They are nearly all exotic, and thus easily distinguished from wild trees. They are obvious insertions into a fabric that did not originally have them: most of them were meant to be conspicuous. They include the gigantic horsechestnuts in the Warren, the London plane by the lake, the swamp cypress and stone pines in Table Coppice, and the black pines at the Eight Wantz.

Besides these specimen trees, which are within the garden tradition, there are small plantations belonging to the forestry tradition. Both in the coppices and the plains, attempts were made to create plantations of pine, larch, oak and other trees in the last century, and again (with varying success) in the 1960s and 1970s.

In Hatfield Forest no planted trees have been coppiced or pollarded. The only known exceptions are a few sycamores and sweet-chestnuts in Table and Collin's Coppices.

Practical woodmanship   Woodmen traditionally make use of the self-renewing powers of trees. As gardeners know, some trees such as pines can be got rid of by cutting them down, but nearly all native species grow again either from the stump or from the root system. Ash, maple, oak, hornbeam and many others *coppice*: the stump sends up shoots and becomes a *stool* from which an indefinite succession of crops of poles can be cut at intervals of years (Fig. 5). A *maiden* tree is one that has grown from seed and has not yet been felled. Aspen, cherry and most elms *sucker*: the stump normally dies but the root system remains alive indefinitely and sends

9

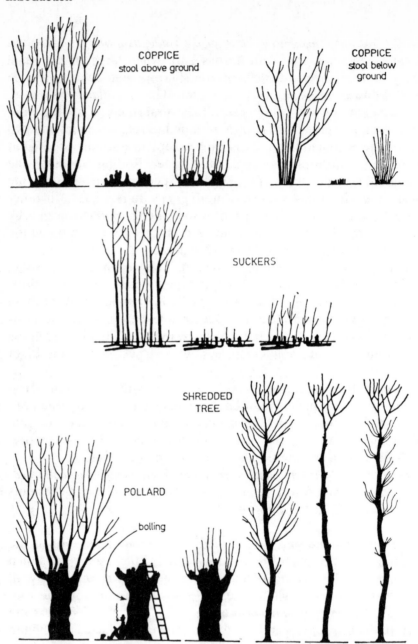

Fig. 5 Ways of managing wood-producing trees. For each method the tree, or group of trees, is shown just before cutting, just after cutting, and one year after cutting. Shredding is a variant of pollarding known only from historical records (p. 68) and foreign practice. All drawn to the same scale.

up successive crops of poles, forming a circular patch of genetically identical trees called a *clone*. (Clones exist not only in trees but in many perennial plants such as dog's-mercury and herb Paris, which have underground stems that creep outwards in circular patches.)

The trees of a wood are divided into *timber* or *standard* trees (a minority) and *underwood*. Every so often a *panel* (several acres) of underwood is felled and allowed to grow again by coppicing or suckering. Scattered among the underwood are the timber trees, which are allowed to stand for several cycles of regrowth and are felled when getting to be full-grown. Timber trees are usually replaced by seedlings. A wood therefore consists of timber trees of various ages; underwood stools; and the herbaceous plants and undershrubs (e.g. bramble) which make up the *ground vegetation*. Coppice stools live indefinitely and over the centuries become *giant stools* many feet across.

A wood is not destroyed by cutting it down. The woods of Hatfield Forest have been cut down many times. Underwood, *if not damaged by browsing*, grows fast and reliably: hazel should reach 5 feet high at the end of one summer's growth, and sallow often exceeds 10 feet (that is, 2 inches a day). The wood yields two products, *timber* from the trunks of the timber trees, and *wood* from coppice stems, suckers and the boughs of felled timber trees. *Timber and wood had different uses and are not to be confused*: we still talk of 'timber' buildings and 'wood' fires. Wood is rods, poles and logs, used for fencing, wattlework and many specialized crafts but in large quantities for fuel. Timber is the stuff of beams and planks and is too valuable (and too big) to burn. Underwood was normally the more important product; woods were traditionally regarded as sources of energy.

An alternative to coppicing is *pollarding*. The tree is cut like a coppice stool to produce successive crops of wood, but at about ten feet above ground leaving a permanent trunk called a *bolling* (to rhyme with 'rolling'). Pollarding is much harder work than coppicing and is not normally done within woodland. Pollards, like coppice stools, live longer than the uncut tree.

Secondary woodland   Some woods are believed to be derived from primaeval wildwood (Chapter 2); others have arisen on land that has at some time not been woodland. Almost all land by nature turns into woodland unless prevented by constant cultivation or grazing.

The easiest way to create a new wood is to take a piece of land and to do nothing to it. It will be invaded by oak, hawthorn, birch or ash, and within ten years will be a young wood. But it will not be the same as an old wood: some trees, such as hornbeam, take many decades to move in, and plants such as oxlip may not appear for centuries.

Woodland is rapidly increasing in this way today, as will be familiar to everyone who goes around Essex by train. Secondary woodland can be of any age: for example, three miles south of the Forest there still stands a wood which appears on a map of 1587 under the name 'Bushy Leyes Grove', which shows that it was then remembered as recent.[3] All over Essex, and in the Forest itself, are woods which (though often ancient) contain earthworks and Iron Age sites which prove that they have at some time been smaller than they are now. The present scrubs are an early stage of such woodland, and bear witness to the uneasy tension between grazing and trees.

Kinds of Wood-Pasture

Wooded commons, parks and wooded Forests   The earliest wood-pastures, and the only ones known a thousand years ago, were *wooded commons*, involving trees, grass and domestic animals, but deer, if at all, only as wild animals. The tradition was given a new lease of life by the Normans' interest in deer husbandry, which gave rise to *parks* (enclosed wood-pastures for deer) as well as to Forests (Chapter 3).

Compartmentation   If a wood-pasture is to be permanent the animals have to be separated from the regrowth of the trees. A simple, though laborious, way to do this is by pollarding instead of coppicing. In Epping Forest local customs did not allow the owners of the trees to interfere with the grazing, and so they pollarded the trees almost throughout the Forest.

A *compartmented* wood-pasture is divided by internal banks into coppices, each of which would be felled like an ordinary wood and then fenced in the early stages to keep out livestock until it had

12

grown sufficiently not to be damaged. For example, in 1336 the de Bohuns, owners of Hatfield, had at Saffron Walden

> a park containing 2 leagues in circuit, and it is divided into 17 quarters in which 10 acres of underwood can be sold every year, worth £4 at 8*s*. an acre. The pasture is worth nothing because of the multitude of deer. The nuts . . . when they happen are worth 12*d*.
>
> *1336 survey*[4]

Hatfield combines both methods. It is a compartmented wooded Forest, in which (as we shall see) each coppice was supposed to be felled every eighteen years and fenced for the first nine years of regrowth; the fences were to keep out deer, as well as farm animals, for the first six years. Livestock had access to the plains at all times. Coppice stools are therefore confined to the woods, and pollards to the plains.

Most parks contained woodland, and some form of compartmentation is recorded in about half of them. The practice was common in wooded Forests but rare in wooded commons.

A coppice in a Forest should (if the compartmentation worked well) have grown in much the same way as an ordinary wood not in a Forest – except that eighteen years between fellings would, until the sixteenth century, have been an unusually long cycle.[5] But the animals will have had some influence, especially on ground vegetation, and a greater influence on trees in the plains. Much depends on the likes and dislikes of deer and other livestock.

The Forest in its Setting

'Ancient Countryside' Most of Essex is traditionally a land of hamlets and scattered farmsteads rather than villages, of a dense network of lanes, deep holloways, ancient hedges and pollard trees. It was little affected either by the introduction of open-field agriculture in Anglo-Saxon times, or by the Enclosure Acts of the eighteenth and nineteenth centuries which abolished the open-fields. This landscape survives relatively intact to the east, south and west of the Forest (Fig. 6). The Forest lies in the parish of Hatfield Broad-Oak, a huge township comprising a decayed market town, a big village (Hatfield Heath), five greens, two-and-a-half 'Ends', a

13

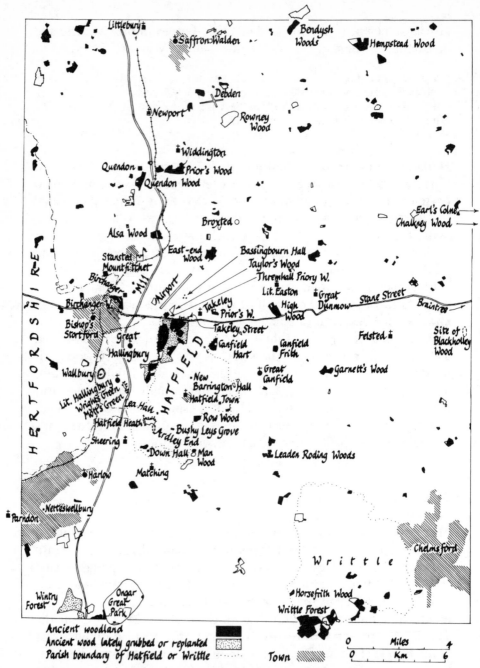

Fig. 6 Surroundings of the Forest, showing ancient woodland and places mentioned in the text.

14

'Street', the boundary-houses of the Forest, and many isolated ancient farms. On the east, the Forest's neighbour was Hatfield Park.

To the west, the Forest abuts on Great Hallingbury, another scattered parish of greens and farmsteads but no village. Little Hallingbury is similar but also has a modern village. Wall Wood is the ancient wood of Great Hallingbury and Monk Wood of Little; Woodside Green is divided between the two. Hallingbury Place, in Great Hallingbury, whose park still survives, was for centuries the seat of the Forest aristocracy.

On the north, the Forest now ends at the romantically overgrown track of the Great Dunmow railway, disused since 1971 and now a public path. Before 1857 it extended to Stane Street, the main Roman road from Colchester to beyond Bishop's Stortford, one of the few reasonably straight lines in Essex. Beyond Stane Street lies Takeley, another parish of greens and farmsteads, with one-and-a-half villages: the modern village of Takeley itself, and the ancient half-a-village of Takeley Street, consisting of old houses strung out along the north side of Stane Street and originally looking out over the Forest. (The houses on the south side of Takeley Street are all new.)

For miles around Hatfield Forest the landscape is agricultural, but with a scatter of woods, many of which have histories almost as long and detailed as the Forest itself: Birchanger Wood, Quendon Wood, Alsa Wood, Prior's Wood (Takeley), Dunmow High Wood, Canfield Hart and Frith, the three woods of Leaden Roding, Man Wood, Row Wood, and many others. They survive rather better than woods in most of Eastern England.

Writtle Forest   Hatfield Forest has a twin sister at Writtle, twelve miles south-east. This also is a huge parish with a great wood called Heywood (now Highwood) which was declared a Forest. Throughout the middle ages the two Forests had similar histories and the same owners.

This Forest had an 'inside-out' appearance, with coppices (called *springs*) in the middle and plains round the edge (Fig. 7). It has mainly acid soils and is much more dominated by hornbeam than Hatfield.

Writtle Forest is private, but has many public paths. It is less well preserved than Hatfield: it long ago lost most of the pollards

15

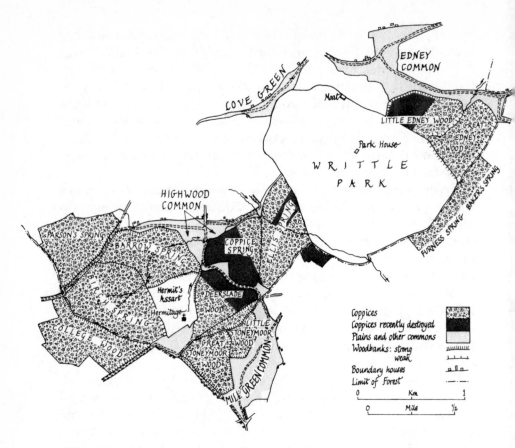

Fig. 7 Writtle Forest. Note that Writtle Park cut the Forest in two. There was an outlying wood called Horsefrith.

and some of the plains, and has been encroached upon in recent years. But it is still a wild and lovely place, with its heathland, pollard oaks, alder slades and woodbanks, and the site of the hermitage in which a solitary monk dwelt. This lonely survival from the depths of the twelfth-century countryside is within twenty-five miles of St Paul's Cathedral.

Place-Names

The Forest has two sets of names: the traditional names, used in this book, and the modern names, which are used in some National

16

Trust publications. (In many recent maps of the Forest, the names are corrupted and misplaced.)

The Forest is divided into 'quarters' by the Shermore Brook and the tracks that once crossed it. Takeley, Bush-end and Fairstead Quarters included coppices as shown on Fig. 3. Wood-row Quarter, in the south, apparently had no coppice; it was mostly lost to the Forest in 1857. The coppices from Hangman's to Emblem's presumably formed another quarter, but its name is lost; I shall call them the Western Coppices.

Every ancient wood in Essex has its own name. Some of the Forest coppices are named after people, probably after someone who was once the woodcutting tenant. Table Coppice is called after an object called the Table which stood at the bridge over the Shermore Brook (p. 114). Doodle-Oak Coppice was named after a famous tree once near it (p. 242). Beggar's Hall and Emblem's are named after nearby farms. Round Coppice, like most woods of that name, is not actually round. What of Hangman's? It would be nice to think that, like a field at Pulham (Norfolk), it was held by a tenant in return for hanging the lord of the manor's thieves,[6] but I have found no such custom here. More likely it was once leased to a Mr Hangman.

There is some trace of place-names within the coppices. In 1807 Hangman's was divided into Norwich, Sharp and Side Quarters.[7]

Most of the modern names seem to have arisen under the Houblon family, owners of the Forest when it was private in the late nineteenth century. They often rest on the sole authority of an annotated copy of the 1915 Ordnance Survey now in the Warden's office. Some may be genuine: 'Eight Wantz Ways' and 'Six Wantz Ways' reflect the Essex dialect word *wants*, a junction of several roads. Some are re-namings: 'Hampton's' for Dowsett's Coppice commemorates a farm steward; 'Elgin's' for Table Coppice honours a relative, the eighth Earl of Elgin (son of him of the Marbles), viceroy of India.[8] Some are corruptions: 'Elman's Green' could be a mis-hearing of Thremhall Green. The name 'Old Woman's Weaver' (or 'Mother's Weaver) is that of a pond on the upper Shermore Brook, but has been applied by corruption to the Brook itself and also to a woodland ride. 'Weaver' is evidently a variant of *wayer*, an Essex word for a pond (p. 114), like German *Weiher*; the spelling 'waver' is known in Suffolk.[9]

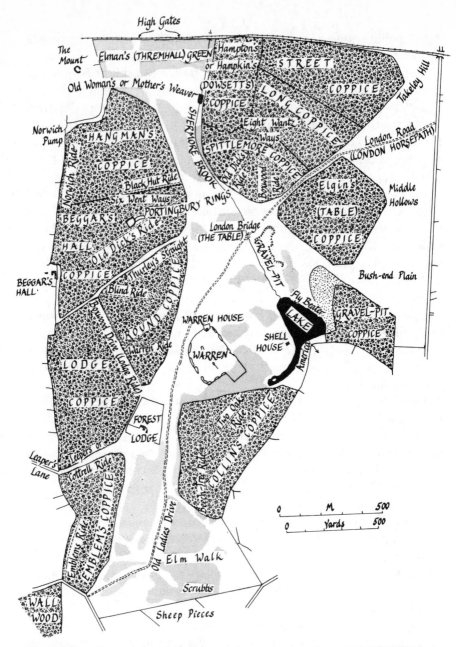

Fig. 8 Minor place-names of the Forest in use in modern times, derived mainly from National Trust sources. Names known to be traditional are in capitals. The topography is shown as in 1960, before the coming of the bulldozer. Shaded areas are scrubs. 'Norwich' is probably corrupted from 'North Hatch' (p. 69).

18

Hatfield Forest in the World of Wood-Pasture

Wood-pasture, of one sort or another, runs deep in human nature. It extends through Scandinavia into Finland;[10] down through Europe, via the pollards and *Lärchenwiesen* (larch meadows) of the Alps and the wood-pastures of the Appennines[11] into Greece, and on into the Himalayas.[12] Pollards, grassland and oakwoods still cover mile after mile of the Pindus mountains in Macedonia; there are huge numbers of pollard oaks, cut in a different style, in the mountains of east Crete. In North America the Indians had a kind of wood-pasture in Michigan, and there was a paleface version in the Appalachians.[13]

Hatfield Forest demonstrates a practice that goes back long before the idea of Forests; our Neolithic ancestors might well find themselves at home in it. In most of the world's wood-pastures the trees' chief duty is to grow leaves on which to feed the animals; in England, at least in historic times, the trees have been meant for timber and wood, with leaves only as a minor product.[14] As far as I know, the English compartmented wood-pasture is a supreme elaboration of the system. Hatfield Forest is the unique survival, in full working order, of this aspect of human affairs at its zenith of complexity.

2 The Hatfield Area before the Forest

Harold held Hadfield in the time of King Edward for 1 manor and for 20 hides. Then 51 villeins, now 60. Then 19 bordars, now 30. Then 20 slaves, now 22. Then 9 ploughs in demesne, now 8, & 3 rounceys & 40 animals & 195 swine & 192 sheep. Then 40 men's ploughs, now 31½ – this loss was in the time of all the sheriffs and through the death of the beasts. Wood for 800 swine, 120 acres of meadow. Pasture whose rent is 19 wethers in the manor & 41 acres of ploughing. To the church of this manor used to belong 1 hide & 30 acres which Swein took away after he lost the sheriffdom ... And 30 acres which 1 smith held in the time of King Edward, who was slain because of Robbery, & the king's steward added that land to this manor. And 40 acres of wood which King Edward's steward held ... The manor was then worth £36 [a year], now £60; but the sheriff receives £80 from it ...

Domesday Book, 1086

[A hide is a nominal unit of tax assessment. A rouncey is a kind of horse.]

The Ice Ages

Our story begins a quarter of a million years ago, during the last but one of the vast changes of climate known as glaciations. Glaciers formed all over north Europe and in Scotland, as they had several times before, but this Ice Age was more severe. Ice-sheets crept over East Anglia and into Essex, passing over the site of Hatfield and ending ten miles further south. The creeping ice brought with it great quantities of clay and rocks scraped off the bed of the North Sea. This muddy debris was deposited over the land surface – very like the mud moraines to be seen round some Norwegian glaciers today – and still covers most of north-west Essex.

The **Chalky Boulder-clay** thus laid down underlies all of Hatfield Forest, except for patches of sand and gravel (probably also of glacial origin) along the Shermore Brook. It is a stiff grey or yellow clay. The boulders in it are most often of chalk or flint, but among them are many other rocks such as millstone grit and sarsen. The local churches are built of these mixed boulders from boulder-clay, picked off fields in the middle ages.

After this Ice Age there was a warm *interglacial* period in which trees and other plants returned and the area became wooded for many thousands of years. Then, around 100,000 years ago, the climate turned arctic once more. Although this time the glaciers did not reach Essex, the vegetation was reduced to tundra. Probably around the end of this last Ice Age, huge dust-storms covered the landscape with a foot or two of a fine mineral powder called *loess*. Over the years, the loess has been washed away or mixed into the topsoil by worms and moles; but in Hatfield Forest, and in many Essex woods, much of it still remains to make the soil less heavy and sticky than pure boulder-clay.

Wildwood

The last Ice Age ended about 11,000 BC, when the climate slowly returned to something like the present and England once again became suitable for trees. Just as today any land, left unattended, turns into a wood, so England was re-invaded by the trees which had retreated to southern latitudes during the glaciation. These came to cover almost the entire land with *wildwood* – that is, wholly natural woodland not significantly affected by human activities. Almost all we know of wildwood comes from *pollen analysis*. Many trees and other plants produce large quantities of pollen grains, which can often be identified as coming from a particular genus. Pollen grains are preserved almost for ever in permanently-wet places such as peats and the mud of lakes (and to a lesser extent in acid soils). The pollen analyst takes a core from a suitable deposit, samples what was laid down at a particular time, and identifies the pollen grains. From this it is possible (taking account of such factors as how much pollen each kind of tree produces) to reconstruct the local vegetation.

The first colonizers of the tundra were birch, aspen and sallow, which are very arctic trees and have light fruits blown by the wind. Next came pine and hazel; then alder and oak; next lime and elm; then holly, ash, beech, hornbeam and maple. All this took place over some 4500 years: generations of trees grew up, died, and were replaced by other species.

Eventually there came the **Atlantic Period**, when the climate was reasonably stable, and not unlike today's, for some 2000 years; long enough for a more or less stable 'climax' vegetation to emerge. This wildwood varied from one region to another: pine was the commonest tree in N.E. Scotland, birch in N.W. Scotland, and oak and hazel in north and west England. The Hatfield area belongs to Lowland England, in which lime appears to have been the commonest tree, followed by hazel, oak, ash and elm.[15] (This was the small-leaved lime, *Tilia cordata*, not the now familiar 'common' lime, *T. vulgaris*, which is only a planted tree.) Native lime is now totally absent from the Hatfield area, but it is still common in a group of ancient woods beginning six miles to the east (p. 217–8).

Pollen analysts have to take their material where they can find it. The nearest sites to Hatfield are at Nazeing and Broxbourne and in Epping Forest, some twelve miles south-west. These show that lime was vastly the predominant tree in an area from which it has now disappeared. This area, however, lies outside the boulder-clay country and has very different soils. For a better parallel with Hatfield we go sixty miles north-east, to the meres in the boulder-clay country of south Norfolk.[16]

Eleven pollen cores have been taken from the mud of these meres. If we leave out the pollen of alder, which probably formed a fringing zone to all the meres, the four principal trees of the dry-land wildwood at the end of the Atlantic Period were lime, hazel, oak and ash. These vary from mere to mere in no consistent way, except that oak was never the commonest. Elm was less frequent, and there was a little birch in places. The differences show that wildwood was not a uniform mixture of trees but varied from place to place. Lime is a tall, densely-shading tree and is gregarious; it probably formed patches of pure limewood. Hazel is of shorter stature, and does not produce pollen if overshadowed by taller trees; there were

22

therefore areas of hazel growing on its own. There were evidently areas of ashwood, perhaps mingled with lime and hazel, and probably of elmwood as well. Oak was probably scattered through many types of woodland as it is today.

The pollen evidence for south Norfolk points, in general terms, to the wildwood having been a patchwork of different mixtures of trees, in much the same way as the woods of Hatfield Forest are today (Chapter 9). Probably this was so in the Hatfield area too. The modern woods around Hatfield differ conspicuously in that there is now no lime at all, but hornbeam and maple, then apparently rare, have become common trees.

In Germany the rise of hornbeam is well known from the pollen record, and sometimes happened within the last thousand years; human activities are said to encourage it at the expense of beech.[17] In England, however, hornbeam is not now a ready invader of coppices or of abandoned farmland, and the previous tree would usually have been lime, not beech.

Why lime should have disappeared from the Hatfield area, but not from the Braintree area, is a mystery. It is possible that there has been no change, and that if we had a pollen deposit at Hatfield it would show that lime had always been rare and hornbeam and maple common. No deposit of the Atlantic period yet found has this particular mixture of trees; but pollen deposits tend to record the wildwood that grew near wet places where pollen is preserved, whereas ancient woodland may perpetuate the wildwood of a different kind of place. As yet this question cannot be resolved.

There can be no doubt that wildwood covered all England over hill and dale; the contrast that archaeologists used to draw between 'heavily forested' claylands like Hatfield and the 'light forest cover' of places like the Breckland cannot be sustained. However, wildwood was probably not quite continuous. All through the Atlantic Period there is a thin but definite pollen record of plants like creeping buttercup *Ranunculus repens*, cuckoo-flower *Cardamine pratensis*, self-heal *Prunella vulgaris*, and sorrel *Rumex acetosa* which are now associated with glades and rides in woods. These do not flower in shade, and their pollen proves that there were small, more or less permanent openings in the wildwood. Possibly wild beasts congregated in particular places and prevented trees from growing. The plains of Hatfield Forest, although mainly an artefact, therefore

23

perpetuate something already present in embryo in the time of wild-wood.

The Cultural Landscape

The first human inhabitants Men have lived in Essex ever since the last Ice Age, and indeed for many thousands of years before. Palaeolithic stone tools have been found all over Essex, including a few not far from Hatfield.[18] Mesolithic men came to Essex well after the Ice Age. At Pledgdon and Wicken Bonhunt, a few miles from Hatfield, sites are known at which they lived or camped and made flint tools.[19] One Mesolithic flint tool has been found in Hatfield Forest, on the edge of Gravelpit Coppice, and was accompanied by two waste flakes showing that it was made there.[20] People already at least hunted in the area, even if they did not live there, but their numbers were very small.

It is probably true that Palaeolithic and Mesolithic men had little more effect on the landscape than the beasts on which they preyed. They made small clearings around their homes and camps, but men were so few that they could have achieved little merely by cutting down trees. Some North American Indians, with a similar way of life, transformed the landscape by burning, but there would have been no scope for fire in Essex. In America much of the leaf-litter, and some of the trees themselves, are inflammable. England is different: trees like oak and lime burn like wet asbestos, and nobody has ever succeeded in burning down a native wood.

The impact of civilization This nomadic way of life was rapidly transformed in the Neolithic period, from 4500 BC onwards. People took to farming and acquired cultivated crops (and weeds) and domestic livestock; they built houses, made pottery, and indulged in earthworks, graveyards and temples. They did the things that define civilization as we know it. Along with this went a much larger population and a transformation of the landscape. Wildwood is no use to barley or sheep. Crop plants and domestic livestock come from the Near East, and Neolithic men began to re-make England into an imitation of the dry open steppes in which they flourish.

Destroying the wildwood was the greatest physical task that mankind has ever undertaken; in Essex it was to take more than 5000

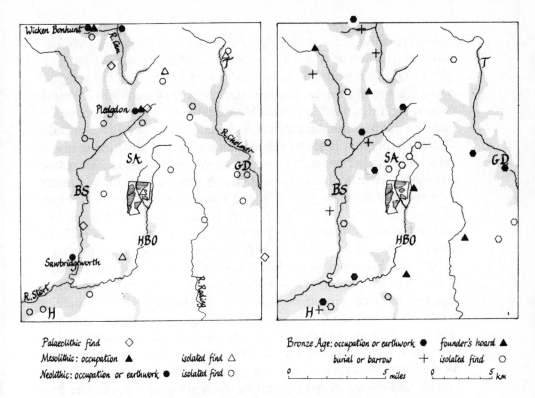

Palaeolithic find ◇

Mesolithic: occupation ▲   isolated find △

Neolithic: occupation or earthwork ●   isolated find ○

Bronze Age: occupation or earthwork ●   founder's hoard ▲

burial or barrow +   isolated find ○

0 _____ 5 miles   0 _____ 5 km

Fig. 9 What is known of the area within six miles of Hatfield Forest in the Stone and Bronze Ages. The present Forest is shown. The main areas of non-boulder-clay soils are shaded. BS: Bishop's Stortford. GD: Great Dunmow. H: Harlow. HBO: Hatfield Broad-Oak town. SA: Stansted Airport. Information chiefly from Deborah Riddy of Essex County Council, and from published sources.

years. We know little of how it was done. Writers still repeat that people made farmland merely by cutting down trees in order to use the timber or wood, but this is a fallacy. Prehistoric peoples would have had no means of using the great trees which formed much of the wildwood; even in our own mechanical age, most of the trees felled in destroying tropical wildwoods are wasted. *They destroyed the woods because they wanted the land*. Cutting down the trees would have been only a beginning; the real task was to get rid of the stumps and prevent them from growing again. Fire, again, would have been of little help.

Although it was probably long before civilized men lived near what was to be Hatfield Forest, they may have had some influence

25

almost from the start. A cardinal sign of the early Neolithic in pollen cores all over north-west Europe is the sudden decline of elm. This Elm Decline has been much debated: archaeologists have attributed it to a change in climate, soil deterioration, or to people specifically destroying, or pollarding, elms. Most of these explanations can now be ruled out because the Decline was so sudden, so vast, was specific to elm, happened both where elm was common and where it was rare, and did not happen in America. In my opinion the only explanation which covers all the facts is that Neolithic men inadvertently let loose Elm Disease (*AW*). There is abundant evidence that Elm Disease has been present in Europe for at least several centuries, and has come and gone in epidemics. In wildwood (I argue) the disease – or the bark-beetles that carry it – did not flourish excessively, and epidemics were small. Neolithic men, by making farmland with free-standing trees, woodland edges, and maybe pollards, created an environment in which the disease and the bark-beetles could get out of hand. The next time there was an epidemic it was a big one. It is possible that Elm Disease helped the spread of civilization, by killing wildwood on the more fertile soils, as well as civilization helping the disease.

Our knowledge of the geography of Neolithic, as of all other prehistoric peoples, is incomplete and biased: it depends on how much evidence has escaped later destruction and on how diligently archaeologists have looked for it. Neolithic activity seems to have been mainly near the Essex coast, but there was a thin scatter all over the county. Much was going on next to Writtle Forest. That mysterious structure, a causewayed enclosure, has been found at Sawbridgeworth, four miles from Hatfield Forest. Higher in the Stort valley, flints and pottery are reported around Elsenham. Occasional flints have been found in Takeley and Great Hallingbury. There can be little doubt that Neolithic men visited the site of Hatfield Forest, but they probably did not live there.[21]

As well as making farmland (and perhaps also heathland), Neolithic men began woodland management. Wildwood would have consisted mainly of trees too big for them to use. They needed rods for the vast quantities of hurdles and wattlework of which most of their buildings and equipment were made, and to grow them they instigated coppicing and pollarding. They appear also to have grown leafy boughs of hazel, and doubtless other species, on which to feed livestock.[22] In many parts of the world, such as Norway, Macedonia and Nepal, tree-leaves are still used as an alternative to hay. In England this would have been less important as grass grows for most of the year; but in Neolithic times, with so many trees and so little grass, leaves might well have provided much of the fodder.[14] Most of the evidence comes from hurdles and underwood structures preserved in the peat of the Somerset Levels, but the same practices may have happened in Essex also.

By the end of the Neolithic, about 2400 BC, Essex was still predominantly wooded, but with increasing areas of farmland, pasture and wood-pasture. These clearings, as far as we can tell, were few in the boulder-clay country around Hatfield. The population was still not large, and although there may have been patches of managed woodland almost everywhere, wildwood still predominated.

The Bronze Age   In this period (2400–750 BC) there is rather more evidence of activity in the Hatfield area; most of it in the form of scattered finds, although settlements are known from Wicken Bonhunt to the north and Great Dunmow to the east. At first, it seems only to have been the river valleys that were inhabited.[23] We used to suppose that Bronze Age people could not plough the claylands and left them still as wildwood, but evidence from other parts of England now makes this unlikely.

Close to Hatfield, the thorough archaeological study of the site of Stansted airport has so far found four barbed-and-tanged arrowheads, and a site of Late Bronze Age occupation a mile outside the Forest to the north-west.[24] From the same period a 'founder's hoard' – a collection of broken tools waiting to be recycled – was found long ago at Hatfield Park, just outside the Forest, and another in the south of the parish.[25] Settlement was still sparse; the boulder-clay was used mainly for hunting visits and was presumably still chiefly wooded; but by the Bronze Age, civilization and metal-working had come to the very edge of the Forest-to-be.

Pollen diagrams of this period show a gradual decline in lime more than other trees; probably it grew on the better soils and so was grubbed out by preference. This does not, however, explain why lime has disappeared completely from some areas but remains common in others.

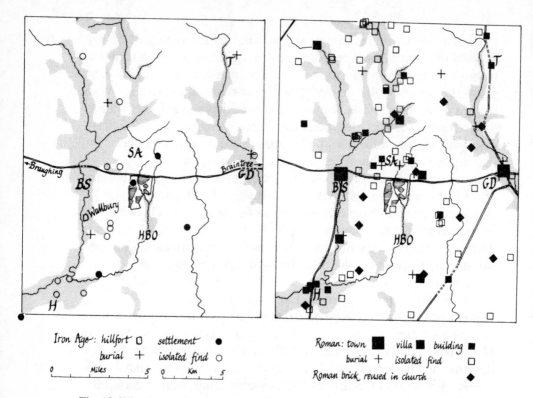

Fig. 10 What is known of the area within six miles of Hatfield Forest in the Iron Age and Roman period, mapped in the same way as Fig. 9.

The Iron Age   With the coming of iron, metal became cheap and could be used for felling-axes, twybills and ploughshares. Almost everywhere could be cultivated, and the landscape of England began to be dominated by farmland rather than woodland. Pollen in Diss Mere, south Norfolk, shows that wildwood there, already partly destroyed in the Bronze Age, was largely swept away for ever in the Iron Age; for the first thousand years the land was used for pasture rather than cultivation.[26]

The importance of the Hatfield area is shown by the great hillfort of Wallbury Camp, but this was probably strategic – a genuine fort – rather than a walled town.[27] People now, perhaps for the first time, lived in the Forest-to-be itself, as shown by Portingbury Rings and possibly other earthworks (Chapter 7). Two other Iron Age sites are known within 1½ miles of the Forest to the north-west,[20, 24] but until the very end of the period this area seems not to have had the dense settlement (at least two sites per square mile) recently found on the boulder-clay around Saffron Walden.[28]

By the end of the Iron Age the area had ceased to be the back of beyond. Stane Street, along the north edge of the Forest, originated as a main road between the Iron Age towns of Braughing, Braintree and Colchester. It is a planned road, running in straight lengths between hilltops, and is usually regarded as Roman; but the changes in direction are more frequent than on genuine Roman roads (*HC*), and I take it to be pre-Roman.

A feature of Essex are the semi-regular grids of fields and roads which cover mile after mile of country – evidently a deliberate landscape designed on a vast scale, with little room for woodland. They still dominate rural south-east Essex (*SEE*), and traces of them are to be found at Saffron Walden and Braintree within twelve miles of the Forest. They appear to date from the late Iron Age – some of them are overlain by Roman roads – but could be earlier.[29]

The Romans   In the Roman period, AD 40–410, Essex was prosperous and highly agricultural. At least a quarter of the county was covered with grids of fields, and presumably much more was covered with fields not regular in shape, whose antiquity we can no longer recognize. On top of this, the Romans tried to impose a triangular grid of main roads: the roads meeting at 60° at Braintree and Dunmow still stand out on the map. There were small towns every few miles, and villas – big agricultural estates – more often still. All this points to a landscape in which the remaining woodland was fully used. A large population consumed timber and underwood, and fuel is implied by bricks, iron, pottery, glass, baths, hypocausts and many other trappings of Romano-British life. Woodland conservation may well have been important.

In the Hatfield area, chance finds of Roman ware have long been known. At Hatfield town, a chest was dug up containing glass and 'Samian' pottery vessels. A decorative green glass basin was once found somewhere near the Forest.[30] Big Roman buildings would have provided the quantities of bricks and roof-tiles re-used in the churches of the two Hallingburys and Takeley. The Stansted Airport surveyors excavated a 'farming village' of wooden houses of the first century AD just over a mile north of the Forest, and found four other sites of various Roman dates within the airport area.[24] In the Forest itself, in 1979, a scatter of late Roman pottery was found south of Collin's Coppice by the digging of a pipe-trench.[31] Agriculture had at last come to surround what is now the Forest, and it is very likely that people were living on parts of the Forest itself.

Anglo-Saxon Hatfield

The coming of the Anglo-Saxons   Most of us have been taught that the collapse of the Roman Empire marks a great discontinuity in the story of the English landscape. The inhabitants – we suppose – perished with their empire; the land reverted to woodland; and out of the ruins invaders from Germany were slowly to hew a land-scape of their own, unrelated to what had gone before.

Undoubtedly there was great disruption, especially in urban life, in the fifth and sixth centuries AD. Since Roman Britain is now known to have had rats, a plausible cause is plague.[32] But country life went on, as is shown in Essex by the persistence of so much of the Roman roads and Iron Age fields, which could survive only if used.

Rivenhall, twenty miles east of Hatfield, is an unremarkable 'back-woods' Essex parish with a supposedly nineteenth-century church. The detailed studies of Warwick and Kirsty Rodwell have shown that it began with a Roman villa which developed continuously into an Anglo-Saxon farm and then into the medieval Hall. The present church is 900 years older than was thought, and a previous church may have begun when the villa was still standing. This is a spectacular example of continuity, but there is no reason to think it unusual. Great and Little Hallingbury, next to Hatfield Forest, with their ancient churches full of Roman brick, could easily have similar pedi-grees.[33]

The Anglo-Saxon landscape   'Hatfield' comes from the Anglo-Saxon *hæþ+feld*, equivalent to the modern Heathfield, though this does not quite give the meaning. *Hæþ* did indeed mean 'heath', an area of heather or similar plants; but *feld* meant not a 'field' as we know it but an open space in sight of woodland with which to contrast it.[34] The place-name Hatfield presumably applied originally to

Hatfield Heath, where a patch of gravel would have made a heath possible.

Heath was very common in Anglo-Saxon England, especially in the neighbourhood of woodland (*HC*).* I know of fourteen places called Hatfield or its variants Hadfield or Heathfield. The Hatfields in Hertfordshire and west Yorkshire are mentioned by Bede, so must date from before AD 730. Our Hatfield could well be of similar antiquity; it is not recorded in writing before Domesday Book, but this merely means that nothing happened there to attract the attention of a writer.

There are several other *feld* place-names in the area, notably the two Canfields immediately east of Hatfield. Also significant are place-names ending in *-lēah*. This Anglo-Saxon word can mean a wood, but is often used for names of hamlets and villages, in which case it evidently means a clearing in a wood, and therefore implies enough woodland to have a clearing. There are many such place-names nearby, such as Thor*ley* (a name which suggests the worship of heathen gods), Take*ley*, and Bex*ley* in Great Canfield; Ard*ley* End and *Lea* Hall lie on either side of Hatfield Heath. These point to the Hatfield area in the early Anglo-Saxon period as being well-wooded, but by no means continuous woodland – rather like S.E. Hertfordshire in the twentieth century.

From the eighth century onwards there are Anglo-Saxon charters, describing the boundaries of landed estates. These show clearly that England in general was not a land of continuous wildwood but rather, as now, of isolated named woods among farmland. The countryside – especially areas like Worcestershire and N.W. Dorset – was full of lanes, holloways, heaths, downland, ponds, and hedges with thorns, oaks, ashes and willows in them (*HC*). The few charters that survive for Essex show that this was another county rich in such things. For example that for Littlebury, 12 miles north of Hatfield Forest, mentions an 'old hedge', a dell and various pits.[35] Other Essex charters mention 'hatches' like those at the corners of Hatfield Forest (p. 69).

The long decline of lime was in its last stage. A pollen record in Epping Forest shows that lime suddenly declined, and later

---

* The earliest document to describe what is now Epping Forest, dated 1062, mentions a heath, remains of which still exist.

disappeared, in the middle Anglo-Saxon period. Possibly this was connected with the rise of a wood-pasture system preceding the establishment of the Forest. Lime, though tenacious of life in all other respects, appears easily to be killed by browsing animals. The trees would first have been pollarded (reducing their pollen output), and when they died would have been replaced by oak, which is much less easily killed.[36] A similar story can be told of several other wood-pastures.[37]

Domesday Book   William the Conqueror's immense survey of England, made in 1086, at last refers to Hatfield by name. The entry, slightly abridged, is given at the head of the chapter. It compares the state of the manor in 1066 with that in 1086.

Hatfield (it corresponded at least roughly to the modern parish) was one of the biggest estates in Essex. Together with the yet bigger estate of Writtle, it belonged to King Harold; they had been Harold's private inheritance, but when he fell in battle William took them over as Crown land. The survey enumerates the various classes of men – villeins, bordars, slaves – who were the King's tenants, and a few gentry more loosely associated with the estate. Some of the land was the King's own farm (*demesne*), on which the survey enumerates the livestock. Most of it was the farms of the tenants.

Essex is one of those unlucky counties for which Domesday records woodland in terms of the number of pigs the woods were supposed to feed. This is not the down-to-earth method that we might suppose. Pigs fed on acorns, and both pigs and acorns varied enormously. Some woods had many oak-trees and some few. In some years oaks yield abundantly; in others there is hardly an acorn to be seen. Although, as we shall see later, pannage was by no means obsolete at Hatfield, Domesday Book counts pigs of the imagination. It is, however, possible to make something of them. From my studies on the relation between Domesday pigs and the known sizes of woods, I conclude that the main entry for 800 swine implies a wood roughly the same size as Hatfield Forest today; it could not have been much bigger.[38]

Hatfield in 1066 had a proportion of land-uses not so very different from what it has now. At the rough-and-ready rate of 120 acres to the plough (*AW*), the 49 ploughs of 1066 would have covered nearly 6000 acres, two-thirds of the parish. Woodland – the present

Forest plus 40 acres – amounted to about one-eighth. Meadow was about one-seventieth. The remaining one-fifth would have been occupied by buildings, gardens and pasture (including Hatfield Heath).

In 1086 England as a whole was roughly one-third arable land and one-sixth woodland (*AW*). Hatfield had much more farmland, and a little less woodland, than the average for England. To the north was a very different type of country. Takeley was divided into three manors, two of which each had 'woodland for 1000 swine' in 1066, reduced to 'for 600 swine' in 1086. Stansted Mountfitchet had 'woodland for 1000 swine'. In Elsenham the chief manor had had 'woodland for 1300 swine' before the Conquest, 'for 1100 swine' afterwards, and 'for 1000 swine' by 1086. Around and on the site of Stansted airport, therefore, we must imagine the equivalent of more than four Hatfield Forests (Fig. 11). These, with other woodland, made up one of the two biggest concentrations of woods in Essex, the other being the present Epping Forest. Most of the big swine-figures are said to have declined between 1066 and 1086, but without any increase of agriculture. This probably means that pannage was declining and the woods were being used in some other way, perhaps by an extension of coppicing. What happened to these woods is not known in detail. The *Colchester Cartulary* gives some hints as to their grubbing-out in the twelfth and thirteenth centuries.[39] As we shall see, the Hallingbury woods (for a total of 800 swine in 1086) were recognizably the present Wall and Monk Woods by 1300. By 1350 the great woods north of the Forest were reduced to isolated, managed wood-lots, much of which still remains in Birchanger Wood, Prior's Wood (Takeley) and parts of East-End Wood.[40]

The archaeological evidence from the Stansted survey corroborates this analysis. Evidence for the Anglo-Saxon period on the airport site, although there is some, is sparse compared to Roman. Not until the twelfth century did the area north of the Forest again become highly agricultural.[24]

Conclusions

The woods of Hatfield Forest today still show, in their variety of types of woodland and in the woodland grassland, some links with

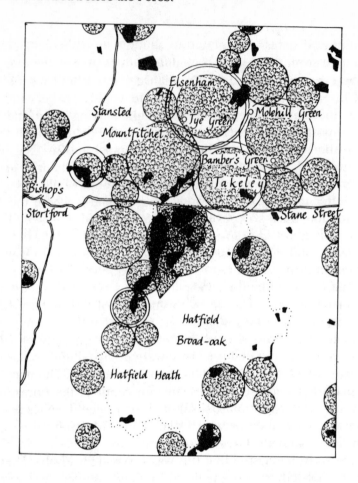

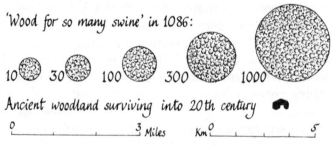

'Wood for so many swine' in 1086:

10 30 100 300 1000

Ancient woodland surviving into 20th century

0 _____ 3 Miles   Km 0 _____ 5

Fig. 11 Woodland in and around Hatfield as recorded in Domesday Book. The size of each circle is intended to represent roughly the actual area of woodland corresponding to each swine-entry (the bigger woods having disproportionately more swine than the smaller). The later Forest is shown in the middle of the map. Hatfield parish boundary is shown as a dotted line.

the wildwood from which they are ultimately derived. The chief differences from most known kinds of wildwood are the complete disappearance of lime and the abundance of maple and hornbeam.

The first effect of civilization on Hatfield would have been indirect, through the Elm Decline. The more definite making of the landscape began almost certainly before the Iron Age. For millennia people were grubbing out woods, digging up stumps, and making fields. Sometimes they had enough livestock to lighten the labour by grazing the regrowth. Of the remaining woodland, some would have been fenced off and managed as coppice, and some – where the trees were not too thick to prevent grass from growing – would have become wood-pasture. The Forest still demonstrates two aspects of the landscape which would have been commonplace for well over two thousand years and here, almost uniquely, still survive. It is quite possible that coppices, and plains with scrubs and pollard trees, were already being operated by the makers of Portingbury Rings, though probably not in quite the same places that they are now.

How far the destruction of wildwood was a one-way process is not known in detail. Doubless there were many failures: fields were made and not tilled, and farmsteads were abandoned. This happened around Hatfield Forest. In the eleventh century, the Forest-to-be was on the edge of an unusual survival for England: miles of near-continuous woodland, in which places like Molehill Green, Tye Green and Bamber's Green would still have been clearings. We should not assume hastily that this was surviving wildwood. Several other *big* wooded areas of medieval England had been less wooded in Roman and prehistoric times. The Wychwood area of Oxford-shire, for example, has an archaeological record going back to the Neolithic; after the Romans cultivation gradually retreated and the land went back to woodland.[41] There is similar evidence on the Grovely Ridge (Wiltshire), in Rockingham Forest (Northants),[42] and even in Epping Forest.

The Hatfield area is an example of *Ancient Countryside*. As far back as written records go, it has always been an intricate and small-scale landscape, with the hedged fields, hedgerow trees, winding lanes, many ponds, and scattered farmsteads that we meet in the next chapters and still see today. In the *Planned Countryside* of the Midlands and the north-west corner of Essex, the medieval landscape consisted of great open fields divided into thousands of half-acre strips, with few hedges, trees, roads or ponds, and with houses grouped into villages. The distinction cuts very deep in the English countryside, and is already present (though not in quite its medieval form) in the Anglo-Saxon charters. In general it appears that Ancient Countryside belongs to those areas that still had much woodland at the end of the Roman Empire; Planned Countryside developed in regions which by then were mainly farmland (*HC*).

Strip-cultivation in great hedgeless fields is not an aboriginal practice but was a definite innovation of the Anglo-Saxons: a collectivization of agriculture that went with communal farming practices and with the aggregation of settlements into villages. This 'rationalization' was introduced in the Midlands and led to what is now Planned Countryside. The strip-cultivation movement never got far into Essex, which still retains the landscape of an earlier age. Medieval Hatfield did have a little strip-cultivation, the embryo of an agricultural revolution that failed to develop.

The present landscape round the Forest is likely to have been made piecemeal over a very long period. Most of it is undatable, though clearly medieval or earlier. I would guess that much is Anglo-Saxon, but Roman or earlier dates are by no means unlikely. The semi-regular grids by which we can identify very early landscapes in other parts of Essex seem never to have been imposed here.

The future Hatfield Forest is first documented as the 'wood for 800 swine' of Domesday. Its proper name, like that of Epping Forest, has been lost; of pre-Conquest names for the great woods of Essex, only Heywood or Highwood (the original name of Writtle Forest) and Hainault are preserved. Domesday Book takes no interest in what was done with the wood, but there can be no doubt that it was a valuable asset and had long had a formal system of common-rights. Anglo-Saxon charters for other parts of England show that some woods were private and others were communal. Probably the common-rights preserved Hatfield from being grubbed out as were the great woods to the north.

Hatfield township on the eve of the creation of the Forest In Domesday Book there is no hint that Hatfield was regarded as a Forest; the Forest system was still in its infancy. In Chapter 4 we shall discuss how and why it became a Forest. This cannot have been because it had unusually much woodland. The woods of Hatfield comprised little more than the present Forest, about 13% of the parish; this was less than in Essex as a whole, which appears to have been about 20% woodland and wood-pasture in 1086.

Domesday portrays Hatfield as a thriving community. Agriculture had suffered a temporary setback, but less than that caused by the Conquest in many parts of England. There was not much room for expansion. The population as recorded adds up to 114; this is usually thought to be the number of households, so that the real population would have been something like 600. This appears to make Hatfield one of the more populous settlements in Essex, but the population was scattered over a huge township and was not more dense than average.

Domesday describes Hatfield, like everywhere else, as a very class-ridden society. Apparently it was inhabited by fifth-, sixth- and seventh-class citizens; there were not any of the freemen (fourth-class citizens) who were common in East Anglia. As we shall see, most of these distinctions were to fade away in the next three centuries. Hatfield was a place of some importance; before 1066 Amwell and Hoddesdon in Hertfordshire, and Hertford itself, had been administered from it. There is no suggestion that Hatfield was yet a town, but it was the kind of place where a town might well be founded in the next century.

3 On Forests and Deer

The Essex countryside has never been so well off for deer as it is today.

D. I. Chapman, 1977[43]

Where did Forests come from?

We owe the word *forest* to the mysterious Merovingian Franks of north-east France, in whose royal charters it appears from the seventh century. Its original meaning is unknown. The medievals thought it signified a region outside (Latin *foris*) the ordinary laws. The learned brothers Grimm, of *Grimm's Fairy Tales*, conjectured that it had been a place of fir (Old High German *forha*) trees.[44] Both of these guesses are still related by modern etymologists, but there is really nothing to be said for either: scholars clutch at any straw sooner than admit ignorance.

The word may originally have meant land covered with trees, but it soon came to mean a region subjected by the king to special laws, usually connected with preserving game. This latter idea, and the word, became widespread in Europe long before they reached England. Throughout our middle ages *a Forest was a place of deer, not necessarily a place of trees*.

Forests were introduced to England by William the Conqueror. They are first mentioned in Domesday Book, which records about twenty-five Forests. The Forest system in 1086 was still in its infancy, but had passed beyond its earliest stages. It was part of the new, un-English doctrine that all land ultimately belonged to the Crown. The king was no longer preserving just the deer on his own land, but was using the Forest Law to keep deer on other people's land:

38

Domesday sometimes says that land had declined in value because it had been declared a Forest. A few great magnates such as the Earl of Chester were setting up Forests of their own. The introduction of Forests was remembered in the Conqueror's obituary:

> The king W[illiam] set up great protection for deer, and legislated to that intent, that whosoever should slay hart or hind should be blinded... he loved the high-deer as if he were their father.
>
> *Anglo-Saxon Chronicle for 1086*

The Forest system grew under Henry I (1100–35). Probably this was a new development after the introduction of fallow deer, which would have enabled him to set up Forests in places where there were not native deer already. Many Forests, such as Sherwood, are first heard of in the twelfth century, and the legal bounds of others were enlarged. There was a third phase of afforestment under Richard I (1189–99) and his successor King John. This brought the number of Forests in England to about 143, of which some 90 were the king's and the rest belonged to the greatest nobility. The increase in Forests and their corrupt bureaucracy caused friction between the king and the nobility, and was one of the abuses curtailed by Magna Carta (1215). After this Forests began to decline.

Forests in Theory and Practice

Forests could be wooded, like Epping Forest or Wychwood (Oxfordshire), although few were *entirely* woodland. They could equally be heath, like most of Sherwood Forest or Wolmer (Hampshire), or moorland, like Dartmoor and Exmoor Forests. There were even fenland Forests, like Hatfield Chase (S.E. Yorkshire), although most fenland was too valuable at this time to be wasted on deer. Forests were most numerous in moderately wooded countries, like Wiltshire and Somerset; the very wooded parts of England, such as the Weald, the Chilterns and Worcestershire, had few Forests, and those mostly not royal. Taken as a whole, Forests contained no more woodland than the average of England.

Forests became a status symbol of the nobility in Wales, which had more than a hundred, and in Scotland, which had about 180. In Scotland the system flourished much longer than in England:

it lost its connection with woodland altogether, and in one form (the moorland Forests of the Highlands) still operates today.

Forest was originally a legal term, meaning the area within which people could be prosecuted for breaking Forest Law. We now use the word to mean the ***physical Forest*** – the area of wood-pasture or other roughland on which the deer actually lived. Nearly always the legal Forest was much wider than the physical Forest: Forest Law protected deer not only while they were in the Forest but also, to some extent, when they strayed into surrounding farmland. In medieval documents the two meanings are usually not differentiated – the reader would have known which was meant – but sometimes the physical Forest is specified by the words 'covert of the Forest' (Latin *coopertura foreste*). This is a most important distinction, and scholars have drawn a wholly false picture of medieval England by overlooking it. They have worked out the legal boundaries (as in Chapter 4), have assumed that these represent the actual extent of the Forests, and have compounded this blunder by the further error of assuming that Forests were wooded. Hence the pseudo-historical belief that medieval England was very wooded.

The location of Forests was determined not by the terrain – though, except in a few merely nominal Forests, some kind of roughland had to be found for the deer – but by where the king had lands or palaces. The biggest concentration of Forests was in the London-Oxford-Dorset triangle, where the king had up to 15 palaces in which to consume the deer.[45]

Parties in a Forest   A Forest was not the king's absolute property, nor was it 'reserved to the king for hunting' as we are often told. All land, even roughland, in eleventh-century England belonged to someone and was used. The king's deer were added to, and did not replace, whatever was already going on.

Forestal rights comprised the right to keep deer, to appoint Forest officials, to hold Forest courts, and to pocket the fines. These belonged to the Crown in a royal Forest, and to some other magnate in a private Forest. (A private Forest is sometimes, though not consistently, referred to as a 'chase'.)

Forestal rights did not include the ownership of the land. The ***landowner*** had the rights to the soil, the timber and wood, and the grazing, except if there were commoners with prior claims.

40

Most Forests were also commons; the **commoners** had rights to grazing and, in some Forests, to wood or timber also. Common-rights did not belong to the public, nor to the local inhabitants in general, but to the occupiers of particular farms or houses. There might be categories of commoners with different rights.[46] The declaring of a Forest did not much affect the common-rights.

The Forest of Essex

Essex had five or six Forests: Hatfield, Writtle, Epping (anciently Waltham), Wintry (a satellite of Epping), Hainault and Kingswood. In the thirteenth century the whole of Essex was Forest, though in the merest technical sense. The Forest jurisdiction was then reduced to four smaller tracts (Fig. 12). The extent even of these was much greater than of the physical Forests: if the Forest of Waltham contained 60,000 acres, of which Epping Forest now covers 6,000, this does *not* mean that nine-tenths of the 'forest' has been physically destroyed.

Why were these places chosen as Forests? Writtle and Hatfield were royal manors, by far the king's biggest properties in Essex. The king was the landowner in both Forests until 1238. Kingswood was attached to the king's borough of Colchester, and he owned the trees and grazing in it. Hainault Forest was next to the palace of Havering, where the king often came; he owned some land in the Forest. Epping Forest had no direct connection with the Crown – the king owned almost none of it – but it was near Waltham Abbey, the favourite royal monastery, where kings often stayed.

When did Forests begin in Essex? Domesday Book has one mysterious reference under Writtle:

> In [King] harold's time there was one pigman (*porcarius*)... sitting on [45 acres of land]; but after king [William] came Robert [Gernon] took him from the manor & made him forester of the king's wood.

Maybe the Forest, thus obliquely referred to, was Writtle Forest itself; or alternatively 'the king's wood' could mean Kingswood Forest. Robert Gernon had some land at Hatfield, but it is unlikely that there were yet any deer there. He had great estates near what was to be Hainault Forest, but that would surely have been too

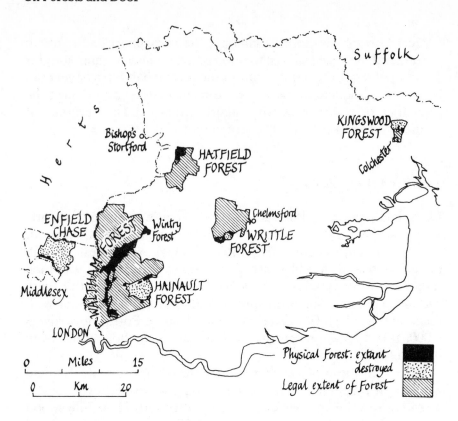

Fig. 12 The Forests of Essex. The legal and physical Forests are distinguished.

big (had it then been a Forest) for a pigman to be made its Forester. From this modest beginning the Forest of Essex was developed, probably by Henry I. It is first expressly mentioned in 1130.[47]

Parks

Deer were also to be found in parks. A park, in the middle ages a place for keeping deer, was more definitely a form of deer husbandry than a Forest. The deer were confined by a special deer-proof fence called a *pale*. Parks were wholly private, though a few had some residual common-rights; there were no special laws.

Parks, like Forests, are a mainly Norman introduction from the Continent. The earliest known park in England, however, was Ongar

42

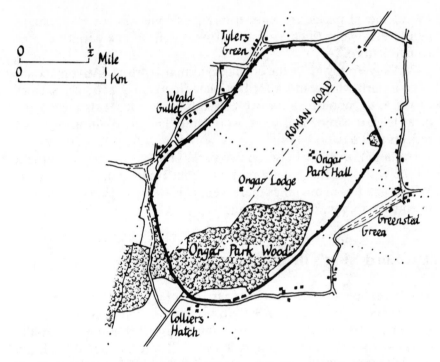

Fig. 13 Ongar Great Park as it survived until *c.* 1950. The parish boundaries are shown, as is the fragment of park boundary which still exists in the south-west. The rest of the park perimeter survived as a hedge (thick line).

Great Park, not far from Hatfield Forest, mentioned in an Anglo-Saxon will of 1045 under the name 'deerhay' (*derhage*).[48] This park can be traced down the centuries, and much of it was still visible until it was tragically destroyed in about 1950. It was very large, about the size of Hatfield Forest, and at this early date was presumably for red deer. It was surrounded by a massive bank and double ditch, in the characteristic shape of early parks – a rectangle with rounded corners, for economy in fencing (Fig. 13).

Domesday mentions Ongar Park and the king's park at Rayleigh (S.E. Essex), and about 33 parks in other counties. Parks proliferated after the introduction of fallow deer. By 1300 they were more prominent in the landscape than ever before or since. In Essex, because parks conflicted with Forest Law, the king's permission to empark was more systematically sought than in non-Forest counties. About

160 medieval parks are known in Essex, one to every 9.6 square miles; they were thicker on the ground than in any county except Hertfordshire.[49]

Parks were lower in the social scale than Forests. Anyone could have a park who could afford it, including gentry and ecclesiastics as well as the nobility. Parks were usually made out of existing woods, or at least incorporated some woodland. The distribution of parks reflects that of woodland.[50]

Hatfield Forest lay between two parks: the king's park of Hatfield on the east, and the private park of Great Hallingbury on the west. Within a radius of ten miles there were at least thirty parks – probably the most parky part of all England.

The Lord King's Beasts

The beasts of the Forest were four: red, fallow and roe deer, and wild swine. These, and these alone, are constantly mentioned in the letters of thirteenth-century kings, our chief evidence for the Forests from the king's point of view.* There are separate Latin words: *cervus* and *bissa*, hart and hind (male and female red deer); *damus* and *dama*, buck and doe (male and female fallow deer); *capreolus*, roe-deer; *aper* and *laya*, wild boar and wild sow. There are also words for various ages: *feto* is a fallow fawn, and *prikettus* is a pricket, a young male with only spike-like horns. Deer in general are implied by *fera* or *bestia*, 'beast'.

In Hatfield (until modern times) *we are concerned only with fallow deer*, the common species in most medieval Forests and nearly all parks. Red deer, then as now, preferred moorland, as on Dartmoor, Exmoor and the moorland Forests of the Pennines; small numbers are recorded from many wooded Forests but not Hatfield nor Writtle. Roe-deer were rare in the middle ages, but are known from various Forests in northern and southern England; they seem to have preferred fenland, and the only eastern record is from the Forest of Huntingdon near Whittlesey. Wild swine were almost extinct: they

---

* In Somerton Forest (Somerset) hares were officially regarded as deer, as were 'wild bulls' – probably related to the 'wild white cattle' still surviving at Chillingham Park (Northumberland) – in Windsor Forest. Claims that wolves and various other animals were beasts of the Forest are pseudo-historical.

are mentioned only in the Forests of Pickering (N.E. Yorkshire) and Dean (Gloucestershire), and a friend of Henry III ate the last dozen of them in 1260. They continued to be kept in parks, including Chalkney Wood twenty miles east of Hatfield Forest, which was maintained as a swine-park by the Earls of Oxford until *c.* 1500.[51]

The fallow deer of Forests did not just happen to be there as wild animals. Red and roe deer were native, but the commonest deer of medieval England was an exotic animal which was not here when Forests and parks began.

Fallow Deer

This animal is, to some extent, the *raison d'être* of Hatfield Forest. It was originally brought from the Near East, runs through the pages of this book for nearly 900 years, and still lives in the Forest. There were small numbers of red deer in Epping and Hainault Forests, but roe-deer and wild swine had been exterminated from Essex before the Conquest.

Properties of fallow deer This summary is based largely on the monograph of modern fallow deer by Norma and the late Donald Chapman (*FD*). It is possible that medieval fallow deer (like medieval rabbits[52]) were less adapted to our climate.

The fallow deer, *Dama dama*, is a sheep-sized animal, a little smaller than the white-tailed deer of America. The buck (adult male) typically weighs about 130 lb, the doe (adult female) 80 lb. They are usually brown dappled with pale spots – the word *fallow* meant yellow-brown – but vary from white to black. The buck's horns, commonly called antlers after those of the red deer,[53] have a distinctive palmate shape; they fall every year and are renewed.

Fallow deer commonly live in woodland, but range over grassland and farmland around a wood. They eat chiefly grass but also brambles, acorns, ivy, dead leaves (and polythene bags). They are very fond of the leaves of some trees and plants; they eat the regrowth of felled woodland, and their likes and dislikes are most effective. In farmland they do surprisingly little damage, considering the amount of crops that they eat: they take a bite here and a bite there, and the damage is made good by more growth of the

45

neighbouring plants. Farmers tolerate fallow deer more than rabbits, which eat a whole area of field bare before moving on to the next.

Fallow deer are gregarious, especially females; I have seen herds of up to seventy. They come together in early autumn, when the bucks' antlers have grown, and spend October observing the sexual rites of rutting. The bucks groan, grunt like pigs, snuffle, scrape the ground, attack aspens and other small trees with their horns, and mark out territories with their scent glands. These ceremonies duly observed, they cover the does. The herds keep together for most of the winter, but then the bucks shed their horns and go their own ways. The does give birth to single fawns, mainly in the second and third weeks of June. This is earlier than in the middle ages, to judge by the 'forbidden month' regulations in Forest Law which were supposed to protect the does while fawning; these ran from 14 June to 8 July, which would be 22 June to 16 July in the modern calendar.

Fallow deer are more suited to semi-domestication in Forests and parks than red or roe. They are easier to keep on a small area of land. They are creatures of habit and stay at home – important in a Forest which has no fence to keep them in. They are less elusive and nocturnal and easier to catch than roe.

Traditionally, fallow deer are for eating; the meat is a little less than half the weight of the animal. In the middle ages it was a priceless delicacy and was never sold. Surprisingly little use was made of the skin, horns or bones.

Deer are prolific: does normally have one fawn every year from the age of two. To keep the population constant, nearly one animal in three each year must die, or be killed, or move away.

How did fallow deer get here?   This deer, though widespread before the last Ice Age, in historic times has been an oriental creature. Its original stronghold was Persia. In Classical times it was known in Rhodes and west Crete. In Crete it was already exotic: the native deer whose bones have been excavated there were of unrelated, and by then extinct, species. The Minoans knew about fallow deer and often depicted them. They probably brought these deer to Crete and thereby began this branch of the wood-pasture tradition in Europe.

The Romans had parks in Italy and Gaul. Writers such as

Columella (first century BC) describe how these were enwalled and stocked with native deer and with exotic beasts such as fallow deer and gazelles. Whether there were such parks in Britain is not known: archaeologists have claimed to find fallow bones in Roman levels, but cannot swear simultaneously to the identification and the date (*FD*). The deer, if they existed, did not survive the end of the Roman Empire. The Anglo-Saxons were familiar with 'high-deer' (i.e. red) and roe, but not with fallow, the only mention of which is in a school textbook of Latin.

Fallow deer are thus a Norman contribution to our landscape. How did they reach the Norman world? In 1061 Roger I, of Hauteville in Normandy, went to Sicily and conquered it from the Arabs. He entered upon a brilliant and cosmopolitan civilization in which Islamic traditions mingled with those of ancient Rome, Greece and Crete. Among these traditions was the keeping of oriental beasts. The Norman kings of Sicily took parks seriously: I once penetrated the awesome ruins of La Zisa, the Arabian Nights palace built by King William the Bad as the chief lodge of the royal park of Palermo.

The Normans in England kept up relations with their cousins in Sicily, and could have acquired fallow deer at any time after 1066. As we have seen, the *Anglo-Saxon Chronicle* notes disapprovingly the Conqueror's introduction of Forests, but knows nothing of a new deer. Fallow were abundant 120 years later. They were probably brought by the earliest extender of the Forest system, Henry I (1100–35), who would have got them from Roger II of Sicily.

Deer in Hatfield Forest Today

The modern countryside is unexpectedly well suited to deer, possibly because many fields and woods never see a man for weeks on end. Deer swarm even over densely populated Essex, except in very urbanized areas. Fallow deer are more widespread than ever before; red deer have returned; and Essex now has roe for the first time, and muntjac, a little deer introduced this century from China.

In Hatfield Forest, fallow deer have their ups and downs but tend to increase. They are very difficult to count (unless food is put out for them in winter) and numbers should be regarded as minimum estimates (*FD*). Mr Lawrence Sisitka tells me that in summer 1987 there were thought to be about 150 head based on the Forest. These included 70 does, 40 fawns and 20 prickets (yearling males). Four separate herds live in Takeley Quarter, Hangman's and Beggar's Hall Coppices, Lodge and Emblem's, and around Collin's. The other forty animals were bucks which move away for the summer and live in surrounding woods. All western Essex is fully stocked with fallow, and elaborate fencing is needed to keep them out of Stansted Airport. In the Forest eighty were killed in 1984, and regular culling is expected in future to prevent the population from exploding.

Fallow deer are most often seen in small groups in the woods; they feed mainly at night on the plains and outside the Forest. Their regular paths, with cloven hoof-marks, extend all over the coppices and into Wall and Monk Woods. There are some light and dark animals, as well as dappled.[54]

Muntjac are a little bigger than a hare, solitary, secretive and seldom seen. They were first seen in 1964;[55] there are now thought to be about twenty. Red deer are well established to the north, beyond Saffron Walden, but only occasionally visit the Forest. Roe deer have never been seen here, although Hertfordshire swarms with them and they are established around Saffron Walden.[43]

4 The Royal Forest 1100–1460

Richard de Toucestr, Walter hunter (is dead), and Alured de Wythinton (who is dead), men and mainpasts[a] of John de Wengham, parson of the Church of Storteford, who is precentor of St Paul's [Cathedral] London, were habitual malefactors of the venison of the lord King in the forest of Hatfeild... [On an unknown day in 1273] they took one Buck in the forest, and also one buck in the park of lord Robert de Brus at Hatfeild, and carried that venison, and always carried whatever they took, to the house of the said John, who consented to their misdeeds and knowingly received them. And they did not come, nor were they arrested. And so the Bishop of London was ordered to make the same John come... and to bring to justice the said Richard his Mainpast. Afterwards the said John came and was committed to prison. And on being released he paid a fine for himself and the said Richard of 40s.

Plea of venison, 1277[56]

[a]A mainpast is somebody who eats out of one's hand.

The King and Hatfield Forest

The making of the Forest No account survives of how Hatfield, or any Forest, was set up: the records of the eleventh and twelfth centuries are meagre. My earliest direct mention is among Henry III's Christmas presents for 1225:

Order to Hugo de Neville to let W., Earl of Warenne, have 10 dry oaks not bearing leaves in the forest of Hadfeld for his fire, of the king's gift.

Calendar of Close Rolls, 27 December

Hatfield therefore became a Forest at some time between 1086 and 1225. During these years, our main source for the Forests is the Pipe Rolls, which often mention the Forest of Essex but do not distinguish its constituent Forests.

Two twelfth-century royal charters mention a Forester at Hatfield, implying that the place had a physical Forest and was not just technically part of the Forest of Essex:

> ... Know that I have given again ... to Humphrey son of Eustace de Barentona and his heirs the land which was Wilfred the forester's in Hadfeld ... for the wardening of my forest ... I grant to him the land which was Adam's, who forfeited himself from the forest, paying for it 12 shillings a year ... I wish and order that the same Humphrey should hold it well and in peace ... in wood and plain ...
>
> *Undated charter of Henry I, 1100–1135*[57]

> ... Know that I have given again ... to Humphry son of Eustace, forester, all the land of his father of Hatfeld and of [Writtle], and specifically the land of Hatfeld ... for wardening my forest. And besides this, the land which was Adam's.... And besides, I have given him again ... his father's office of my forestry ... to hold it from William of Monte Fichet in Essex, as his father did.... And all the foresters and officials of the said forest shall take orders from Humphrey himself as they used to do from his father.... Let him hold it well ... in wood and plain and meadows and pastures and waters and ponds.
>
> *Undated charter of King Stephen, 1135–54*[57]

I am wary of early Forest charters. The medievals liked to think that the Forest system was of venerable antiquity, and forged such documents as the 'Laws of Pseudo-Canute'[58] which still deceive credulous authors into repeating that the Anglo-Saxons had Forests. There is a famous 'charter', in doggerel verse, by which Edward the Confessor (king 1042–66) purports to give the keepership of the Forest of Essex to one Randolph Peperking; but it is written in a rude imitation of Chaucer's English, not the Old English of the Confessor's time, and makes anachronistic mention of pheasants etc. The Henry and Stephen charters, however, which are known from fourteenth-century certified copies, contain no such obvious impostures, and are consistent with what we know of the history of Essex and of the Forest system. I see no reason to doubt them.

By 1135 Hatfield Forest was well established: there were Forest officials, with a hereditary chief, and Adam had already forfeited land for some crime against Forest Law. It is possible that the Forest was founded by William II (king 1087–1100), but more likely it dates from the early years of Henry I, who is known to have extended the Forest system.

Shortly after 1100, therefore, the king decided to set up a number of Forests in Essex, including Hatfield and Epping. At Hatfield the land belonged to the Crown and there would have been little need for formality, except to define the bounds – in effect, to put up notices saying 'This is a Forest'. But a branch of the Forest administration would have had to be set up, and there would have been the practical matter of introducing deer. A hint as to how this might have been done comes from two royal orders, apparently for starting a Forest in Belgium:

> To Richard de Muntfichet... to cause to be taken within and without the king's park of Havering [*i.e. in Havering Park and Hainault Forest*] 80 live does and 40 live bucks for the use of the count of Flanders, and to deliver them to Reynold Ruffus, the king's yeoman, and to have made... such cages as shall be needed to put them in.

> To the sheriff of Essex... to cause 120 bucks and does that the king ordered to be taken alive in the Forest of Essex for the use of the count of Flanders to be carried in carts to the Thames and to cause Reynold Ruffus... to have a ship to carry them to Flanders.
> *Liberate Rolls, 3 and 2 December 1238 (editor's translation)*

Hunting   One of the common factoids that we learnt at school is that English kings were 'passionately fond of the chase', and that Forests were 'reserved to the king for hunting'. This may be true of William the Conqueror; but what real evidence is there of other medieval kings hunting in person? William II met his end in 1100 by a shooting accident (?) in the New Forest; Edward II, the playboy king, was blamed by his contemporaries for spending too much time in the field; Henry VII once slew a deer in Savernake Forest (Wilts);[59] but there is little more. The ordinary working king might or might not care for an occasional day with the hounds, but had little time or opportunity to hunt in ninety Forests. Records of actual royal hunts are remarkably few until Henry VIII, who was a great emparker but took little interest in forests. His daughter, Queen Elizabeth, was a mightier hunter than himself or any of the kings before him. Most of what we 'know' about medieval hunting is based on Continental sources, and it is a fallacy to assume that medieval England was like France.

As far as I know, the king only once visited Hatfield. Henry III was there on 21 August 1229,[60] and at that time of year would probably not have come for the hunting. There was nowhere in Hatfield for a king to stay. There was a small palace at Writtle, and Edward I stayed there for a day or two three times in 35 years;[61] the dates again make it unlikely that he hunted.

The king's hunting was done for him by professionals. This is clear from hundreds of letters of Henry III and his successors, filed in the Close Rolls and Liberate Rolls, ordering deer to be slaughtered for the table royal, for example:

> Order to the seneschal of the forest of Essex, that he allow to be captured the 15 bucks which the king ordered to be taken for his use in the forest of Hatfeud, not reckoning in the number of those bucks the little beasts killed with bows and arrows; and besides those 15 bucks he allow another 10 bucks to be taken.
>
> *Close Rolls, 14 September 1252*

> The king sends Hugh Franceis and Robert de Suninges to the parts of Essex to take in the wood of Haffeld 20 does for the king's use, and in the wood of Blacholehey[a] 15 does. And Richard de Munfichet is ordered to allow them to take [the deer] and to give them advice and help.
>
> *Close Rolls, 8 January 1253*
>
> [a]Between Felsted and Braintree; one of the few woods in Essex, outside the Forests, to have had deer. Part of it survived (as Blackholly or Blackley Wood) until *c.* 1850.

> To the sheriff of Essex ... to receive 12 bucks to be taken in Haffeld forest and delivered by Henry de Candevre and have them well salted and carried to the king at Westminster without delay.
>
> *Liberate Rolls, 20 June 1270 (editor's translation)*

Medieval kings were great eaters of salt venison, especially at feasts. Orders often include arrangements for salting the carcases and transporting them to the palace. Preparations for a big dinner might take a month. At Christmas 1251 Henry III ate 430 red deer, 200 fallow, 200 roe, 200 wild swine, 1300 hares, 395 swans, 115 cranes, and thousands of other beasts and birds, besides salmon and lampreys.[61]

Kings also gave deer to their friends, either as carcases, or as permits to hunt, or alive for stocking parks. For example:

> The king to Richard de Muntfichet, greeting. Know that we have given ... Hugh de Nevill 20 does to re-stock his park at [Great] Halingebery. We have also given [him] two oaks in our park of Hathfeld to fence his said park of Halingebery. And therefore we order you to let him have the said 20 does in your Bailiwick, and the said two oaks in our park ...
>
> *Close Rolls, 26 February 1221*

> P. de Rivall is ordered to let H. earl of Oxford have 3 bucks and 12 does in the king's forest of Hathfeld to stock a certain park of his, of the king's gift.
>
> *Close Rolls, 8 September 1233*

The king's permission to hunt probably gave Hatfield something of the formal pageantry of the chase; but it could easily be misunderstood:

> Presented that Robert de Ver, Earl of Oxford, Robert Carbonel, William Pycot, William de Lauenham huntsman of the said Earl, and several others of his retinue came to the forest of Hatfeld on [14 September 1279] and took four bucks. And that the same Earl and John de Beauchamp . . . came to the said forest on Monday [11 August 1281] and took four bucks. From which the senior forester showed that . . . the King had given the said Earl five bucks that year, and that there was still one to come. But about the said four bucks taken [in 1279] nothing was shown, nor any permit produced; but it was well inquired into . . . by the forester, verderers, and other staff of the forest [and shown] that the said Earl [had a permit] which Michael de Lond, then senior forester, received . . . and that he had not taken them without permission, so he was acquitted.
>
> *Plea of venison, 1292*[62]

A fallow deer is not easy to catch in an unfenced Forest. Before firearms, hunting was a very skilled profession, but we know little about it. There is no shortage of medieval books on hunting, such as *The Master of Game* attributed to no less an author than the Duke of York, *c.* 1400;[63] but these are all derived, if not translated, from Continental originals, and are concerned with the hunt and its etiquette as a courtly science rather than with filling the royal pot. For workaday hunting in England we rely on a few hints in the king's correspondence, for example:

> To the sheriff of Oxford. Order to pay their wages to the king's yeomen William de Balliolo, John Lovel, and Robert Lespuier, whom the king is sending with two *haericii* berners and four *haericii* veutrers and two *daemericii* berners and two *damericii* veutrers, and 24 *haericii* dogs and 24 coursing *damericii* dogs and 30 greyhounds to take the king's fat venison (*pinguedinem*) the present season in the forest of Whicchewode [Wychwood, Oxon], paying them from the present day . . . 12*d*. a day each, 2*d*. daily for each of the two *haericii* berners, 2*d*. daily each for the four *haericii* veutrers, 1½*d*. a day for each of the said *damericii* berners, and 2*d*. a day for each of the said *damericii* veutrers. He is also to provide the said yeomen with salt for the venison and with carriage for the same, as they shall inform him on the king's behalf, making an indenture . . . of the costs expended . . . .
>
> *Close Rolls, 25 July 1312 (editor's translation)*

I leave it to others to investigate just what these technicalities mean.

There were three specialized sorts of hound: the *damericius* was evidently a buckhound, for hunting *dami* or fallow deer; the *haericius* sounds like a Latinization of the word 'harrier', though this does not explain what exactly it did. Of the two houndsmen, the word *berner* is said to mean one who feeds dogs on bran made into dog-biscuits, and the *veutrer* or fewterer to have been in charge of the *veltre* (a breed of hound used for bear and boar).[64] Both words, however, are of much earlier French origin, and who shall say what they meant in fourteenth-century English? Berners and veutrers received the lowest wages for unskilled labour, but yeomen were professional men and were paid accordingly.

Nets are seldom mentioned, but presumably were used for the tricky job of catching deer alive. I have found no mention of snares, which to the modern poacher are the obvious (but illegal) way to catch fallow deer.

A possible method is suggested by this order for Havering Park, next to Hainault Forest:

> Richard de Muntfichet [is ordered to assemble at Havering] a supply of men from the neighbourhood of Havering, to make a breach in the pale of our park of Havering, and to form a line to drive beasts from the forest through that breach into the said park . . . .
>
> *Close Rolls, 1225*

This would have been feasible also at Hatfield. In several places (Writtle is another) the king had a park abutting on a Forest; the park may have held a stock of deer to be caught easily for ready use, replenished from time to time by driving deer out of the Forest.

The dates of orders for venison show that deer were killed all the year, regardless of their condition; for instance, the 10 does ordered from Hatfield Forest for Easter 1248 would have been sorry eating. Males were taken from April to September and females from October to March. (At present, bucks may be killed from August to April and does from November to February.)

Henry III's orders for venison run from 1231 until his death in 1272. In those 41 years he ate 228 deer out of Hatfield Forest, gave away 106 in the form of carcases or permissions to hunt, and gave 125 alive for stocking parks. (These figures take no account of unrecorded or unfulfilled orders.) These add up to 459 fallow deer, 11 head a year, two-thirds females and one-third males (Table 2). The

Table 2   Deer ordered by King Henry III from Hatfield Forest, 1231–1272

	Bucks	Does	Total
Used by the king	38	190	228
Gifts for stocking parks	36	89	125
Gifts of carcases etc.	84	22	106
Total	**158**	**301**	**459**
Epping and Hainault Forests, 1234–63	567	639	1206
Havering Park, 1234–63	428	878	1306

excess of females was rather unusual: in general the king took rather more bucks than does. Hatfield produced about 2% of Henry III's entire consumption of fallow deer (about 600 animals a year (AW)). This was much more than its share for so small a Forest. Epping and Hainault Forests, ten times the area of Hatfield, produced only three times as many fallow and a few red deer.

The parks to which deer were sent ranged from Hallingbury, next to the Forest, to Edwardstone thirty miles away (Fig. 14a).

The king's deer were not an intensive use of the land. Even if we double the recorded figure to allow for poaching, unrecorded orders and deer taken by Foresters as perquisites, one fallow deer annually from some 50 acres of Forest would be well under its capacity. Deer-farming in parks could be much more productive. Havering Park (Table 2) yielded four times as many deer as Hatfield Forest from the same area of land, as well as grazing for the king's cattle and wild swine and grazing rents from local farmers (EF).

The king made very little use of the deer in Hatfield Park, even before he parted with it in 1238. There were deer in Writtle Forest, but as far as we know they benefited him only indirectly, through poaching fines.

The king's orders came very erratically. In 1241 and 1243 he ordered 40 does at once, and a further 20 in 1244, but at other times there were several years without an order (Fig. 15). Gifts of dead deer were usually of bucks, doubtless to make up for the excess of does killed or sent to parks. After Henry III records of this kind were kept only sporadically. To some extent Edward I

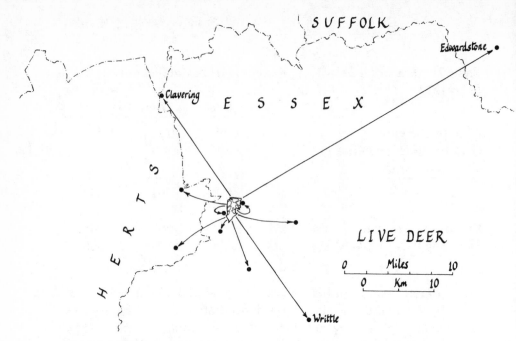

Fig. 14 (a) Parks to which King Henry III commanded live deer to be sent from Hatfield Forest, 1231–63.

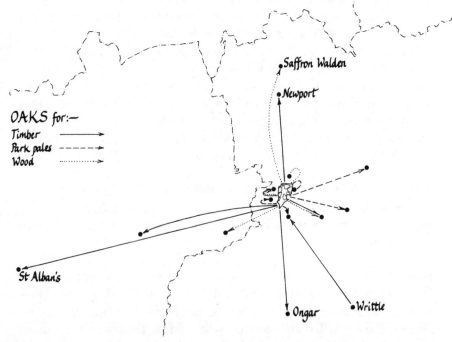

(b) Places to which the king sent oaks from Hatfield Forest, 1225–52.

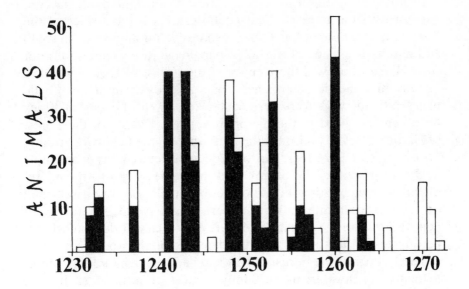

Fig. 15 Numbers of fallow deer ordered by Henry III from Hatfield Forest for all purposes. Black: females. White: males.

kept up Henry's practices: for example in 1280 he gave 12 live deer from Hatfield 'wood' to Robert the Bruce VI to put in Writtle Park.

In the fourteenth century the king ceased to eat the deer out of Hatfield, but assigned his rights in them to others. In 1340 Edward III granted the venison of the Forest for life to Robert de Morle, a neighbouring squire. In 1383 and again in 1408 all the deer were granted to members of the De Vere family of Castle Hedingham.[61]

Forest bureaucracy: officials and courts   In the Forest system we enter a complex bureaucracy that the modern mind cannot easily cope with: a never-never world of perquisites and sinecures, of courts that try offences committed so long ago that the participants are dead, and of nearly as many officials as deer. Scholars have been fascinated by this amazing system, but have never fully understood how it worked in practice; it was probably not quite so inefficient as it sounds. Those who share this interest are referred to C.R. Young's book (*RFME*). Here I summarize those aspects that affected Hatfield.

A 'Forester', *forestarius*, was anyone with any kind of official connection with the Forests. The top Forester was the Justice of the Forest on This Side of the Trent, responsible for all Forests in south and middle England. This exalted personage rarely comes into our story. Under him was the Keeper of the Forest of Essex; we have already met the de Muntfichets, of Stansted Mountfitchet Castle near Hatfield, who were responsible for all the Forests in Essex for a century. Next in the hierarchy was the Keeper of the Forest of Hatfield. Below him were the men who did the fieldwork: riding-Foresters, foot-Foresters, and 'boys'. The structure was not as simple as this in practice. The offices, and the names given to them, frequently changed. Some Forest offices became negotiable assets, and others were hereditary. Hence there was a parallel hierarchy of deputy Foresters. Typically the Foresters received deer and other perquisites of their offices, and the deputies did the work if any.

The Keeper of the Forest of Hatfield had been a hereditary office, belonging to the Barrington family, almost from the start. It went with the post of Woodward. A woodward is somebody who manages a wood, whether in a Forest or not. At Hatfield this post too had become attached to the Forest and hereditary, so that after Henry III ceased to own the woods in the Forest the Barringtons continued to be hereditary woodwards. They were important people, with estates in several other parishes.[65] Their house still stands at Little Barrington Hall, surrounded by the broad tract of land, seemingly bitten out of the Forest (Fig. 3), which they had taken over either from Wilfred the earliest Forester or from the hapless Adam. Later they became virtual owners of a third of the Forest itself. (There is a parallel with the Sturmy family of Savernake Forest, Wilts, who claimed to have been hereditary wardens since William the Conqueror, and whose descendants rose to become Marquesses and owners of the Forest.)

Besides the permanent officials, there were *verderers*, a kind of elected magistrate who held the lower Forest courts. *Regarders* were commissioners, appointed to report on the state of each Forest, in theory every three years.

I have found orders to the sheriff of Essex to arrange for the election of verderers for Hatfield Forest in 1377, 1384, 1389 and 1421. They seem to have been local men of leisure. In 1384 the sheriff himself had taken on the job, but was ordered to elect a successor 'as he is too much occupied with the office of sheriff to busy himself with that of verderer'.[61]

We learn about Forest justice mainly from the rolls of the *eyre*, a kind of grand assize court which met every twenty years or more and which purported to try all the infringements of Forest Law accumulated over the last quarter-century. The eyre for the most part merely reviewed cases which had already been settled in lower courts, such as the attachment courts, in theory held every six weeks, whose records rarely survive. The verderers were supposed to collect the fines at these courts and to hand the money over at the eyre. History seems to be silent on what happened to the fines from the one-third or so of defendants who died before the next eyre.

Forest courts dealt mainly with offences of *venison* and *vert*. Anyone killing a deer without the king's permission trespassed against the venison. Vert – the word (Latin *viride*) merely means 'green' – was divided into trees and other vegetation. A landowner cutting down his own tree, or a farmer stealing a landowner's tree, within a legal Forest both, in theory, trespassed against the vert. So did a commoner or other resident who put animals on the Forest in excess of his grazing rights. There were prosecutions for *assart* – grubbing up Forest roughland and making it into farmland. A provision of Forest Law, though apparently not in Essex, was the *expeditation* or 'lawing' of dogs – cutting off part of one of the animal's feet lest it run after the deer, or in practice drawing a fee from the owner for not doing so.

Every time a deer was found dead an inquest was supposed to be held, with a jury of twelve good men and true sitting on the body, as if it had been a man:

> It happened on Sunday [20 January 1241] that Clement Godcop walking towards the monastery of Hadfeld Regis saw a buck lying dead in the field of Agnes Wood which is called Estfeld; and at once informed Wilfred de Barenton, forester, who ordered the foresters and verderers to hold an inquest in the four [neighbouring] townships [Hatfield, Great and Little Hallingbury, and Great Canfield].
> The township of Hadfeud say that they know and have heard nothing from which the buck might have died except from murrain, that it had no sore (as it seemed to them) and was almost pulled to pieces by pigs . . . .[66]

Not surprisingly, dead deer were seldom reported, and when this happened they were always found to have died of 'murrain' – the general word for unidentified disease.

Poaching   Everyone 'knows' that Forests were places where deer were protected against poaching by 'harsh laws and savage punishments'. This factoid is apparently based on the *Anglo-Saxon Chronicle*'s claim that the Conqueror blinded the slayer of hart or hind. Some obscure statutes of the twelfth century mention confiscation of the offender's testicles as well as eyes (*RFME*). However, medieval legal documents seldom mean what they say. None of the authors who have quoted such Byzantine penalties has ever produced a single actual court proceeding where these organs were even mentioned, let alone forfeited. Offenders were in practice fined, imprisoned, outlawed or pardoned. The Pipe Rolls make it clear that already by 1150 the main effect of Forest Law was to provide revenue.

From the next two centuries records of Forest justice are very copious, and the following cases relating to Hatfield and Writtle illustrate the varied things that happened to people caught trespassing against the king's venison.

> Pardon to John le Vannere of Hatfeld Brodok... of having killed in his close at Hatfeld and carried away a buck which broke that close and often trode down and consumed the grass of his curtilage there.
>
> *Calendar of Patent Rolls, 1354 (editor's translation)*

> Alex who was parker at Hatfeld Regis, with someone else who is dead, hunted one... buck in the forest on Wednesday [30 December 1277] and wilfully carried it away; and now does not come, has not been arrested, and has not been found. And the same Alex was a habitual malefactor of the venison in the same forest. Afterwards Simon de Kensinton came and paid a fine of 10*s*. for the same Alex.
>
> *Plea of venison, 1292*[62]

> Presented... that Ralph de Gynges (who is dead) and Luke Tany came to the forest of Hatfeld on [30 September 1264] with the hounds of Roger de Leyburne (who is dead) & took four does & carried them away without a licence. [The surviving defendant failed to turn up, and an order was made to get him to come.]
>
> *Plea of venison, 1277*[67]

> On Saturday [6 September 1242] William Waybard came to Horsfrith [an outlying wood of Writtle Forest] and saw there Hawe le Esart and three others with him whom he did not know with bows and arrows, and he went away from them and went to Roger de Weulaueston, the Forester, and

60

showed him how he had found them. And this man took men with him, and searched the said wood and could find nothing. And the Foresters and ver-derers met *ad hoc*, and held an inquiry among the four nearest townships ....
Fingrie [Fingrith, now Blackmore] came and say that they know nothing about Forest malefactors, nor their receivers.
Abbess's Ginges [Ingatestone] say the same.
Queen's Ginges [Margaretting] say the same.
Writtle came and say that they have heard from William Wayberd that on Friday [12 September 1242] he saw two running-hounds at a doe worried (*tesatam*) to death; one being black, the other brindled, and he pointed this out to Roger de Weulaueston ....[68]

I have found ten prosecutions for poaching in Hatfield Forest between 1264 and 1368. The humble individual killing an occasional deer rarely came before the courts, and when he did was pardoned. Usually a gang was involved, including on several occasions an important person or the park-keeper from Hatfield or Writtle. In at least three cases somebody went to prison. The Precentor of St Paul's, quoted at the head of this chapter, was an exalted, though not an unusual, clerical gang-leader. His fine of £2 (about £1000 in today's money) would have been meant to deter as well as to provide revenue.

Fallow deer were just as much the king's property as cattle or sheep. In an age when stealing a large sheep was (in theory) a hanging matter, it would not have seemed wholly unreasonable to maim the deerstealer. But the king made nothing like full use of his deer, and had no strong reason to suppress poaching. Even if the medieval fallow deer, like the medieval rabbit, was less prolific than it is now, the official killing of less than a thousand deer a year out of ninety royal Forests cannot have been anything like enough to keep down the population. As often, the medieval law barked harder than it bit, and in a rough-and-ready way got the balance about right. The king could not eat or give away all his deer; he needed to oppress the nobility, but had a duty to protect his humbler subjects; he had no use for eyes or testicles, but had need of the money which Forest transgressions, even in so small a Forest as Hatfield, gave him.

Hermits No Forest was really complete without a hermit. In Essex there were official hermits in Hainault and Writtle Forests. At

61

Writtle, Henry II had endowed a solitary Cluniac monk, later increased to two,

> ... perpetually staying in the same hermitage always to beseech God for the salvation of the living king and for the souls of departed kings.

They were granted a small farm, exemption from vert, and 4*d*. a day pocket-money.[39] Perhaps Hatfield went without a hermit because it had a Priory already.

The Medieval Topography

We make a big mistake if we think that Hatfield Forest existed to supply deer for the king's feasts. This was a relatively minor use of the land; the main users were local countryfolk and their lords. We learn little about them from the royal records; we have to pore over the everyday accounts and court rolls kept in Essex County Record Office. Let us begin with the one official record which says something of what Hatfield Forest looked like in its environment.

The Hatfield Perambulation These are the bounds of the Forest as seen on 28 January 1298. I translate the Latin text (from a seventeenth-century copy[70]) in a form which enables it to be followed on the map (Fig. 16).

> This forest [or] chase ... of hatfeild begins at the end of Shiringelane between the lands formerly of Robert de Shrowes and Peter de haselingfeud [1] –
> *[Shiringelane is the road to Sheering. Shrowes is Shrubs, an ancient farm [1a]. Haslingfield is in Cambridgeshire.]*
> – thence through the field of the said Robert towards the South, & so straight by the ditch which divides Shiringe, hatfeud, and Cowyks [2] –
> *[South must be an error for north. Cowyks is Cowicks, a manor in Sheering [2a].]*
> – & so by the same division as far as a certain place called Pokewoldeshach [3] –
> *[A 'hatch' is the ancient Essex word for a gate across a road. The spot must be where the road from Hatfield Heath crosses into Little Hallingbury. The heath was a common, and like most commons funnelled out, and still funnels, by 'horns' into the roads that ran across it. A hatch would be needed at the tip of the road-funnel to prevent beasts grazing on the common from straying.]*
> – and so thence straight by the ditch of Walter Attehach as far as the pale

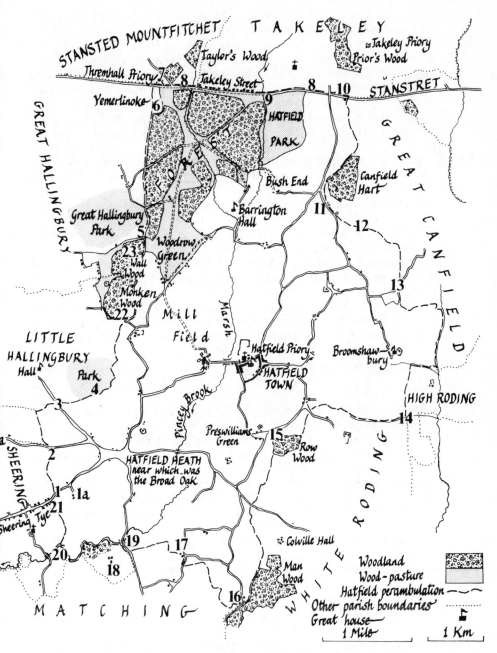

Fig. 16 Hatfield Broad-Oak in the Middle Ages. Numbers refer to the 1298 perambulation. Not every road is shown.

of the park of little hallingbery [4] as the said ditch is the division between Sabrightesworth, hatfeild, & little hallingbery –

[Walter Atte-Hatch would have been the gatekeeper. There is still a farm called Little Hallingbury Park. Sawbridgeworth parish just touches Hatfield.]

– & from the side of the said park towards the North straight by the division which divides the township of little hallingbery & hatfeilde . . . as far as the ditch of the park of Robert fitzWalter in Hallingbery bury [5] –

[The division is a stream most of the way. We pass by Wall Wood [23] without noticing it. We arrive at the great park which adjoined Hatfield Forest on the west.]

– & so from that ditch as far as a certain other ditch which extends through a certain land called Yemerlinke [6] straight up to the priory of Thremhale [7] –

[Yemerlinke – another manuscript says yemerlinoke, *an oak-tree place-name – is evidently the name for the curious bite which Thremhall Priory took out of the N.W. corner of the Forest. The site is now part of a prairie-field. The moats of the Priory are still to be seen.]*

– & so thence by the king's Road [8] which leads towards Dunmowe as far as a certain bridge called martinesforde [9] –

[The bridge over the Pincey Brook.]

– And so from that place straight by the said Road as far as the house of henry loveth [10] straight by the division which divides the townships of Hathfeud & great Canfeud as far as the messuage formerly of Richard Moose [11] –

[Along the border of Great Canfield; we pass the wood called Canfield Hart without noticing it. The messuage is probably Hart Farm, anciently Wood End in Canfield.[71]

– And so by the said division between the same townships as far as a certain meadow called Holmad [12] –

[A meadow must be by a stream, probably that coming out of Canfield Hart.]

– And from that meadow by the division between the said townships as far as a certain pasture called littlehach [13] –

[Another 'hatch' place-name implying a road across a common – probably where Bexley Lane in Canfield met Change Common in Hatfield.]

– & from that place by the division which divides the township of hathfeud heyrothinge & Whiterothinge [14] –

[The boundaries of White and High Roding are mainly streams.]

– as far as the ditch [Latin *fossatum*, which can also mean a woodbank] of the wood of Wilfred morel called Rowewod [15] –

[Row Wood is still there, and has a massive woodbank (Chapter 7) round it. It is now claimed to be partly in Hatfield parish.]

– & from that place by the same division between hathfeud & Whiterothinge as far as the messuage of Walter Chalenar, which messuage is the division between Whiterothinge Matchinge & hathfeud [16] –

[This point is Manwood Green. We have failed to notice Man Wood in White Roding, which until World War II adjoined the boundary.]

–... by the division between matchinge & hathfeud as far as the messuage of hugo de Peruill [17] –

[It is still called Parvill's.]

– And so by the same division ... as far as the messuage of Godfrey Attedonne [18] –

[Mr At-Down was doubtless so called because he lived on a prominent down or hill. His house has come up in the world and is now Down Hall.]

– And from that messuage by the division ... of hathfeud & matchinge as far as a certain bridge called Gysebregge [19] & from that bridge by the division between the said townships as far as a certain bridge called Wassingpol [20] –

[These must be Downhall and Sheering bridges.]

– And thence as far as a certain place called Shiringetye [21] at the end of Shiringslane.

[A tye is a green or small common with houses round it, e.g. Matching Tye nearby. Sheering Tye has evidently become Sheering village.]

And let it be known that everything within the said bounds and divisions ... remains in the forest. Including ... a certain Wood called Monkenewode [22] adjacent, next to the Wood called Walwode [23] in little Hallingbery.

Like all Forest perambulations, this is useless for finding the extent of the Forest; it defines the *legal* bounds of Forest jurisdiction, of which the *actual* Forest was only a small part. As a description of Essex countryside in 1298 it is of the greatest value. Hatfield has changed remarkably little: it is still possible to walk with certainty where the surveyors walked nearly seven centuries ago, and to identify the landmarks. The boundary is evidently that of the whole parish of Hatfield. The only place where one hesitates is around points [19] and [20]; here it looks as if the boundary has later been changed to bring the Down Hall estate within Hatfield. All the roads, bridges and hatches in the perambulation are identifiable in terms of roads or lanes that still exist.

The perambulation should dispel any notion that Forests imply woodland. Only three woods are mentioned – Row Wood, Monk Wood and Wall Wood – and all three still exist. The perambulation might have mentioned Canfield Hart and Man Wood, which undoubtedly existed at the time, as well as the woods in the Forest itself; these too are still extant (Man Wood much reduced by the making of Matching airfield). As far as I am aware, these were all the large and middle-sized woods in or around Hatfield at the time.

Essex, then as now, was a land of dispersed settlement and not of villages. This description of the parish boundary manages to pass through six houses and mentions two others. Several of these, such as Shrubs, Parvills and Cowicks, are still known by the same names as in 1298. It is quite possible that some of the actual buildings are still standing (Chapter 8); the perambulation just misses the magnificent medieval farmstead of Colville Hall.

The interior of Hatfield parish   There are several surveys of Hatfield, including detailed ones of 1328[72] and *c.* 1450.[73] The fifteenth-century rolls of the manor court give us many allusions.[74]

Hatfield comprised a market town, many hamlets and scattered farmsteads, various greens and small commons, some with houses round them, and the houses round the perimeter of the Forest. There were two chief manor-houses, one in the town and the other isolated. Adjacent to the present church was Hatfield Priory, a smallish Benedictine monastery, founded in the 1130s, of which John Lydgate, the poet, was once Prior.[75]

The court rolls and *c.* 1450 survey mention all the hamlets and scattered farmsteads now in Hatfield, and maybe others now deserted. Hatfield Heath was evidently a real heath (Latin *bruera*) as well as a settlement. Woodrow Green, the south end of the Forest, had rather more houses round it than there are now. In 1434 there is an allusion to Bush End, which defines the east corner of the Forest.

The market town is first heard of in 1222.[60] By 1328 it was much more flourishing than it is now. The survey relating to the market-place mentions 14 shops, 12 houses, 35 stalls (belonging to 19 owners), 7 'purprestures' (that is, encroachments – possibly stalls that had turned into permanent buildings), one 'place' (a vacant site?), one cottage (i.e. a house with some land), and a smithy. A century later, Hatfield town had probably been ravaged by the plague; yet it had an astonishing number and variety of tradespeople, to judge by those who were fined (often time after time) for infringing the consumer-protection regulations. For example, in 1447 eleven brewers and eight bakers of human bread were fined 1*d.* or 2*d.* each. In 1448 four butchers, two fishmongers and a tanner of ropes [made of leather?] were fined for excessive prices. We hear likewise of a baker of horse-bread (in 1441) and a leather-tawer (1443).

Estimates of population inevitably include the whole vast parish and not just the town, but all through the middle ages Hatfield was certainly one of the bigger country towns of Essex, comparable in relative importance at least to Braintree today.[76]

What did the countryside look like? The earliest map, dated 1587, covers part of the south of Hatfield, and shows that all the present roads and most of the hedges now surviving were already there.[77] In 1450 all these roads existed – each with its own name – and several others now vanished. Petty courts spent much of their time on road offences, for example:

> Richard Haber appropriated from the king's highway at Preswilliamesgrene one piece of land 1 perch [16½ feet] long and 1 perch wide on which he placed a dead fence to the annoyance [of passers-by] ... [fined 2d.]
>
> *11 June 1443*
> [Pierce Williams is a hamlet near Row Wood, named after a thirteenth-century inhabitant.]

> [Richard Gyva, turner, of Takeley, established] a purpresture on the town waste at Stanstret ... in length ... by the ditch of the close of the tenement of the said Richard in Takeleghe on the north, and the king's way called Stanstret on the south ... 65 feet long by the said ditch by a ruler, and in width at both ends and in the middle 3 feet by the ruler ... [charged an annual rent of 1d.].
>
> *20 July 1448*
> [Takeley Street half-village fronts on to Stane Street, now the A120 road, on what used to be the north edge of the Forest. Mr Gyva had been pushing his garden fence out 3 ft into the road, as gardeners still often do today. As the Tithe Map for Hatfield (1838) shows, the boundary between Takeley and Hatfield is the north edge of the road, not the middle.]

There were many such purprestures, encroachments on to public or common land, especially into the width of roads. In 1447 John Nedeman was fined for appropriating 14 × 8 feet of the king's way for 'one layby (*diversorium*) to put his cart in it'. The Vicar and many of his flock put muckheaps in the road. In 1443 William Barbor, junior, was fined 2d. for blocking the king's way with wood. He had also 'erected one latrine ... running into the king's way to the annoyance of passers-by'; he did nothing about it and was fined at every court for at least four years.

There was some open-field strip-cultivation. For example, the courts had recurring trouble with Woodrow Hatch, the south gate into the Forest, through which beasts in the Forest were liable to get out and do damage to 'the tenants who have any corn growing in the field called mellefeld'. This implies that Mill Field was a small open-field, with several occupiers and without hedges to keep beasts out. There were several such small open-fields in the area: Bush-End Field in Hatfield, and Beetle and Mill Hide common fields in Little Hallingbury, survived into the nineteenth century.[77] There is no suggestion that these were relics of a time when open-field had been general: most of these parishes, like most of Essex, has always been 'conventional' fields with hedges and single occupiers.

Hedges are abundantly mentioned, often in the context of disputes between neighbours; in Canfield they were sometimes allowed to overgrow and obstruct the highway.[71] A hedge in Essex then was much the same as it is now. For example, Richard Tye complained that on 10 March 1442

> ... John Palmer senior entered his land called Heggefeld in Hatfeld... & cut down to the ground certain underwood growing there, to wit maples, white thorns & black, and other trees & took and carried away the underwood ... value 6s. 8d.

Some hedges, by the 'hedge-dating' rule of one species per century, should already have been ancient.[79] A year later:

> James Mede complains that John Palmer senior in the month of March cut down to the ground, took & carried away divers Trees... viz. oak, ash, Maples, white thorn & black, lately growing in a certain hedge of the said James between heighfeld and hegfeld, and had been repeating this trespass from time to time for 7 years... by which the said James has been wronged and has suffered damage to the value of 20s.

Pollard trees, which are still a common, though rapidly diminishing, feature of Essex hedges, are mentioned in the court rolls. Medieval hedgerow trees often included black poplar, which is now rare (probably extinct in Hatfield). John House sued William Bene for 10s. because

> ... in February [1436] William shredded (*defrondauit*) certain trees of the said John, viz. poplars and maples, growing in a certain hedge belonging to three rods of land... in a certain field called Moltfeld & took & carried away the underwood cropped from them [and came back seven years later and lopped the same trees again].

Hedges and trees were worth a lawsuit because, apart from the Forest, Hatfield had very little woodland. There were a few small woods, such as Down Hall Wood and this one, now unidentifiable:

> Thomas Brond and John Whitaway... who have some land abutting on the grove of the lord of this manor called Balneygrove [are summoned] to

answer ... why they cut down very many oaks lately growing on the edge of the said grove against their land and took them and carried them away, viz. the said Thomas 8 oaks, the said John 15 oaks, bigger and smaller ....

Court roll, 18 July 1444

The extent of the physical Forest   Woodland is very stable. Medieval woods often survive even where the rest of the landscape has been transformed as it has not been here. In the neighbourhood of Hatfield Forest, almost every single large and middle-sized wood which existed in the middle ages is still there, or was until the era of the Ministry of Agriculture and the Forestry Commission (Fig. 7).

What of Hatfield Forest itself? Was the medieval Forest bigger than it is now? I shall take 'now' to be the year 1857, just before the Forest was truncated by an Enclosure Act (Fig. 3).

On the north and west sides the Forest was confined by the bounds of other parishes, and by the perambulation which we have just followed; the legal and physical boundaries coincided. To the east it was fixed, as we shall see, by Hatfield Park. The south boundary is fixed by Wood Row, a settlement not only recorded in writing from the fourteenth century,[80] but having several medieval buildings and a moat still extant.

The south-east side of the Forest abutted on the Barrington lands, and is fixed by one of the Forest's oldest documents, the Barrington Claim. The full text we shall discuss later. The Barrington lands are said to lie 'from fflouentie Herne to Bugenhach in the forest'. The latter place-name is evidently a misspelling of Bush-end Hatch. The former name includes the word 'tye', discussed on p. 65. *Herne*, which occurs in several Essex place-names, is Old English for a corner; specifically it may mean a funnel where a common narrows out into a road, as with the 'horns' of Blackmore Forest in Dorset. Flowentye Herne would be an appropriate name for the funnel of Forest that projected from Wood Row towards Little Barrington Hall (Fig. 3).

The Forest probably had, as later (p. 131), eleven gates or hatches. Woodrow Hatch, *alias* Houseshatch, often came before the manorial courts in the 1440s because the people responsible had not repaired it. There was a Bush-end Hatch, and presumably another at Flowentye. On the Great Hallingbury side, there was a North Hatch, mentioned in *c.* 1450, and presumably also a South Hatch. (A 'way which leads from *Alingbir'* [Great Hallingbury] to the forest of Hatfield' is mentioned as early as 1238.[81])

In some Forests there were frequent prosecutions for *assart*, encroachment on the physical Forest. I have found only two at Hatfield (apart from minor purprestures at Woodrow Green). In 1324 the Prior of Thremhall was convicted of having enclosed a croft – a private field – from the Forest in 1305; he was fined 2*s*. and allowed to keep it.[82] Presumably this was an extension to the Yemerlinoke land mentioned in 1298. In the 1328 survey he is said to have 14 acres of land; the modern area of Yemerlinoke is 17 acres. The assart was more important than its area would suggest. In the middle, until recently, there was a small moat, evidently for the Prior's windmill; the site was called 'Mill Fields' in *c.* 1800.[78]

I conclude that the thirteenth-century Forest had, with very minor changes, the same area (1100-odd acres) and outline as before the enclosure of 1857.

Owners of the Forest

Originally the king was owner of the deer in Hatfield and Writtle and owner of the soil of the Forests – as lord of the principal manors, owner (on paper) of almost everything in both parishes. At Hatfield he had two manor-houses, Hatfield Bury and Broomshaw Bury, each with a substantial farm attached. The rest of the farmland, about two-thirds of the parish, belonged to the king's tenants, who were supposed to work the manor farms for him and to perform various services by way of rent.

In 1238 all this was disposed of into private hands in a curiously casual way. The Earl of Chester had died, leaving his estates and the earldom to his children John and Isabel. Isabel had married into what was to become the illustrious Scots family of Bruce. Henry III intervened, offering to take over Isabel's share of the inheritance and to make her a fair exchange:

> Grant to Isabel de Bruys that for her [share of the inheritance of the late earl] in [Cheshire], the king will make her a reasonable exchange in that county; and for her greater security the king has committed to her the manors of Writel and Hathfold, co. Essex, in tenancy, until an extent of her [share] be made and the same assigned to her.
>
> *Patent Rolls, 11 June 1238 (editor's abridgement)*

Morant, the eighteenth-century Essex historian, remarks that the king took over the earldom 'lest so fair an inheritance should be divided among females', but perhaps Henry merely did not want to be cluttered with two half-earls. Isabel the Bruce thus had Hatfield and Writtle in lieu of a more permanent settlement which the king never got round to making.

The king retained the Forestal rights. Hatfield and Writtle passed into the category of Forests, like Epping, in which the king kept deer on land belonging to somebody else. Isabel owned the land, the trees and all that was on it, and was lady of the manors, but like other landowners within a legal Forest, was expected to obey the Forest Law or to pay the penalties.

In 1252 Isabel died. Her son Robert was a distinguished English judge as well as Competitor for the throne of Scotland. When he died in 1295 his son was another Robert the Bruce, Earl of Carrick and Annandale in Scotland, and on his death in 1304 Hatfield and Writtle passed into the hands of *the* Robert the Bruce.

Robert the Bruce had much to occupy him in Scotland, but he came to England to settle his father's affairs, and is known to have been in Hatfield on 4 April 1304.[83] He had no chance to come again. In 1306 he was crowned Robert I, king of Scotland, and thereby was held to have committed high treason against Edward I, who claimed to be king of Scotland too. Edward confiscated Robert's English estates, but allowed Eleanor his wife to keep a one-third interest in Hatfield and Writtle until she died in 1332.

Hatfield was not long to remain in Crown ownership. On Edward I's death, Edward II bestowed Hatfield and Writtle (less Eleanor's life-interest) on his own sister Elizabeth, who had married Humphrey VIII de Bohun, fourth Earl of Hertford and Essex. This time the king parted not only with the manor but also with part of the Forestal rights, namely the proceeds of the courts:

There is there a certain forest called hatfeldforest, whose venison belongs to the Lord King, and the wood and soil belong to the Earl . . . it is common to all the tenants, but the lord gets the fines & transgressions.

Inquisition post mortem, *1336*[4]

The de Bohuns, lords of Hatfield for two centuries, were as exalted as the Bruces: they were warriors (one of them had the honour

71

of being split with a battleaxe by King Robert in person on the field of Bannockburn), patrons of manuscript illumination,[84] and great landowners in Essex and elsewhere. Their estates included Quendon Wood and Dunmow High Wood.[4] The de Bohuns clashed with Forest Law more than the Bruces; at one stage the king even applied the supreme penalty of temporarily confiscating his brother-in-law's woods. However, in 1360 Edward III gave William de Bohun the unusual gift of permission to hunt in Hatfield Forest until further notice.[85]

The de Bohuns nearly came to a bad end in 1397, when Thomas, Duke of Gloucester, who had married Eleanor de Bohun, meddled in politics and, in Morant's sinister phrase, was 'taken off' by Richard II and his lands confiscated; but when Richard himself was 'taken off' in 1399 the de Bohuns were rehabilitated. In 1421 their estates were inherited by Anne Stafford and King Henry V. Anne's share included 'le manor de hatfeld', valued at £81 4s. 7½d. per annum – a very valuable manor indeed – together with 'un fforest', 1 parc', and 7 outwoods (woods outside the park).[86]

Anne's son Humphrey Stafford rose in the royal favour and was made Duke of Buckingham in 1444. Probably as a further favour, Henry VI relinquished the Forestal rights in 1446, and thereby brought to an end Hatfield's history as a royal Forest.

Woods and Trees

The king's oaks In his earlier years, Henry III used or gave away trees from Hatfield Forest and Park much as he did deer. Here are some examples:

> Order to R[ichard] de M[untfichet]... to let W[alter] de Kirkeham have 20 oaks in the king's wood outside his park of Hadfeld, to repair the king's fishpond (*vivarium*) at Newport; he is to have them entirely, with the foliage and everything else, without keeping anything back.
>
> *Close Rolls, 18 July 1231*

> Order to Walter de Burgh to let the sheriff of Hertford have in the king's wood of Hadfeld enough timber to make 20 thousand shingles to roof the king's buildings in Hertford castle.
>
> *Close Rolls, 19 October 1236*

> Order to Richard de Muntfichet to let W., Earl Warenne, have six oaks,

of the gift of the Lord King, in the park of Hathfeld to repair his buildings at Roinges [probably High Roding].

Close Rolls, 14 January 1224

Order to Hugo de Nevill to let W., Earl Warenne, have 10 dry *robora*, not bearing leaves, in the forest of Hadfeld for his fire, of the king's gift.

Close Rolls, 27 December 1235

Trees specified are either oaks for timber, or *robora*. This last is not just another Latin word for oak; it occurs often in Forest records, nearly always as firewood. The interpretation that best fits is that *robur* means a dead pollard (*EF*).

The numbers of trees mentioned are very small. The records cover 22 years (1221–1242); in that time 81 timber oaks, plus 30 *robora* and dead oaks, were ordered from Hatfield Forest, 49 oaks from Hatfield Park. This cannot represent all the felling there was. The buildings, equipment and fires of Hatfield would have consumed vastly more than seven trees a year; but most of this was routine woodcutting, recorded (if at all) in the estate accounts, which have not survived. The Rolls record only those gifts and special uses which were unusual enough to require the king's authority. Forests in general, as I have shown, were a source of specially large and costly oaks (*HC, AW*). Some of those which Henry III gave to religious houses still, to this day, hold up the great roofs of Lincoln Cathedral and Gloucester Blackfriars.[87]

The Hatfield oaks were not used for such exalted purposes, nor were they transported long distances like some of those used at Gloucester, but the small numbers suggest unusual size. For example, in 1236 the king gave 5 oaks from Hatfield Park to the Dean of St Martin's, London, to make posts for a barn at Newport (eight miles away), together with 5 oaks from the 'Forest of Essex' and 10 oaks and 100 'rafters' from private woods temporarily in the king's hands. This suggests an aisled barn, built round a small number of great internal posts, like the marvellous Wheat Barn, of almost exactly this date, which still stands at Cressing Temple, 16 miles from the Forest. The recipients were mostly local dignitaries and magnates; we wonder why the king twice gave *robora* to Roger de Ros, tailor.

Such oaks were rather few in the Forest: when the king gave Hatfield Priory twenty oaks for repairs in 1230, ten came from the Forest and ten were brought from Writtle (Fig. 14).[74]

The Bruces and Bohuns After the king disposed of Hatfield and Writtle, Forest Law might have applied to the new owners in respect of the trees. In theory, felling timber or wood within a legal Forest was a contravention of vert, and required the king's permission; even carting wood incurred a fee called *chiminage*. In practice this did not happen. The men of thirteenth-century Essex made the same use of their woods as those of Suffolk, who were not under Forest Law. We do not, alas, find in the Public Record Office a file of felling licences for every wood in Essex; nor did a prosecution result from building every timber-framed house. There was evidently an understanding that normal woodmanship and trade in timber and wood did not infringe Forest Law. In Epping Forest it was the custom that only holly, hawthorn and crabtree counted as vert (*EF*). Prosecutions were rare and resulted from something unusual, such as grubbing out a wood.

Such understandings were often unwritten, and scholars have overlooked them. The men of Hatfield and Writtle claimed at the Forest court of 1324 to have the existing right to cut their woods without permission.[82] There survives a specific dispensation for a wood in Hatfield:

> Order ... to let the Prior of Hadfeld & the men of the same township have maintenance (*sustentacionem*) in the wood of Hadfeld as they used to have ... at the time when the township of Hadfeld was in the hands of Guy de la Poscener.
>
> *Close Rolls, 1225*

When Henry III settled Hatfield on Isabel the Bruce, a dispensation was written into the grant:

> Isabel de Bruys and her heirs are granted the manors of Writtle and Hatfield in perpetuity ... quit of waste of forest and assart ... they can take dry and green wherever they wish in the woods ... they shall be free of Chiminage, and their said woods shall be in their own keeping .... Excluding only ... our Venison in the outwoods of the said manors outside the Parks.
>
> *Close Rolls, 1241*

The king was not whole-hearted about parting with the trees in the Forest. He continued to take them from 1238 to 1242, and once in 1258. (I have noted elsewhere that Henry was absent-minded about taking trees from lands he no longer owned.) In 1242 he was worried:

74

Order to Richard de Muntfichet to guard the forests of Writtle and Hatfield as before, and not to let Ysabel de Bruys destroy or assart the wood of the said forest, because the king granted the manor and woods to Ysabel, excluding... the venison of the same forest, which will be worth nothing to the king or his heirs if the wood of the said forest is destroyed.

Close Rolls, 1242

More serious conflicts came in the de Bohun period. In 1315 one Roger le Haukere was bailed out of Colchester gaol, awaiting trial at the Assizes on a charge of vert.[61] A vert offence of this rare degree of gravity would have had to do with trees rather than grass. The king confiscated the woods of Writtle and Hatfield for the life-time of John de Bohun, Earl of Hertford & Essex,

because it was lately... convicted by the steward of the forest in the county of Essex and by the foresters, verderers, regarders and twelve free men dwelling within the forest... that John wasted and altogether destroyed his wood called 'le Heghwode' in the town of Writtle to the harm of the king and his beasts, and that W. de Fynchyngfelde, who was the king's steward, sold 100 oaks in the cover of Hatfeld when the earl was in Scotland, and that Walter had four charcoal hearths (*astra ad carbones*) in the said cover, to the destruction of the forest and the detriment and escape of the king's beasts....

Close Rolls, 1336 (editor's translation)
[Heywood or Heghwode, nowadays corrupted to High Wood, is the collective name for all the woods in Writtle Forest.]

The next Earl made his peace with the king and got the woods back, and we hear no more of such disputes.

I wish I could find those charcoal-hearths. Charcoal-burning is rarely recorded in medieval Essex. Charcoal was an urban and an industrial fuel, made in huge quantities in the industrialized Forest of Dean, where it was an important source of revenue for the king.[88] In rustic Essex, every manor used small amounts for the smith's forge.

Uses of wood and timber   The normal use of medieval woodland was coppicing, which provided most of the regular income. For example, when John de Bohun died, his lands at Debden included

Wood called Rowenhey in which can be sold (after the six years next following) 20 acres of underwood per annum, which are worth 100*s*. per annum at 5*s*. an acre; but there is no pasture... the parson of the church of Depeden shall have... every year half an acre of underwood... And the pannage is worth... 6*s*. 8*d*....

Post-mortem survey, 1336[4]

Rowney Wood is still on the map, though the Forestry Commission has wrecked it. Its area, 158 acres, indicates an eight-year coppice cycle. The same survey, at Great Dunmow, mentions a coppice cycle of apparently 8 years in High Wood (still extant) and 5 years in Nattok Wood. These figures illustrate the medieval practice of cutting woods on short rotations; as in all such surveys, they are estimates of the average of what would in practice have been a varying number of acres cut each year (*HW, AW*).

In wood-pastures, normal coppicing was precluded because the grazing animals would have eaten the regrowth. There are records of both solutions to the problem: pollarding and compartmentation. Compartmentation, exactly as we find it in Hatfield Forest, was practised in John de Bohun's park at Saffron Walden (p. 13).

How much of this applied to Hatfield itself? The documents already quoted imply all three kinds of tree typical of the Forest down to this day: timber trees, underwood (implied in charcoal-burning) and pollards (*robora*). More details come from surveys, and from the Barrington Claim already mentioned:

> John son of Nicholas de Barenton of King's Hatfeld puts in a claim... to the forest fee and Woodwardry...
> [of which the perquisites include] sufficient fuel in the said forest of hatfeld from underwood for his consumption in the manor, without selling any;
> and also sufficient underwood to fence the said lands lying against the said forest (that is to say, from fflouentie Herne to Bughenhach in the forest);
> and also all the wood brought down by wind from any manner of tree;
> and also all branchwood (*escheetes*) of every manner of tree which is cut down in the said forest which is not suitable for work on ploughs...;
> [and the stump of any ancient 'stock-oak' cut down (p. 240)]
> [and the second-best haycock in the common marsh]
> and also to have [right of] common in the said forest with every manner of animal...;
> the said John & his ancestors have used the said rights from time of which there is no memory....[89]

There were two Sir Nicholas de Barentons, who flourished *c.* 1240 and *c.* 1300;[90] the Norman-French language makes the former more likely. A later version of the Claim adds, as a perquisite,

> the topmost branches and *robos* [?error for *robora*] cut down for pasturing the deer....[91]

This document appears to relate to conditions in the thirteenth, if not the twelfth, century. It clearly mentions timber and underwood.

The mysterious 'ancient stock-oak' would appear to be an oblique reference to a pollard; one purpose of pollarding in wood-pastures was to provide 'browsewood' for the deer to gnaw when times were hard (*AW*).

The survey of 1328 unfortunately falls in the period when the king had confiscated the Forest woods; it therefore mentions underwood in the farm groves and park, but says of the Forest 'nothing can be got from the underwood in the same'. However, the tenants' labour services included carting underwood, termed *busca* – a Latin word generally meaning firewood:

> [The tenants] shall carry four cartload of *busca* from the forest to the manor [-houses] of hatfelde or brunshoo [Broomshawbury] with 1 cart, 1 man, and 1 horse. So that they shall carry as much great *busca* as two men can lift together and put in the cart; or they shall fell the *busca* for the said 4 cartloads.

This presupposes long-rotation coppicing producing heavy logs.

The '7 outwoods' inherited by Anne Stafford in 1421 (p. 72) probably mean the Forest coppices – excluded from the park, as the word *foreins boys* implies.

The 1328 survey mentions a curious perquisite of the blacksmith, John Phelippe, who in return for looking after the lord's ploughshares and coulters

> shall get from the lord every Year in Hatfield forest one oak. So that the lord shall choose the best and the same John shall get the second-best. And this concession to the smith is worth 13s. 4d.

This hints at the size of the Forest oaks. Oak-trees in ordinary woods normally sold for between 0.3d. and 20d. each; the largest, to judge by the bigger oaks to be found in ordinary medieval buildings, would be a tree about 15 inches in diameter and 20 feet in usable length. Hatfield Forest produced each year at least one oak of eight times this value: not especially enormous – the post on which a windmill turned could cost £1 or more – but an outsize oak which commanded a special price. As the timbers in the Lantern of Ely Cathedral, built at exactly this time, show, outsize oaks were more difficult to get in the 1320s than ever before or since (*AW, HC*). The smith's oak might have had a trunk 30 feet long and 20 inches thick, not so very large by modern standards – many in the Forest now are bigger.

After the de Bohuns got the woods back, we have estate accounts for the year 1377–8, which detail those uses of trees which involved money.[92] Four acres of underwood were sold in the Forest at 13s. 4d. the acre, a price which implies a long coppice cycle of about 20 years (AW). The park produced 400 faggots, sold at 3s. 4d. the hundred – they cost 9d. a hundred to make.

Timber in that year was used only for work on the estate, although by-products such as branches and bark were sold for small sums. In the usual way, trees were used at once without seasoning. Three carpenters were hired for 30 days to fell and work timber for repairs to the gatehouse of Broomshaw manor-house. Three carpenters spent four days felling and squaring timber and rebuilding a broken bridge, and one carpenter four days on the Lady's henhouse. Two men were hired for five days to split timber and make 32 hurdles of oak sapwood (cost' querc') – evidently the type of hurdle which looks like a small gate. Most of this was oak, except for one ash felled in the park to make carts. The working woodward of the Forest was paid 2s., which would have been a part-time salary, and the smith duly got his oak.

If this account is representative, the Forest was not a big asset to the de Bohuns. The Forest, park, and hedges produced between them all the timber, and doubtless the fuel, for a huge estate, but only a few per cent of the total cash income of £158 12s. 3½d.

In the next century the manor was leased out to a 'farmer' or lessee, and hence we have no accounts, but the Forest was excepted. In a valuation of 1435, 'sale of underwood in the forest' was valued at £1 16s. 4d. a year.[93] Buried in the court rolls are accounts of some of the sales of trees, for example:

Sales of faggots & ashes in the park and the forest. £6 12d.
John Yenge, Woodward, certifies to the court on his oath that there were made in the forest this year 6½ hundred faggots priced at 4s. the 100 (besides 12d. paid for making the same), whence the total of 26s.; which faggots came partly from the boughs of the oaks which were felled in the said forest for making a new stable on this manor, partly from other underwood felled there . . . .
There were sold this year in the forest and the park . . . divers ashes, viz. to Walter Short of Takeleghe 12 for 18s., to Henry Deepham at [Bishop's] Storteford 8 for 9s., to George Whelewrighte of Storteford 3 for 4s., . . . [a total of 34 ashes from the Forest and 35 from the park, sold to 18 people] . . . whence the total for the said ashes £4 15s.

Court roll, 15 September 1442

To be inquired into . . . about all the ashes, maples, & other trees felled in the forest & the lord's park & sold to divers persons by the officers of this manor . . . .

Court roll, 18 May 1443

Sale of faggots and ashes in the forest 19s. 6d.
From the report of John Yenge, Woodward . . .
made in the forest this year 320 faggots . . . total 12s. 4d.
[and 5 ashes sold for 6s. 4d.]
Item, there were felled in the park and forest this year for making the new windmill of this manor 58 oaks, 2 ashes & 2 aspens; of which 49 oaks, 2 ashes & 1 aspen in the forest, & 9 oaks & 1 aspen in the park. From which the boughs were delivered to John Baldewyne, Millwright, with the rubbish (*quisquelijs*) and all the by-products . . . in part-payment of his stipend . . . .
Item, there were sold in the said park 12 ashes . . . for 10s.

Court roll, 20 July 1443[74]

Though incomplete, this gives some indication of the landowner's uses for trees. Timber trees included oak (always the commonest) but also ash and aspen. The ashes fetched an average of over a shilling each, which must imply big trees, since an ash was normally rather less valuable than an oak of the same size. They were not of outsize importance, for all the purchasers came from Bishop's Stortford or Takeley or Hatfield itself.

At Writtle the accounts are fuller and tell us much about pollarding. Beech at that time was native there, and grew in Writtle Park and Heywood Common, the principal plain of the Forest. The accounts for five years between 1396 and 1426 include sales of *lopp' fagorum* and *capita fagorum*.[94] These 'lops' and 'heads' of beeches are distinguished from *cropp'*, the boughs of trees felled for timber; for example, 'To John Howchin in Heywode for five heads of beeches 15d.' There are also occasional mentions of shredding, *defrondacio* (Fig. 5). In 1397–8, 119 beeches were pollarded, realizing £2 16s. 6d., and smaller numbers in other years.

Thirty beeches in the Park were equivalent in value to an acre of underwood; they were therefore big trees pollarded on a long rotation. This is confirmed by a dispute in 1396–7 between John Bachelor, who had bought eight lops, and John Borell, a haulage contractor, who had not turned up to cart them. Borell brought a counter-claim for 3s. 4d. in lost time, alleging that Bachelor

should have faggotted up the topmost branches of the said lops and should have split with wedges all the great underwood ready to load on to the cart according to contract, which was not duly done; so that the said John Borell took 3 days longer to carry the said wood than if it had been faggotted and split.

The Writtle accounts also tell us about coppicing. For example, in 1397–8, twenty-seven people bought 6.3 acres of underwood in Horsefrith wood, in lots of from $\frac{1}{16}$ acre to 1 acre each, at a price (13s. 4d. an acre) which indicates, as at Hatfield, a coppice rotation of about 20 years.

Many actual trees of the medieval Hatfield Forest are preserved in buildings around. Like most medieval houses, Forest Lodge and Forest Cottage (Chapter 8) is built of what would nowadays be very small oaks. They tell us that the Forest woods, like woods generally, were full of such oaks, growing quickly, felled at no more than 50 years old, and very easily replaced (*AW*). Hatfield's status as a Forest, with compartments, therefore affected the growing of underwood but not of timber. The growing of large numbers of small oaks was a function of the Forest which, because it was ordinary and not disputed, hardly appears at all in the records.

Nuts Until the coming of the grey squirrel, woods produced hazelnuts in abundance. In prehistory, nuts had been an important foodstuff, and medieval documents occasionally mention them. A version of the Barrington Claim says that every tenant of Sir Nicholas

> ought to have ... one man in the outwood [i.e. the Forest] to gather nutts to his vse as often as the workemen of the Towne gather nutts to the vse of the Lord ....
>
> *(17th-cent. translation)*[90]

The hermit of Writtle was allowed to have 'his men gathering nuts in the forest around' – a provision which surprises us as much for the Forest of Writtle (where there is now very little hazel) as for the life-style of hermits.

Hatfield Park The park, though often mentioned back to 1221, is first described in the 1328 survey:

> There is there one park containing 180 acres of land, from which the herbage (if the deer were not there) would be worth 41s. per annum. And there can be got in the same 6s. [worth] of underwood, besides [what is used in] maintaining the fences. And the pannage in the same, when it happens, is worth 6s.

As we have seen, the park, like the Forest, produced modest quantities of timber and faggots. It was a sufficiently early park for the tenants of the estate to have been made partly responsible for the upkeep of the boundaries:

> there are 49 tenants... which pale about the Park 151 perk of pale with the Lords timber, and they shall have the ould wood of the sayd pale [*the Latin text adds* when it is not worth putting back in the said pale] and that custome is worth per ann. 3s. 1¾d. and they shall inclose and maynetayne 119 perks of hedge about the sayd Parke and they shall have the ould hedge of the same and that custome is worth per ann. 9s. 1½d.
>
> *Survey, 1336 (17th-cent. translation)*[95]

The total of 270 'perks' or perches, that is 0.84 mile, would have been rather less than half the perimeter of the park (Figs. 3, 16). The pale was a special deer-fence of cleft-oak stakes. The word 'hedge' should read 'fence' – the original Latin *sepes* can mean either, and the court rolls make it clear that this was not a hedge. It needed more attention than the pale; how it was made deer-proof I do not know, but then deer appear very seldom in the records of this park.

A regular item at manorial courts was the parker's report, stating how much perimeter was in bad repair; whether it was pale or fence; whether it was against the Forest, or 'the king's way called Stanstrete' on the north, or 'Gotelesmede' (the meadow on the south), or against a field; and who was responsible. For example, in 1441, fourteen people were called upon to repair 60½ perches of fence and 23½ perches of pale, or rather to pay fines of between ½d. and 2d. per perch for not doing so. In 1442 it was the lord's share of the park fence that needed mending:

> 25 perches of new fence & 48 perches of old fence to be re-pointed (nou' barbat')... 4d. per perch of new fence & 2d. per perch of old fence re-pointed.

The purlieu woods Wall Wood and Monk Wood can be traced back to the thirteenth century. Wall Wood was the wood of Wallbury Manor in Great Hallingbury, named after Wallbury hillfort. Monk Wood in Little Hallingbury belonged to the monks of Bermondsey, a Cluniac priory in Surrey. As we shall see, they formed a miniature compartmented wood-pasture with Woodside Green.

These were private woods but subject to Forest Law; presumably they were coppices, but any deer in them were the king's. Monk Wood was confiscated by Henry III because the Prior's woodward had failed to answer a summons by the Forest officials; the monks got it back in 1256.[61] It was again seized in 1323, this time ostensibly for 'waste' of the trees, although Edward II may have been influenced by just having thrown the Prior into gaol for helping rebels.[66, 85]

Commoners and Grazing

The surveys state baldly that tenants of the manor have common-rights in the Forest. Attached to the Barrington Claim is a list of permitted animals:

> that is to say horses, Mares, foals, Oxen [with] Horns, cows, steers, Heifers, calves, Sheep . . . pigs . . . Goats, Kids & Geese.

We hear about common grazing chiefly when it infringed Forest Law or manorial by-laws. People pastured too many animals, or the wrong animals, or at the wrong time of year, or not having rights at all. Most business of Forest courts was with such minor vert offences. In Hatfield and Writtle the king relinquished this jurisdiction to the Bruces, and we hear little of it.

In the 1320s, however, Edward II had seized the woods and reimposed this part of Forest Law, and some light is thrown on grazing practices. Goats were unexpectedly important. In most Forests, including Epping and Hainault, they were prohibited and automatically seized if found, though usually released on payment of a fraction of their value (*EF*). At Hatfield, where local custom allowed goats, the fines were usually lighter. I have found five cases in the Forest pleas for 1325 and 1332. William Serle 'called le Heerde', i.e. the goatherd, was fined 1*d*. a head for 30 goats 'besides those which he has in his keeping'; Andrew Petteworth, a stranger from Bishop's Stortford, paid 20*d*. for twelve goats. Goats were worth something like 10*d*. each,[96] so the fines were not deterrent. At Writtle, the hermit was fined 20*d*. for 28 goats. Important people may have been fined more: the Prior of Hatfield paid 40*d*. for twelve goats.[97]

For grazing in general we turn to the manorial court rolls. Fines were incurred mainly, if not entirely, by persons living outside Hatfield who were not entitled to use the Forest, for example:

> Order to distrain ... the Prior ... of Thremhale ... because he has trodden down & consumed the pasture of the lord & tenants of this manor in the forest with his cattle, sheep, pigs, geese & other beasts.
>
> *Court roll, 14 January 1447*[74]

On 29 April 1447 Michael Colman of Great Hallingbury was 'fined' 1*d.* each for 16 sheep (*bidentes*) on the Forest, and John Bedwell, John Muskham and Michael Hascle of the same place were fined for 44 more. On 30 September Muskham, two Colemans, and six others paid a total of 9*s.* 2*d.* for 122 sheep, one cow, two bullocks, and a horse. Fines ranged from 0.2*d.* to 1.3*d.* per sheep, 4*d.* per cow and 2*d.* for the horse. Seeing that a sheep was worth about 18*d.*, a cow 10*s.*, and a horse more than £1, there is clearly no punishment intended; the court was merely being used as a convenient way to collect a reasonable grazing rent.

The Sharers The men of Takeley Street were special: they fronted on to the Forest but did not belong to it. In the 1328 survey twelve persons

> claim to have common with their animals in the forest of Hatfelde, for which they render per annum on the feast of St Martin 5 ploughshares, worth 12*d.* each.

We duly find *quinque vomeres* among the income on the account-roll of 1377–8. Probably not all Takeley Street had the privilege: men 'of Stanstret' were occasionally 'fined' for trespassing with animals. The twelve Takeley men were challenged in 1358 for 'destroying the herbage' with 160 sheep, but the jury found that they were tenants of 'Shariers land' who gave their five ploughshares and paid double avesage for their pigs.[98]

Pigs and pannage Until recently, historians often thought of woods as useful chiefly for feeding pigs: of great grunting herds gorging acorns every autumn. This may be true of parts of the Continent, or of Corsica and Sardinia,[99] but in medieval England it is largely mythical: there was not enough woodland, much of it was not oakwood, and our acorn crop is not dependable. However, pannage is better documented and went on longer in mid Essex, especially

Hatfield and Writtle, than elsewhere in Eastern England. The complex relations between men and swine that I shall unfold were not to be found everywhere.

Pannage properly refers to driving pigs into the woods between Michaelmas and Martinmas (7 October to 19 November in the modern calendar) to fatten. It was widely accepted that, even on wood-pasture commons where grazing was free, the lord of the manor was entitled to a payment for the acorn crop in years 'when it happens'.[46] Pannage does not imply woodland: we hear of payments for the pannage of hedgerow trees, of stubble and pasture, and even of a garden (windfall apples?).

Pigs could be in the Forest outside the acorn season. If they were there in the Forbidden Month (p. 46) they should have been confiscated under Forest Law, presumably lest they eat new-born fawns. On the roll for 1324 there are two rather serious cases, of which this is one:

> Adam Bush who was riding forester (who is dead) confiscated one piglet, value 4*d.*, of Richard Brice of Peryndon [Parndon] in the covert in the forbidden month [in 1309], and one piglet of Godfrey le Lord (who is dead), value 4*d.*, and one piglet of John le Dryvere, value 4*d.*, and impounded them. And the same Richard, Godfrey, and John broke the pound and drove the piglets out . . . .[97]

The surviving defendants failed to turn up – it all happened 15 years ago and thirty miles away – and the court went through the motions of ordering their arrest.

We learn more about pigs from the manorial surveys. In 1328

> [the lord's swineherd] shall keep the lord's pigs for the whole Year . . . both in the forest and outside. [He is excused the ordinary services and] shall get from the lord one weaned piglet after Michaelmas, when he shall go with the lord's pigs up to the next Easter to look after the lord's field pigs. And from the pigs which he keeps, fattened for the larder, he shall get all the tails, viz. every whole tail with 3 vertebræ in the backbone nearest the tail . . . .

At Hatfield (and Writtle) a distinction was made between pannage and *avesage*. Avesage was due to the lord from all tenants who kept pigs. This is given in two versions. There are three ages of pigs, Latin *porci, porculi* and *porcelli*, which I translate 'pigs', 'piglings', and 'piglets'.

[Each tenant pays the lord two pigs.] If he has two pigs he shall give them [both] for Avesage. And if he has one he shall buy another identical pig and give them for Avesage. And if he has no pigs he shall give nothing . . . .

For every pig of the age of 2 years or More 2*d*. For a pig of the age of one and a half years 1½*d*. For a pig of the age of one Year 1*d*. For a pigling of the age of half a Year ½*d*. For every piglet piggletted on the feast of St Peter-in-Chains [1 August] or earlier ½*d*.

In practice we hear only of the second kind. Avesage was, in effect, a tax on pigs, imposed at acorn time regardless of whether there were any acorns in the Forest or whether any use was made of them. It was not an onerous tax – the value of a pig was at least 3*s*. – but year after year the manor court discussed what to do about people who hid their pigs and would not pay. In 1446 a committee was appointed to look into the matter. Usually the animals were confiscated but redeemed for about half their value. In March 1444, John Turner, butcher

had . . . this year one sow not Avesaged . . . openly in the market-place and elsewhere . . . he said that all the . . . Jurors were liars and perjured . . . .

Contumacy got him a fine of 3*s*. 4*d*.

For 1413 there survives a complete list of the swine that paid avesage: 7 boars, 82 sows, and 85 pigs at 2*d*. each, 259 piglings at 1*d*., 333 piglets at ½*d*.[100] These 766 animals belonged to 128 people. About half the pigkeepers had three or fewer, but the numbers per person varied from 27 swine to a single piglet. In addition, ten of the twelve Takeley Street commoners had 101 animals (one boar, eight sows, five pigs, 64 piglings, 23 piglets). For these they paid at double rate. The monies add up to £3 13*s*. 7*d*., rather less than strict arithmetic would expect. (The accounts of 1377–8 include £2 19*s*. 4*d*. for avesage.)

Pannage in Hatfield meant the use of the Forest by the pigs of 'foreigners', for which they were charged double the avesage. For example, in 1446 four men of Takeley (not Sharers), six of Great Hallingbury and one of Thremhall paid 9*s*. 7*d*. for 47 animals.

Acorns were the lord's property. At Writtle in 1397 six people were fined up to a shilling each for gathering them in the Forest and warren.[101] I have one such instance at Hatfield, in 1452.[102]

Did Hatfield have a pig economy based on the Forest? Pigs may have been somewhat of a local speciality. At Writtle, an even bigger manor with much the same customs, an avesage roll for 1397 records only 327 animals.[101] There, too, 'foreigners' were 'fined' for 'trespass' of pigs in pannage time, but not only in the Forest; pigs were pannaged in the (wooded) rabbit-warren and on stubble.

Hatfield was probably the biggest stronghold of pannage in Essex. At times there were nearly a thousand pigs in the manor, local ones being augmented in good acorn years by animals brought from neighbouring parishes. No attempt was made to discourage outsiders: even double avesage was only a modest fee. Only in the best acorn years might all the pigs have been in the Forest; many of them would have fed in stubbles and elsewhere. The best indication of which were the good acorn years is the number of pigs which 'foreigners' paid for:

1440	124 pigs	1444	none
1441	55	1445	no record
1442	none	1446	47
1443	67	1447	none

The fair Hatfield had had a fair since 1336. Presumably it was held in Fairstead Quarter, the south-east part of the Forest. This may explain why, in 1980, a magnificent thirteenth-century ring was found outside Collin's Coppice: a gold ring set with a sapphire, adorned with dragons and written with words of love.[103] Was it lost or cast away at the fair?

Conclusions

How did the people of Hatfield live, and what difference did it make belonging to a Forest? Since the days of Karl Marx, historians have thought of England in the Middle Ages, and for long after, as a land of peasants growing their own food and clothing, making their own tools, living out their lives under rigid rules of family and society, rarely touching money, and seeing nothing of the wider world. Often they are thought of as poverty-stricken peasants oppressed by powerful lords – 'People who Did Not Matter', in Rowland Parker's phrase.[104] If they had the misfortune to live in a Forest, they should have been doubly oppressed, their faces ground by the Forest system as well as the manorial system.

Were the peasants of Hatfield like this? Indeed, were there peasants at all in Hatfield? The researches of Professor Alan Macfarlane show that the peasant stage in England, if ever there was one, lies further back than the thirteenth century. His evidence comes from many parts of the country, including even the open-field villages of the Midlands which seem designed for peasant cooperatives. Much of it is from Essex, especially from Earl's Colne, a small town very like Hatfield and twenty miles away. In Earl's Colne, and in much of medieval England, people did all the things that textbook peasants do not do: they behaved as individuals and not as families, still less as communities; they had money and went to shops and bought things; they lived in substantial wooden houses – many of which are still lived in six centuries later – with gardens and orchards; they hired workers and hired themselves out; they bought fields and houses and sold them; they quarrelled with their families and bequeathed their property to somebody else.[105] They did what Essex people were still doing in the 1940s; they were not like the peasants of medieval Ireland or France or of nineteenth-century Norway or Russia.

It is not my business to prove Macfarlane's conclusions specifically for Hatfield, but a glance at the records reveals many non-peasant habits. There were many shops (what small Essex town today has *two fishmongers*?); there were many payments in cash and few in kind; surnames like Turnor and Haslingfield indicate specialist businesses and people moving from a distance. There were many independent women, for example:

> Juliana Clement and Alice Tourtelhof... shall keep the prisoners arrested inside and outside the town, and prisoners arrested in the manor, and shall take them to Colchester Gaol.
>
> *Labour service in the 1328 survey*

A measure of the independence of local farmers is the number of moats. Moats were dug round farmsteads mainly in the twelfth and thirteenth centuries. They had many functions, but their chief significance appears to be as status symbols. A moat symbolizes the independence of a man whose house is his castle. Hatfield is in the midst of the biggest concentration of moats in England; there are at least fourteen in Hatfield itself.[106]

On paper, Hatfield manor, like manors generally, was set up for a peasant, or at least a moneyless, society. The lord had a demesne farm and consumed its produce; the tenants, by way of rent, worked the lord's land, guarded his prisoners, paled his park, etc. At Hatfield the services can never have been very onerous, for the tenants had about twenty times as much farmland as the demesne. In practice services were nearly always commuted for money and the work done by contractors, although as late as the 1370s we find someone working off his services by digging post-holes for the Lady's henhouse. The lord had little opportunity of oppressing the tenants. Powerful though the Bruces and de Bohuns might have been, they were remote, and could claim their rights only through the manor courts. The courts were composed of local people, and although they did not make the rules it was they who interpreted and revised them. As we have seen, the rules were often bent, and seldom in favour of the lord. Fines for not mending the park pale were only a fraction of the cost of getting the work done. Medieval Hatfield appears to have been an easy-going, well-to-do society of independent small farmers, traders and craftsmen. It was insecure, but not from fear of the lord; the insecurity came from the plague (nobody knew whether he would see another spring) and from the neighbours. Fists and weapons were readier than they are now; a fifteenth-century Barrington was prosecuted six times for attacks with a dagger, a sword, a lance, a billhook and knives, for a shooting, and for assaulting the police.[65]

If a thirteenth-century inhabitant were to return to Hatfield today, he would notice some physical changes: the shrinkage of Hatfield town, the disappearance of Hatfield Park and the Priory, the growth of a substantial village around Hatfield Heath, and the very recent destruction of many of his familiar hedges. But surprisingly much of the fabric of the landscape is still there, and the Forest would be instantly recognizable after 700 years. This is not a particularly unusual degree of stability. We find nearly the same stability in the parallel documents for Writtle, and the same story could be told for Great Canfield, Leaden Roding, Earl's Colne – indeed for all the nearby parishes for which sufficient records survive. The popular notion that the English landscape has been continually changing is less than a half-truth.

Deer and the Forest system   The making of Hatfield into a Forest can have had little direct effect on the countryside. There need have been no more deer in Hatfield than there are now: the king's needs could amply have been met by a herd which never rose above 150 head. Such numbers do not now cause most farmers to complain of damage to crops; but they would have altered the woods by eating ash, oxlip and other plants that they are fond of.

What did the king get out of the Forest? An average of a dozen deer a year hardly justified the trouble of keeping it going. Revenue from fines is difficult to measure, but at times was important. Medieval kings were poor, and had no income-tax to pay for running the country. As the twelfth-century Pipe Rolls show, Forest fines contributed an appreciable fraction of the entire exchequer.

In an age when power did not go with wealth, Forests were an important part of the prestige by which the king reigned. They were the supreme status symbol and a source of gifts which money could not buy, such as deer and giant oaks. Honorific sinecures in the Forest hierarchy were a means for an impoverished king to reward those who had served him well. There was no Order of the British Empire; knighthood was reserved for valour in battle; how else could Chaucer have been honoured than by being made under-Forester of an obscure Somerset Forest?

The enormous value of these privileges is shown by the one occasion when money did buy them. When Edward III gave Robert de Morle permission to hunt in Hatfield Forest for life, he got out of repaying a debt of £1100 – something like half a million pounds today.

Was the Forest system oppressive? The king used it to oppress the nobility; that was one of its functions, until King John went too far and brought Magna Carta upon himself. Kings used Hatfield Forest to keep the Bruces and de Bohuns in their place; but did the oppression extend further down the social scale? C.R. Young has produced instances of Forest officials being a nuisance, or worse, to ordinary folk: 'it was so easy to get into trouble unintentionally simply by being in the wrong place at the wrong time' (*RFME*). But with rare exceptions the severity of Forest Law, as of manorial regulations, was neutralized because the cooperation of local people was needed to put it into effect. To us it might seem irksome to have to attend inquests on dead deer and on strange goings-on, but these summonses were rare and possibly were a welcome excuse for a day out.

In Essex the Forest courts were almost always concerned with raising revenue from fines, rather than deterring people from doing things. Routine felling of timber or wood was rarely prosecuted at all, except in woods belonging to French religious houses such as Bermondsey and Felsted priories. Courts imposed modest fines on people who grubbed out private woods. The courts acted as a supra-manorial authority regulating the grazing of Epping and Hainault Forests, which ran into many manors (*EF*). In the single-manor Forests of Hatfield and Writtle the *manorial* courts dealt with grazing, except for goats and for pigs in the Forbidden Month.

Only for venison offences did Forest courts punish with prison or deterrent fines. In Hatfield this happened much less than once a year. Deer must often have been killed for the pot or to protect crops (otherwise the numbers would inexorably have risen), but this was rarely reported, and when it did come before the courts was condoned. Organized poaching was made a source of revenue: fines were heavy enough to prevent a black market in venison, but were not so systematic as to stop poaching altogether. Poaching gangs prosecuted in Essex included remarkably many knights and clerics, and the occasional earl or bishop.[66]

Trees, grazing, highwaymen and the fabric of the Forest   As a wood-pasture common, Hatfield Forest was an asset to the landowner, who owned the trees; to the commoners, who had the grazing; and to the Barringtons, who had rights in both. About one place in four in middle or south Essex had such a common; Hatfield was not appreciably different through being a Forest.

Scholars often assert that Forest Law preserved woodland, but it is most unlikely that they are right. Forest authorities never seriously tried to prevent people from grubbing out woodland. Woodland survived no more often – maybe somewhat less often – within the bounds of Forest Law than outside. The survival of the medieval landscape at Hatfield is due to the checks and balances which prevented any one person from getting too much control over it; the manor court counted for much more than the Forest court.

Grazing, as in later centuries, was by all the farm animals, and on a considerable scale with hundreds of sheep etc. Woodland would rapidly have been turned into grassland-with-trees had these live-stock had access to all of it all the time. The men of Hatfield seem not to have regarded the Forest as over-grazed: they allowed people from other places to use the common, and did not charge them excessively.

Coppicing, pollarding, and ordinary and outsize timber trees are recorded (in rather more detail at Writtle). Trees included oak, hazel (nuts), ash, maple and aspen. There is no mention of hornbeam, but this is an undistinguished tree, with no specific uses, which is easily overlooked in the anonymity of 'underwood'.[107] Lime had probably already disappeared, and birch was not yet abundant. The indications of coppicing point to a long rotation. It would have been a normal manorial practice for the men of Hatfield to require their lord to provide them with timber and underwood for maintaining buildings, fences and equipment. The Forest was not the only source: there was little other woodland, but plenty of hedges and hedgerow trees.

Woods as big as those of the Forest are likely to have attracted small industries. The de Bohuns tried to set up charcoal-burning. Among the surnames in court rolls that of Turnor is prominent. Turners were an important trade in an age of wooden plates and cups; they are often supposed to have been associated with wood-land, although they would hardly have been big consumers of trees.[108]

Who made the system of coppices in the Forest? Woodcutting and grazing in the middle ages could hardly have been combined without it. Some form of compartmentation is recorded in about half the wooded Forests, for example the eighteen 'copses' of Grovely Forest (Wilts), the scores of coppices in Cranborne Chase (Dorset and Wilts), and the 'Copses' and 'Lights' of Wychwood Forest (Oxon); in the New Forest, compartments existed in the middle ages but were abandoned later (*NF*). Compartmentation favours the owner of the trees: coppicing produces more wood per acre, and for much less trouble, than the pollarding which has to be done in an uncompartmented Forest. It is unfavourable to the graziers, who are excluded from at least a third of the Forest at any one time. A compartmental Forest therefore implies strong land-owners and weak commoners.

Hatfield usually had weak lords and strong commoners, who pre-vented any encroachment on the Forest. As we shall see, in later

centuries it was difficult to maintain even the existing compartmentation. The compartments were set up at a time when there was
some connection with Great Hallingbury, for the western compartments provide for two lanes from that direction (Fig. 3). It is possible
that the Crown was responsible, although kings were reluctant to
diminish the rights of commoners:

> Order to Wilfred le Chamberleng [and others] sellers of the king's underwood
> in Wiltshire... to fence in all the places in the king's wood of Grovely,
> from which they have sold underwood by the king's order, so that the king
> may not suffer damage, nor the men of Barford and Wishford [who had
> the common-rights] be inconvenienced by having their beasts shut into the
> enclosure.... And the king orders, that when the said underwood shall
> have grown up, the said men may have their common-rights there, as they
> used to have earlier.
>
> *Close Rolls, 1252*

More plausibly the compartmentation, if not of much earlier origin,
is a relic of the early de Bohuns' attempt at commercializing the
Forest. Is it more than a coincidence that there were seventeen
'quarters' in the de Bohun park at Walden and seventeen coppices
in Hatfield Forest?

Another pointer to this early period is the existence of a strip
of open land between the northern coppices and Takeley Street
(through which the railway was later to pass). Such narrow clearings,
called *trenches*, were customarily made alongside main roads to give
travellers a sense of security from highwaymen lurking in the bushes.
A statute of 1284 required underwood and woodbanks to be removed
from within 200 feet either side of the king's highway.[109] As far
as I am aware the making of new trenches ceased soon after.

5 The Disputed Forest 1460–1857

We find the said Forest or Chase to consist of Wood ground and Plains (that is to say) in Woodground usually incopsed and inclosed 646 acres, in open Wood and Bushie ground 109 Acres, and in Playnes, Ridings and highways 240 acres. The Forest appears irregular, full of angles and narrow Passages which wee conceive to be dangerous for the safetie of the Game of Deer there, in respect that besides the angles the Forest extends in length near two Myles[a] and in most places not above halfe a mile in Breadth, so as by reason of the small Quantitye of Playnes the multitude of Sheep and other Cattle that depasture there (by pretence of Comonage) and unsufferable taking of Estovers[b] Stakeboot Hedgeboot at all Times of the Year for repair of the Forest[c] . . . the Deere are forced to stray abroad for their Food and the Wood are in a great Measure decayed insomuch in case the abuses be not speedily prohibited both Deer and Woods will receive a totall Destruction.

We find little Timber in the Forest worthy valuation. The open Woods consisting of Pollard Ash and Maple of small worth.

We find some Misdemeanurs often comitted and usually practised by the pretended Commoners in Digging of Lime Loam Mortar and such like. . . .

Wee find great abuse by cutting of Grass with Sickles and other Instruments within the young Springs in the time of their incopsing by the pretended commoners whereby the Underwoods are greatly Spoiled.

There is a parcell of Wast ground[d] a Member of the said Forest called Woodside green containing about 67 acres having in some part thereof a small Quantity of open Wood of Sallow Ash and Maple of small growth and of little value. . . . The game of Deer do seldom feed upon any part thereof for that the . . . Hedge dividing the Forest and Green are maintain'd at so great a height by the Commoners and adjacent Inhabitants as without great Danger the Deer cannot Leap them. . . .

The feeding Playnes within the Forest are so irregular and of so small content that his Majesties Game there can hardly bee maintain'd being near 400 in Number . . . having no other Fodder or Hay . . .

through the daily Concourse of People in driving their Sheep to and from the said Forrest, the Deere are much disturbed.

Report of [corrupt] Royal Commission, 1639[110]

---

[a] So the draft reads; the fair copy has 'near Five Miles'.
[b] Common-rights of woodcutting.
[c] The word 'hedges' seems to have been left out.
[d] Meaning 'common-land'.

Lords and Commoners

The medieval fabric of Hatfield and of the Forest was not much altered by the king relinquishing the Forestal rights. It was to endure for four more centuries, through four dynasties of landowning families. For all this time, Hatfield remained a small Essex town surrounded by hamlets and scattered farms. The kind of society in which the Forest operated is portrayed in the wonderful and learned books of F.G.Emmison on life in Elizabethan Essex.[111] Essex was then probably more populous and less prosperous than before; its people remained fiercely independent and surprisingly violent. This was very true of Hatfield Forest affairs. The farmers were technically the lord's tenants, and even in the eighteenth century occasionally performed labour services; but he had very little control over them, especially over how they used their rights in the Forest.

The accident-prone Dukes of Buckingham   Humphrey Stafford, first Duke of Buckingham, had inherited from his mother the Hatfield estate, including the landownership of the Forest. In 1446 he was given the Forestal rights as well:

> the sport[a] of the deer [is] reserved to the king; and since the said sport by reason of bad keeping is much destroyed; the king ... grants to the said duke all the said sport with the punishment of all trespasses of venison ... without rendering aught to the king.
> *Calendar of Charter Rolls (editor's translation)*

[a] Latin word *deductus*, in this context better rendered 'game'.

Buckingham was one of the greatest men in England, of royal descent and a vast landowner. In the Wars of the Roses he fought for Lancaster, and was killed at the battle of Northampton in 1460; his son was already dead in battle.

The dukedom and estates went to Humphrey's grandson Henry, who again took up the dangerous game of fifteenth-century politics. It was he who sentenced the Duke of Clarence to his death in a butt of malmsey. He supported Richard III, but in 1483 committed high treason against him and was beheaded and his lands confiscated.

This setback was only temporary. Two years later Richard met his own end, and the new king Henry VII rehabilitated Henry Stafford and returned the estates, including Hatfield and Writtle, to his family.

The third Duke, Edward, became a personal friend of Henry VIII. He was the biggest landowner in England, and Hatfield was only a small part of his property; he did, however, go there in August 1508. He had a reputation for enclosing common-land and making deer-parks. In 1519 he tried to enclose the Forest, but the commoners objected and he gave in.[112] Two years later the Duke, having made too much of his royal blood and grown too big for his boots, was suddenly beheaded on a mysterious charge of high treason and his lands were confiscated.

Henry VIII held on to Hatfield Forest, rather unusually among confiscated lands, for the rest of his reign.

The infamous Lord Rich   The Forest was next owned by the wickedest of Englishmen. Sir Richard Rich, after a misspent youth, had been appointed Solicitor-General, and whenever Henry VIII had any dirty work, he had the doing of it. He betrayed Bishop Fisher to a traitor's death, swore away the life of Sir Thomas More, and personally tortured Anne Askew. Although he did well out of the dissolution of the monasteries, he was not adequately rewarded in the king's lifetime. After Henry's death in 1547, Edward VI promoted Rich to Lord Chancellor and gave him most of the Hatfield estate, including the Forestal rights, 'does and beasts, both male and female'.[113] Sir Richard was also ennobled and was given other dignities, including the jocular honour of the Wardstaff of the Hundreds of Harlow and Ongar.*

Lord Rich managed to retain the favour of Queens Jane, Mary and Elizabeth, founded Felsted School, and died an undeserved death in bed in 1567. His son Hugh lived until 1581. Hatfield was managed by his grandson Robert, who discontinued the ancient park.

---

* The men of those Hundreds had held their lands for at least 300 years on condition of rendering ceremonial service once a year to the king in the person of a Wardstaff. This was 'some Willow Bough growing in Abbasse Rothing Wood', 2 ft 3 in. long and 4 inches round. It was cut on the second Sunday after Easter and was taken to Rookwood Hall, where it was rolled up reverently in a fair linen cloth and placed on a cushion on the high table. After a break for refreshment, the Wardstaff took its seat on a cushion beside a certain lane, across which a great rope with a bell hanging on it was stretched, and received the homage of the men of Abbess Roding and of passers-by. After armed men had watched over it all night, a notch was cut in it. Next day the Wardstaff marched in procession, doggerel verses being recited before it, to Fyfield where these rites were repeated. The Wardstaff received royal honours at eight other places on the following days, ending either at Magdalen Laver or (in another account) being ceremoniously cast into the sea.[115]

The arbitration of 1576   Meanwhile the Barringtons had been coming up in the world.[114] By 1530 they were claiming to have been hereditary woodwards since before the Conquest. They became large country squires by purchasing the dissolved Hatfield Priory. With it went fields and meadows and houses and Man Wood.[116]

The Riches had to deal not only with the claims of the commoners but with the Barrington family as woodwards. This venerable office had acquired great privileges and vague rights, which Robert, third Lord Rich, wanted to delimit. The Court of Star Chamber, called in to arbitrate, came to a decision in 1576, later confirmed by a special Act of Parliament.

The decision, as far as it concerns the Forest, was that in return for relinquishing the woodwardship Sir Thomas Barrington was to become the owner of the trees (but not the soil or pasture) of the north-eastern third of the Forest, and was to have common-rights of pasture in the whole Forest for specified animals. His share was defined as:

> all the Woodde Tymber trees vnderwoodes and busshes . . . in those partes . . . called Busshende quarter conteyninge of Woodde Lande grownde Two hundrethe thirtie and three Acres . . . and Takeley quarter Conteynynge One hundreth and one and Twentie Acres of Woodde land grownde . . . devided from the Residewe of the said fforreste by A certen Brooke called Sheremore Broke. . . .[117]

These 354 acres were presumably modern acres (p. x); although the actual area involved was about 405 acres, not all of it had trees. Thus began the traditional distinction between the 'Barrington Side' of the Forest, north-east of the Shermore Brook, and what was later to be known as the 'Morley Side'.

Barrington was required to operate a scaled-down version of the Forest's coppicing system. After felling each wood, he had to fence it to keep out livestock which would eat the *spring* or regrowth, but he was not allowed to cut down and enclose more than 26 modern acres of wood each year:

> there shall not . . . in any one Yeare be taken . . . nor inclosed by . . . Sir Thomas Barrington . . . above Sixtene Acres of woodd lande . . . according to the measure of xxi foote pole . . . for the preservacon of the Sprynge thereof after the same shalbe felled.

This restriction was presumably to protect the rights of the commoners, which are mentioned in another clause. Each enclosure was to stand for nine years, during which time Barrington was allowed to take the herbage growing in the woods.

Barrington's common-rights were to be for 140 sheep, 20 cattle, 10 yearling calves, 10 horses 'or mares with theire foles by theire sydes', and 30 swine.

Lord Rich, as owner of the Forestal rights, was to continue to pasture his deer on the Barrington side of the Forest, and to have access for himself and his keepers, except within the nine-year enclosures. Sir Thomas (doubtless continuing an ancient perquisite of the woodwardship) might demand from him every year three bucks and three does, 'good and seasonable'. If Rich did not produce them within two days, 'yt shalbe Lawfull to the said Sir Thomas ... to Kyll & take awaye the said Buckes & Does'.

Ruffianly lords The Rich family was never closely connected with Hatfield. In 1592 they sold their interest in the Forest to Lord Morley & Mounteagle, and in 1612 they sold the rest of the Hatfield estate, including the lordship of the manor, to Sir Francis Barrington.

The Morleys were ancient neighbours of the Forest. They had been lords of Great Hallingbury, *alias* Hallingbury Morley, since the fourteenth century. They thus already owned Wall Wood and by now had acquired Monk Wood also.[118] Hatfield Forest was to go with Hallingbury for three centuries.

These sales set the scene for 200 years of quarrels between the two lords as well as between the lords and those who had the common rights. The Forest had been the Crown's, and the manor someone else's, for much of the middle ages, and this had led to disputes; but the new separation was different. Lord Morley had bought not only the Forestal rights (by now reduced to little more than the right to keep deer) but also the soil of the whole Forest and the trees in the western two-thirds. Barrington already had the trees (but not the soil) of the north-eastern third and the right to pasture animals throughout the Forest; he now bought the manorial jurisdiction over the whole Forest, including the right to hold courts and to fine offenders (including Lord Morley) against the by-laws. As lord of the manor he now had to deal, not with distant and complaisant Royal Forest authorities, but with a resident owner of the Forest eager to enforce his claims. There was plenty of room for the two lords to dispute which rights each had acquired, and for high-handed commoners to play off one lord against the other.

In the early decades, political differences aggravated the friction. The Morleys were strongly Royalist. Lord Morley's son, who discovered the Gunpowder Plot in 1605, was – if we believe even a tenth of what was said about him – a very ruffianly lord indeed. Sir Francis Barrington, although he had been created one of the original baronets in 1611, was of the opposite persuasion. Charles I in 1626 commanded him to lend him money. He refused, and the king threw him into the loathsome Marshalsea; we find him petitioning to be let out, his doctor certifying

> his Stomach is almost lost, his flesh is greatly wasted, Rhewmes and coghs which abound even of Phlagme doe increase and all by reason of the ill and close ayre of the Prison.[119]

(He was released after a year,[120] but died soon after.) The course of history went against the Morleys, who were to pay dearly for their support of Charles I. This affected their Hatfield affairs, so that by 1650 the then Lord Morley was a very downtrodden lord indeed.

As time went on, disputes between successive lords gradually lost the violence of those years, but did not die out. Well into the eighteenth century two respectable county magnates chased each other through the courts on matters such as whose grass they could trample and whose rabbits they could shoot. They evidently regarded the Forest and its ancient complexities as a subject for their hobby of litigation.

This is not a book on Forest personalities, so I shall give only an outline of the disputes as they provide a framework for the Forest's history. A fuller account has been published by Derek Shorrocks (*SC*); to this I am indebted for much of the material of this chapter. The documents in the disputes were themselves often the result of historical research by lords and their lawyers; this is why so much survives of the history of the Forest. (I have not been able to discover the outcomes of many of the cases.)

The first *casus belli* was the periodic enclosing of the coppices after felling. This, as I have shown, is the mark of a Forest with a strong landowning interest. At once, in 1612, the commoners disputed Sir Francis Barrington's action in fencing his coppices, on the grounds that he was only the lord of the manor and not entitled to do so:

Alledging that because *the Soil* is not ye Complainant's ... the Statute will not warrant the Complainant Fencing & Inclosing.[121]

The trouble started when Richard Chalke,

a very malitious and turbulent person, had of late Claimed Common of pasture on ye said young spring, being not above three years' growth, & had not only put in his own Cattle but also caused the Cattle of diverse other persons to come into ye said Young Spring.[121]

The matter went to the Court of Chancery, and witnesses put the point of view of both sides. Abell Hurley pointed out that by the time the coppices were made available to the commoners' animals, any pasture in them was

become so thick with bushes that in many places a Man can hardly go or ride between them. ...

On the other side, Philip Kent testified that some of the coppices

have been so fed with great Cattle ... that ye same Spring ... hath been cut again over or pruned for the better Growth thereof wch biting hath been by the Cattle wch have been put into ye said Inclosures ...

but he claimed that the cattle were those of Sir Thomas, Barrington's son. Thomas White and others thought it would be better if Sir Thomas were to pollard the trees instead of coppicing and enclosing the woods

for that if it were not inclosed the wood would be ye better ... being lopped & would be out of the reach of Cattle & so ye plaintiff every few years might lopp & Crop & have sufficient firewood by that means ... but now by reason of ye said Inclosures made & Cutting up of great trees therein the Springs that come after of the Stumps of the Trees are bitten with the deer & Cattle that they dye & never come to any great profit.

Thomas Northage

> hath seen that Draw Bushes have been placed in the Hedges [i.e. the coppice fences] for Hogs to go in & out.

Henry Gates, keeper of Lord Morley's deer, also tried to get Barrington's enclosures disallowed, as being

> dangerous for the killing of Deer ... by Deerstealers & Hunters of Deer whithin ye said Copices by reason of the Hedges more Subject to be Ensnared with Buckstalls & ropes or Snares which may be set in Creepers thorough the Hedges. But he saith that ... ye said Copices are some relief to the Game of Deer that got into ye Copices in Winter time where they find some better food then in the Mayne open fforest.[122]

The court found in favour of Barrington, allowing him to continue fencing off each wood for nine years after each felling; he was even authorized to 'cut and dispose of the Grass' growing in those nine years.

Matters got more ruffianly in the next two years. People had been breaking down and setting fire to Barrington's 'hedges' – which would have been dead fences round the coppices, and therefore combustible – and it was alleged that Lord Morley's son was the ringleader. Thomas Leventhorp (Morley's bailiff, and a member of a respectable Hatfield family) admitted that his Lordship came from time to time with seven or eight roughs, 'some of them with Bills and some bowes and some with swords and such like Weapones', and

> did ... giue Commaund and Direction ... to breake gown a gate leadinge into a Coppice Wood of the Complainants and alsoe to Cutt downe some of the hedges ... both wch was donn. ...

Leventhorp also claimed that Morley 'did Commaund ... the said hedges to be sett on fire', but had not seen this done. After the fences had been repaired and again broken down, two Justices of the Peace intervened, and Morley declared that if he had been there 'he would have beate them off his grounde', or, in another version, 'he would have hacked them in peces like Doggs'. It was alleged that Barrington, for his part,

> had placed an ambushe of men in a place Called the Gravell Pitts in the ... fforrest to have sett vppon and assaulted ... Lord Morley and his Companie. ...

100

Sword and pistol at Hatfield Fair By 1600 the fair, held on St James's Day (25 July), took place on Thremhall or Thremnall Green in the north of the Forest by the main road. Doubtless it was an important occasion for buying things like tools and crockery cheaply – like Midsummer Fair, Cambridge, today – and was a valuable privilege of the lord of the manor. When Lord Morley bought the Forest he discovered that this did not include control over the fair, which continued to be held on his land by a lessee of Lord Rich. Morley coveted the fair for himself, and for twenty years it was a source of friction and violence between the Morleys and the Riches.

When Barrington bought the manor he found Morley in illegal possession of the fair, and tried to get the authorities to stop him. Morley and Leventhorp were continuing their malicious damage to Barrington's wood-fences. At the fair in 1613 there was a riot. One Salmond, the Deputy Sheriff, tried to arrest Leventhorp for pulling down fences,

> wherevppon [Leventhorp] tooke him a box on the eare and triped vpp his heeles and then hee the said Salmond told [Leventhorp] that hee was the Deputie Sheriffe. ... [Lord Morley's men] all began to assaulte [Salmond] and tooke a Way his sworde and [Leventhorp] seeing it kam beetwene them and haueing a pistoll and a sword bent his pistoll against his fellowes ... in the defence of the said Salmond ... and gott his sword againe and gaue it to him. ...[123]

Barrington, having won the dispute, transferred the fair to Hatfield town, well away from Morley's land. In 1660 Sir John Barrington moved it to Hatfield Heath,[124] where it was held until it faded away in the 1860s.[76]

The dispute over hedgebote Lord Morley next contemplated proceedings against the commoners himself. As owner of the soil, not lord of the manor, he had no authority to prevent them from exceeding their common-rights. In Hatfield Forest the commoners had rights only of pasture, not of woodcutting. But they found a way of exploiting *hedgebote*, the ancient right of tenants of the manor to have underwood and bushes given them by the lord's woodward to repair their hedges and fences – here especially the hedges between the Forest and the fields adjoining (p. 130). Morley alleged that the commoners had 'plotted Combyned and Confederated among themselves' to get up a claim

101

that for want of a woodward or other officer to assigne the same it was lawfull for them to take woode and busshes at their pleasure within the said fforrest. . . .[125]

As far as I can discover the allegation was not pursued.

A corrupt Royal Commission As is well known, Charles I, among the other stratagems by which he raised money, tried to reactivate the Forest Laws; this abuse was one step on his road to the scaffold. Sometimes, as in Epping Forest, the cash came from huge fines imposed for technical breaches of the Laws.[66] Alternatively, landowners might be persuaded to pay lump sums to be exempted. In 1634 the Forest court arraigned Barrington, but he was able to prove ancient exemption.[126]

This example was evidently not lost on Henry, the next Lord Morley, who in 1639 got up a scheme of his own in the form of a Royal Commission 'touching the intended disafforestacion and ymprovement' – ominous words – of Hatfield Forest. The Commission recommended that the Forest should become Morley's absolute property; the common-rights were to be suppressed, and the commoners fobbed off with 100 acres of land in exchange; another thirty acres were to be given to the poor; and the Crown was to be bribed with £6 6s. 8d. a year in consideration of terminating non-existent right to the deer.[110]

Disafforestation – abolishing the legal status of the Forest – would almost certainly have resulted in the Forest being physically destroyed and made into ordinary farmland, as was, for example, a third of Neroche Forest (Somerset) at about the same time.[127] But 1639, with the Civil War only three years away, was not a good time to play this game. The Vicar of Hatfield smelt a rat and appealed to the Inner Star Chamber, who promptly suppressed the Commission,

finding the proceedings of ye Lord Morley his Commissioners and Agents to have been very Irregular. . . .
Lord Morley . . . the better to attain to his own Ends therein, did voluntarily Intitle his Majesty to a Yearly Rent of Twenty Nobles, issuing out of the said fforest or chase, and thereupon procured a Commission out of his Majesty's Court of Exchequer to such persons as ye said Lord Morley was pleased to Nominate, one of them being the Steward of his Courts, another his menial Servant, and a Third a prisoner in the ffleet [*the Fleet Prison*] who

by Colour of the said Commission Summoned the said Inhabitants who claimeth right of Comon, threatning them with his Majesty's high displeasure and using other Menaces in a high Nature. . . .[128]

With this comic ending Hatfield Forest was saved.

Valuable though the Commissioners' report is, we cannot take it all at face value. The Commissioners present the Forest, as an asset of Lord Morley's, in the least favourable light; they make the most of 'abuses' of common-rights, and indeed do not admit the existence of common-rights at all. It was part of the scheme that they should pretend that the deer still belonged to the Crown. They made inquiries and report the answers of some of the persons they questioned. They claimed to meet with less opposition from those inhabitants who lived nearer the Forest, who, the Commissioners alleged, had a less weak claim to common-rights: 'those tractable persons have more pretence and coullor of comonage'.

The Shares of Takeley Street duly make their appearance. They no longer rendered five ploughshares, but exhibited each year a

> straunge substaunce of ould Iron which they termed a share . . . hauing noe semblaunce of a ploughshare, but rather like vnto that wod phraise le browne bill; wee conteyne the same noe authenticall Record to warrant further Clayme . . .

No mention is made of the Barrington interest. By this time the Morleys and Barringtons had composed their differences, and Barrington had lent Morley a large sum of money on the security of the Forest.[129]

A downtrodden lord and his rabbits Lord Morley got into serious trouble through being on the wrong side in the Civil War. He became the fifth owner of Hatfield Forest to be held to have committed treason; although he kept his head, his estates came under the Act of Parliament in 1649 confiscating the assets of 'malignant' Royalists. Fortunately the estate was not his abolutely, but was entailed in the family; Morley had tried to break the entail, but his mother – doubtless foreseeing this contingency – had forbidden him (*SC*). Morley thus lost the estate, but when he died Parliament had to return it to his son Thomas.

The commoners took advantage of the lord's troubles and put him to various petty indignities. In 1649 he was charged before the manorial court 'for digging Soil in the Forest'. He was repeatedly fined in connection with keeping rabbits, and later the Sharers got up a petition to 'the Honorable the Commissioners for removeing Obstruccions in the sale of delinquents Lands', accusing his Lordship of

> lately making a Warren in the Forest and enclosing divers parcels of land, to the great preiudice of yor Peticoners, and many of their Cattle lost and spoyled. . . .[130]

We shall return to these rabbits in Chapter 7.

During Morley's disgrace the Forest was leased and sub-leased into the hands of distant personages such as the Earl of Cardigan. We can well believe that, as was said a century later, 'the Deer were killed, the ffences let down and the fforrest or Chace filled with Sheep & Hoggs'.[131]

Turnor Thomas, Lord Morley inherited estates encumbered by mortgage and by claims arising from his father's sequestration.[132] In 1666 he sold Hallingbury and the soil and deer of the Forest to Sir Edward Turnor, Speaker of the House of Commons. 'The Chase' was valued at £1500, no great sum for so large an area.[133]

The new owner asked his lawyer to find out what exactly he had acquired. He looked into whether Barrington might have forfeited his right to cut the north-east coppices 'he not having performed the Covenants agreed upon'; he claimed a right to the fair; and he even contemplated having the 1576 award set aside and making Barrington revert to his ancestral duties as woodward.[134]

As far as we know, Sir Edward did not pursue these matters, except for unseemly disputes with Sir John Barrington and his tenants over deer. It was Turnor's genial custom to hang or shoot any dogs that came into the Forest.[135] Barrington, having thus lost some hounds, responded with the traditional defiance of nailing a buck's head to the market cross (*SC*). Turnor was still being high-handed in 1682:

> Sir Edward has upon hunting rode out of the fforrest and over the Tenants Corne; and when they have civily desir'd him not to ruine their Corne he has ... bad them tell their great Landlord that he would hunt there, and that if they would have Corne they must sowe it farther from the fforrest ... now Sir Edward claims all Hatfield broad-oake to be fforrest.[136]

Turnor evidently thought his Forestal rights entitled him to hunt in person over the whole of Hatfield as defined in the 1298 perambulation. He revived the warren, brought in new rabbits, and employed one Robert Cass as warrener.[135]

From Turnor's time there are two important but undated valuations of the Forest and of the purlieu woods, evidently by his agent. One of these seems to date from *c.* 1700,[137] the other from *c.* 1690.[138] (A more shaky version of the same handwriting appears in a memorandum of 1720.) They mention coppice-woods, deer, 'a very good Lodge for a Keeper' and 'a large Connywarren'.

The Houblons   Turnor's son died in debt, and the estates were sold in 1729. The Forest thus passed into the hands of its last private owners, the Houblon family (pronounced 'Hubblan'[139] and sometimes spelt 'Hubland').

The Houbelons, burgesses of Lille, had moved to London in the 1560s and had prospered. Four of them founded the Bank of England in 1694, Sir John Houblon IV being its first Governor. In 1724 the family fortunes converged on a fourteen-year-old heir, Jacob Houblon III, whose uncle as trustee had been directed to buy him a suitable estate. This happened to be Great Hallingbury, with the Forest. Houblon, after graduating at my own Cambridge college, came to live there as a country squire.[140]

The Houblons were as disputatious as their predecessors but more genteel. In their time we find a new strand of motive in the management of the Forest. It became treated as an extension to Hallingbury Park, and thus came within the scope of the landscape-park movement. Parks as beautiful landscape go back to Norman Sicily, if not to the Garden of Eden, but by now they were being designed by professionals.[141] Jacob Houblon III began by making the lake and the Shell House and planting a few trees. Jacob IV, who succeeded his father in 1770, consulted the famous landscaper, Lancelot 'Capability' Brown, about Hallingbury Park.[142] This was doubtless connected with the building of a new Palladian mansion of Hallingbury Place, rivalling the magnificent Barrington Hall which had been built (on a new site) twenty years or so before.

At Hatfield the violence of a century earlier had faded into litigiousness between Houblons, Barringtons and commoners. This was not usual in England. Many Forests, including Enfield Chase not far away, became the resort of armed gangs of poachers and highwaymen, against whom the law reacted in kind. Stealing deer, which in Queen Elizabeth's days had been a minor offence, had grown into a hanging matter by Houblon's time. The most ferocious of all English statutes, the Black Act of 1723, which created fifty new capital crimes, was directed against Forest criminals.[143] As far as we know, all this passed Hatfield by.

Enclosure of the Forest Meanwhile, the idea was gaining ground that all land ought to be absolute private property and ought to be used for conventional agriculture. The fashion of the age was against multiple land-uses, especially Forests. At first this affected mainly open-fields and strip-cultivation, which were abolished by Enclosure Acts; this phase had little effect on Essex, where strip-cultivation was unusual. Later, landowners applied Enclosure Acts to Forests and other commons, expropriating the rights of commoners and (where they still existed) of the Crown. In this way Essex lost most of its heaths and open spaces, of which, as county maps show, there were still vast ramifications in the 1770s but only fragments by 1840. It is surprising that Hatfield Forest remained as long as it did.

There was a quiet period in the time of John vi, the third of the Houblons at Hallingbury, who in his Emmanuel College days had had a remarkably expensive taste for 'Ice Crame'.[144] Forest matters were again taken up by John vii Archer Houblon. On inheriting the estate in 1831 he made inquiries about rights and their exercise. Sir Fitzwilliam Barrington, the last of the ancient family, died in 1832, and Houblon bought the Barrington interest in the Forest. At about this time he bought out five of the Sharers of Takeley Street.[145]

Finally, in 1857, Houblon promoted an Enclosure Act to make him the absolute owner of the Forest. He had bought out much of the opposition, and the remaining common-rights were no longer highly regarded; but, like most enclosures, this was expensive. The Act of Parliament cost him £2819, plus £385 in legal fees. He compensated some of the commoners for £1834;[146] others were given pieces of land cut off the edges of the Forest. Five-sixths of the Forest passed intact to the Houblon family.

Topography of the Forest

The Forest in its setting   At the head of this chapter is the description of the Forest in the report of the Commissioners of 1639. Remarkably little has changed in these 350 years; it would almost do for a description of the fabric of the Forest today, with its 'Woodground usually incopsed and inclosed', 'open Wood and Bushie ground' with 'Pollard Ash and Maple of small worth', and its 'Playnes, Ridings and highways'.

Hatfield parish was still much the same as it had been in the middle ages. Hatfield town was no longer important, and was to shrink further: the market was abandoned and many houses fell down. It still had its Council of Four-and-Twenty and its headboroughs, alefounders, fishtasters and other officials as a reminder of former grandeur.[147] The population moved back to Hatfield Heath, where a village grew up.[76] The roads, hedges, greens, miniature open-fields and hamlets changed little. Maps of 1587[77] and 1624[148] show that some new groves had sprung up, and that some hedges had been grubbed out – these appear on the maps as rows of trees across fields.

In 1638–40 a new perambulation of the parish boundary was begun. It is much more detailed than that of 1298 and took at least three years. The part passing the Forest appears to be lost. I cannot discuss it all, but an extract gives the homely flavour:

> ... hearts Mead & hearts field to a Corner there, where we Crossed over to an Oake standing by a pond in the next field, and from there along the mydle of the lane to Manwood greene and to a bushe standing there. And soe went throwe ffosters Barne into puntMasters field. ...[124]

Although a very large parish, Hatfield lacked a proper vicar. The living was so poorly endowed that for more than a century Trinity College Cambridge, the patrons, refused to present an incumbent.[149]

Maps   The earliest large-scale map to show anything of the Forest was made for Sir Francis Barrington in 1624.[148] It covers the south-eastern edge, with 'The Coppice' marking Gravel-pit Coppice, Warren Coppice (shown but not differentiated), and 'Woodd Roe greene' as a treeless plain tapering into a road and with houses round its edge. Barrington Hall is drawn as a many-gabled Jacobean house;

in 1613 John Skingle had contracted to make 100,000 bricks for it in a place called Brickhills, which the map shows south of the house.[150] (This edifice has long ago bitten the dust, revealing the medieval Hall behind, which still stands.) The fields between the Hall and the Forest have changed little in 360 years.

In 1757 Jacob Houblon III commissioned the cartographers Hollingworth and Lander to make a beautiful map (Plate 2). It shows the Forest at exactly its medieval extent, the coppices and plains, the Shermore Brook, the Lodge and Warren House, and the newly-made lake with the Shell House. There is some indication of pollard trees in the plains. 'London Road' ran diagonally across the Forest; this highway was evidently a short-cut for people further east along Stane Street to go to London avoiding Bishop's Stortford. The Forest still had its complicated boundary running out by 'horns' into lanes, with houses at intervals round the perimeter. It is named 'Takeley Forest', a common error at this time.

The map shows seventeen coppices, nine on the Barrington and eight on the Morley side. In the north-east are three compartments which, though counted as coppices, are shown with scattered trees. Evidently Barrington had given up trying to maintain these as coppices. This area is now a plain with pollard trees, some of which still show their origin as coppice stools (p. 249). Of the remaining coppices, Warren and Doodle-oak disappeared later, leaving twelve extant today.

In 1766 Sir John Barrington had an atlas of his estates drawn by the cartographer Mackoun. The family fortunes were now at their height; the property included a deer-park and thirteen woods, among them the medieval Row Wood, Man Wood, and Taylors Wood (now lost in Stansted airfield). His Hatfield Forest map gives much the same information as its rival, but the three former coppices were by now indistinguishable from the plains.[152]

The next map is in the atlas of Essex by Chapman and André, surveyed 1772–4 (Fig. 17). It is on a small scale, but shows alterations to the lake (p. 129) and Warren Coppice (p. 130). The first edition Ordnance Survey, surveyed 1799–1805, is also at a small scale, but clearly shows trees and scrubs in the plains as well as the coppices (Fig. 18).

The last map in this period accompanies the Tithe Commutation Award of 1838, which shows the Forest in beautiful detail (Fig.

19), though it does not distinguish between grassland and scrubs in the plains.

Early lists of the coppices   Although on archaeological grounds the coppices must be medieval, the earliest lists of them are from the seventeenth century. The Morley coppices are first listed in a lease of 1654, which mentions 'springs or Coppices of woodgrounds ... Dudlowe, Northwood, Beggarshall, Round, Lodge, Emberlings, Scalemoore, ffirestead'.[156] Five of the names are familiar. Dudlowe is evidently the later Doodle-Oak Coppice, now lost, named after the Doodle Oak (p. 242). Firestead Coppice is evidently Fairstead, now Collin's. Scalemoore may thus be what Warren Coppice was called before there was a warren (p. 163); the name would be appropriate on account of the nearby 'moor' or fen where the lake now is. An earlier Morley lease, of 1597, mentions 'Ten parcells of ground which are now inclosed or copi[c]ed';[157] I cannot say whether two of the coppices were then subdivided, or whether there were two others lost soon after.

On the Barrington side, a lease of 1639 mentions Table, Middletrench, Takeley-gate, Gravelpit and Huttons coppices; each of them supposedly 16 acres measured with a 21-foot perch, that is 26 modern acres.[158] Table and Gravelpit Coppices are still so called; Middletrench and Takeley-gate are presumably two of the lost north-eastern coppices; Huttons may be Dowsett's (see later).

A curious undated document of a few years earlier surveys the woods on the Barrington side. I quote it in a slightly simplifed form, with my identification of the coppices (Table 3). It looks as though the Barringtons were in financial trouble, had been coppicing their woods for all they were worth (despite the 1576 agreement), and were making a last effort to raise a few more hundreds by selling timber – possibly to bail Sir Francis out of his dungeon.

The Doodle Oak is here mentioned for the first time, and we encounter London Horsepath (later London Road), Takeley Street and Hatfield Park (then defunct). The Table, which gave its name to Table Coppice, was some object at the middle of the Forest where London Road crossed the Shermore Brook. White's Wayer was a pond (p. 17) and the Gore was a triangle of land; they were somewhere at the north edge of the Forest. From these features I can identify all the Barrington coppices as they were later. It is impossible

Fig. 17 Hatfield in 1772–4, from Chapman & André's atlas of Essex.[153] Note the difference between wood-pasture and woodland. Forests and commons are accurately shown, but the shapes of woods are very inaccurate. The area shown is 5½ by 4 miles (9 by 6 km).

110

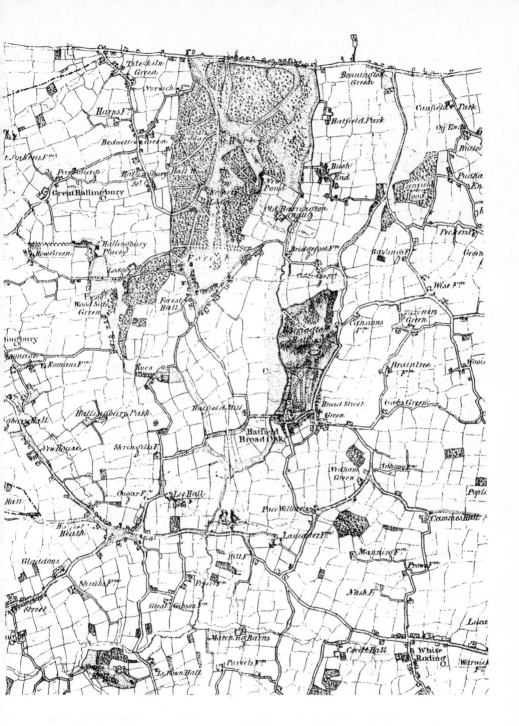

Fig. 18 Hatfield in 1799, from the Ordnance Survey survey manuscript drawing.[154]
Woods are quite accurate. The apparent field boundaries are a conventional
indication of enclosed land; they do not depict individual fields.

111

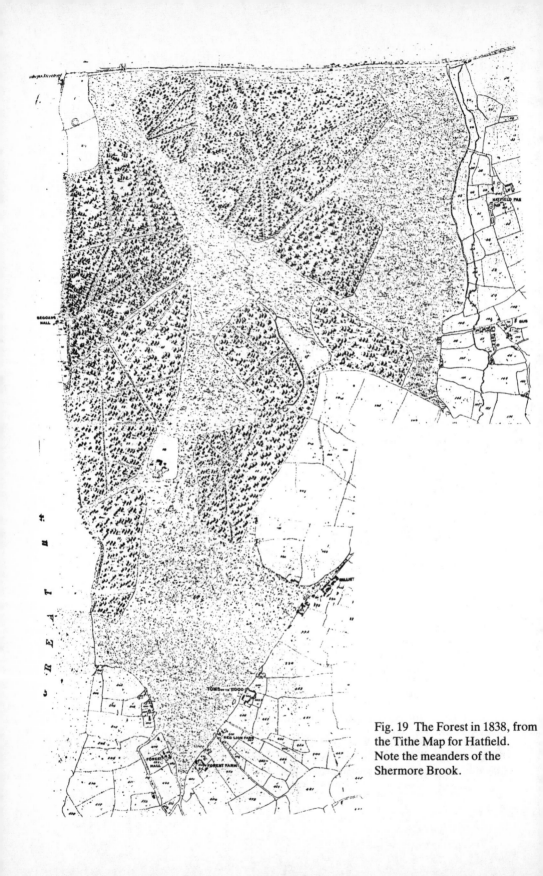

Fig. 19 The Forest in 1838, from the Tithe Map for Hatfield. Note the meanders of the Shermore Brook.

to make the acreages fit, even if we assume that they are estimated in big acres (p. x), and I can only suppose that they are vague guesses. In this private document Barrington makes no pretence of keeping to the 16 big acres which the 1576 agreement allowed him to fell annually, whereas in the 1639 lease Sir Thomas evades the agreement by deeming each coppice to be of 16 acres. The first three items in the list were evidently in the far north of the Forest, but cannot more closely be identified. The high values indicate big trees or long-neglected underwood. I suggest that the strip of land between the coppices and Stane Street, once an anti-highwayman trench (p. 92), had been allowed to get overgrown.

Woodland Management

Underwood and woodcutting   Coppicing is implied in Henry VIII's lease of Hatfield, other than the Forest, to William Tyrrell in 1546. Tyrrell was allowed to take 36 cartloads of underwood in the Forest yearly, by permit from the Master of the Sales of the King's Woods, as well as timber for repairing the estate's buildings and equipment.[160]

The Forest seems designed for felling one coppice annually on a cycle of 17 years, or 18 years if one coppice is missing. The division of the coppices between two owners would have made this awkward. The practice is summarized by Morant, the Essex historian, in 1768:

> John Barrington Esq; hath *nine* copses of wood, besides outlands that lye open. Jacob Houblon Esq; has as many, about thirty acres in a copse one with another. When they fell any, they must enclose it for nine years to preserve the wood, and then it must lye open for nine years more, before they fell it. The Poor are to have the hedges [i.e. fences] at the nine years end.[161]

This long cycle was usual in compartmental Forests and parks; ordinary woods, where animals could be kept out all the time, were cut more often (*AW*). In practice felling was irregular, especially when the coppices were not properly fenced. For example, in 1677 Turnor claimed that all Barrington's coppices were neglected, 'ye Wood thereon being of many Years growth'.[162] (This could be exaggerated, since Turnor was investigating whether Barrington might have forfeited his rights by not exercising them.)

Table 3

A note of the veewe, and value of all Sr ffrancis Barringtons wooddes in Hatfeilde fforrest, to be cutt vp by the roote, and the same hath been estemed by Edwyn Lukyn, John Neuman, and Richard Manne . . .

	Acres	Value, £	Identification
Imprimis, the frunte of woodde that is from the brooke, to White Waier, and betweene the streate, and the longe Goare	8	£50	not heard of again
Item the rounde parcell of woodde, betweene the Goare, and the coppie hedges, and from the stile of the little coppie alonge the West side of the waye that leadethe to Whites wayer	10	£50	not heard of again
Item the parcell of woodde, called the olde coppie, betweene the waye that leadeth from the little coppie stile, to Whits wayer, and London Horse pathe, against Takley streate, and the trees vpon the Grene, and in the horse pathe	16	£70	not heard of again
Item the first coppie, betweene Hatfeilde Parke, and the horse pathe, over against Takley streate	20	£60	Low Street Coppice [40 acres]
Item the foure coppies that were last laide out, adioyninge alonge Hatfeilde Parke hedge, to Bushe End Gate	20 40	£60 £80	Middle and Bush-End Coppices [81 acres]
Item the coppie that is betweene Barrington hall grounde, and the high Waye, that leadethe from the table, to Bush Ende, downe to the brooke . . . with the trees on the plaines	25	£30	Gravelpit Coppice [26 acres]
Item the olde coppie called the table coppie	14	£16	Table Coppice [40 acres]
Item the Woodde from the table to Dowdle oke, betweene the brooke and the coppie hedges . . . This parcell hath beene since newe felled and coppied	22	£50	Spittlemore Coppice [32 acres]
Item the inclosed coppie against Huttons	14	£30	Dowsett's Coppice [26 acres]
the inclosed coppie against Kats	20	£40	Street Coppice [42 acres]
and the inclosed coppie against London horse path	10	£14	Long Coppice [32 acres]
Total	**219**	**£550**	

4

Memor, his Woodd hathe of late yeres been so felled, and coppi[c]ed, that, savinge thre parcelles, which maye make present profitt, there is none vpon his side without cuttinge vp timber trees, by the roote : which parcelles in all will amounte but vnto 60 acres, or there abouts.[159]

114

The Turnors themselves did not fell their woods in a rigid rotation. The agent, planning a visit to Hatfield in 1720, intended

> To take Brices Account this year of Embellins Coppice felled this Spring and of severall other Coppies which are not yet finished and to have some of those Coppies to be measured. . . .[163]

A report on the Forest in 1730 says that Houblon had:

> 434 Acres of Copices and Woodlands. . . .
> The Woods & Copices which now want to be cut & are above ye Common
>
> Growth being some of 15, 16, 17, 18 and 20 years, 193 acres.
> Note ye Remainder of ye Copices & Woodland are much of them 8, 9, 10, 12 & 13 years Growth. Severall of which are now also fellable.[164]

This agrees roughly with Barrington's statement in 1758 that the Houblons and their predecessors had always kept to an 18-year felling cycle.[165]

In many woods the underwood products are recorded in minute detail. Some was used for specialized things like hurdles, thatching spars, hop-poles, and (in Essex) on sea-defences. Some went on fencing and mending hedges. Most of it, however, was used for fuel: faggots, logs, and occasionally charcoal. Firewood was scarce in Essex in the desperate winters of the late sixteenth century.[166] At Hatfield little such detail survives. In 1664 'Roundwood, blocks and ffaggotts' are mentioned, which would be appropriate for a long coppicing cycle.[167] Accounts of the 1800s and 1810s occasionally mention hurdle-making and faggots.

The valuations of *c.* 1690 and *c.* 1700 state that the coppices in the Forest made £100 per annum. This comes to £0.14 per acre per year, just over half the average value of underwood in Essex at the time (*AW*). Wall and Monk Woods together made £37 or £50 a year, that is £0.35 or £0.47 per acre per year. The difference is a measure of how livestock damaged the growth.

Competition between timber trees and underwood was well recognized at this time, and an example comes from the Town Grove (no longer extant) in Hatfield. The charity owning the grove was allowed, with some legal difficulty, to fell the timber in it

> for the Improvement of the said Grove, the underwoods being spoiled by the thickness and droping of the Timber trees. . . .[168]

Little is known of how woodcutting was organized. The 700 acres of woodland in the Forest would have required fifteen men, at the very least, to keep up with cutting them. Many woods were leased to contractors to be felled, but this was probably not done here, since I never find the behaviour of contractors made an excuse for litigation. We learn a little of everyday woodland scenes from a case in *c.* 1750 about a wounded deer. John Bawcock, a woodman, said that he saw the deer when on March 2 'he was employed in making up ffaggotts' in the coppice. A colleague

> denied he knew anything of it, but said it might happen by the Hind's running upon his Ax amongst ye Wood.[!]

Matthew Gray deposed

> that he was carting Bushes for Inclosing the said Coppice ... that the Hind was very tame ... insomuch that it used to follow persons & take bread & other things from Woodhands.[169]

The 1800s and 1810s These decades alone are well recorded, through John VI Houblon's rent books which survive among the family archives. The eight coppices on the Houblon side of the Forest were cut on a 17- or 18-year rotation. In some years a whole coppice was cut (all the underwood together with such timber trees as were saleable), in other years nothing. This was a clumsy arrangement for the Houblons. They had other woods, but these had their own coppice cycle (p. 123), and no attempt was made to integrate them in order to have the same acreage to cut each year. Possibly in 'off' years the Forest woodcutters were cutting the Barrington coppices, of which I have no similar records.

In 1808, a typical year, we find:

To 46 a[cres] 3 r[oods] 20 p[erches][a] of Underwood felled in Hangman's Coppice in Winter 1807 and Spring 1808 – including what was taken for the Use of Hallingbury Place, the Keepers Lodge and Cottage	£857 7s. 6d.
To 2 a[cres] 0 r[ood] 11 p[erches] of Ditto fell'd in Wall Wood at the same Time, including a small Quantity reserved for the Place	£26 17s. 0d.
Ash & Oak Tops sold out of Hatfield Chase	£40 19s. 6d.
24 loads 5 feet[b] of Oak Timber out of Hatfield Chase in 1808 @ £8 10s. per Load naked	£204 17s. 0d.
44 loads 44 feet of Ash out of Hatfield Chase @ £6 10s.	£291 13s. 8d.

116

1 load 10 feet of Elm @ £6 10s.	£7 15s. 4d.
46 feet of Poplar @ 1s. 10d.	£4 5s. 2d.
100 faggots out of Wall Wood	18s. 0d.
283 Fathoms of Bark from Off the Oak Timber felled in Hatfield Chase 1808 @ 7s.	£99 1s. 0d.

[a] That is, 46.88 acres, being the area of the coppice minus its rides.
[b] The load here is evidently of 50 cubic feet, computed by the method of p. 245; one load would be (by modern standards) a single biggish oak-tree.

The cutting of this one coppice earned a total of £1506, about a quarter of the income (including rents) which the Houblons derived from all their estates in Essex and Herts. About half came from timber trees (including bark) and half from underwood.

Table 4 summarizes the income from timber and wood for these years. The coppices, except for Warren (p. 130), were flourishing. Underwood prices work out at from £0.79 (Collin's) to £1.12 (Beggar's Hall) per acre per year of growth. Allowing for inflation, this is from $2\frac{1}{2}$ to $3\frac{1}{2}$ times the value of the 1690s. Woods in general had become more valuable, but the Hatfield coppices were now selling for twice as much per acre-year as the average for Eastern England at the time (AW); they were now worth the same as Wall and Monk Woods. There can be no doubt that the grazing problem had at last been solved.

Underwood was sold to at least 17 buyers, probably woodmen who cut it themselves, processed it, and sold it retail.

Timber in the Forest brought in a little less income than wood. More ash timber than oak was sold, but oak made more money. The timber of oak was worth rather more than ash, and oak had also a valuable bark which at this time was worth nearly half the value of the timber. Since 1790 a boom in shipbuilding had begun to monopolize the supply of oak timber, affecting prices even in places remote from the sea. The parallel and explosive boom in the leather industry had an even greater effect on the price of oak-trees via the bark. Ash was of no use for shipbuilding or tanning.

In comparison with other woods, the Forest coppices were producing rather less timber than usual, which no doubt helped the underwood to flourish. It was most unusual for so much of the timber to be ash. Hangman's and Beggar's Hall produced a little elm and 'poplar', presumably aspen. The oaks fetched a lower than average price for timber and a higher than average for bark, which probably means that they were small trees (AW). Ash prices were about average.

117

Table 4   Abstract of wood and timber cut in Hatfield Forest, 1801–19[7,170]

Year	Price index[a]	Coppice cut	Acres cut[b]	Value of underwood	Oak timber	
					cu. ft	£
1801 or '02		Collin's – *no details survive*				
1803	1268	Warren	[42]	393	49[e]	6[e]
1804	1303	Doodle-Oak	[24]	414	686	103
1805	1521	none				
1806	1454	none				
1807	1427	Beggar's Hall	[53½]	1080	965	154
1808	1476	Hangman's	46.9	859	1205	205
1809	1619	none				
1810	1670	Lodge[h]	56.8	1042	1510	302
1811	1622	none				
1812	1836	none				
1813	1881	none				
1814	1642	Emblem's	30.8	545	nil	*nil*
1815	1467	Round	36.1	689	nil	*nil*
1816	1344	none				
1817	1526	Collin's	48.2	689	362	72
1818 record missing						
1819	1492					

[a] After Brown and Hopkins ; see Fig. 1.
[b] Figures in square brackets are estimates.
[c] Includes small sums for branchwood and for timber other than oak and ash.
[d] Fellings of Thremhall Priory Wood and of various small Houblon woods are omitted.

Oak bark	Ash timber		Total income out of Forest[c]	Acres cut in purlieu woods[d]	Cost of feast
	cu. ft	£	£		£
48	4375	367	944	Monk [0.6]	23
36	1100	110	591	Monk [2.6]	22
			60[f]	Monk [7.6]	16
			nil	Wall [8.6]	?[g]
70	1843	240	1625	Wall [7.5]	33
99	2244	292	1509	Wall 2.1	34
			nil	Wall 7.4	19
102[i]	1788	264	1751	Wall 0.2	42
			nil	Wall 7.5	15
			nil	Wall 8.7 + Wallis 3.4	23
			nil	Monk 5.7 + Wallis 4.5	23
nil	361	54	613	Monk 4.4	25
4	140	21	714		18
			nil	Monk 10.8	21
51	571	80	895	Monk 5.0	36
			nil	Wall 15.9	29

[e] A large amount of oak was used on the estate; the figures record only what was sold.
[f] From 400 cu. ft of walnut.
[g] The feast was held but the cost is not recorded.
[h] Timber includes some from farmland trees on the estate.
[i] This figure is low because the buyer paid for the peeling.

Pollarding in the plains is probably implied by an item in 1812 of £23 for 'Topwood and Faggots from Woodrow'. It is surprising not to find this regularly; annual rings (p. 247) show that pollards were being cut at this time.

The 1808 account concludes with the item

Wood Feast Dinner and Liquor at the George Inn Bishops Stortford   £34 9s.

The feast was held most often in October, and usually in that excellent hostelry the Green Man, Takeley Street. As the table shows, there was a feast every year, though in 'off' years – when only small areas of woodland, outside the Forest, were felled – less was spent. I suspect that the expenditure depended on how many buyers there were to be feasted.

Coppice boundaries   In 1612 the coppices 'had Gates to them with Locks and Keys to go out of one Coppice into another'. Some coppices had been divided into two or more 'Quarters, with a Hedge going between'[171] – maybe one such division survives between Long and Spittlemore Coppices, where there is no bank.

As we have seen, the compartmentation did not then work very well, and livestock often got into the coppices and ate the young shoots. A footnote to the survey of c. 1625 says of the Barrington coppices:

Memor. that many timber trees since this veewe haue been felled, and many lopped, and at Sr ffrancis overthrowe, at the comon lawe, the vnderwoodde of two young coppies ware spoiled [by the Commoners Cattle].*

* Note added in another contemporary hand.

In 1624 Lady Elizabeth Morley, in a moment of good sense, removed some of the family differences with Sir Thomas Barrington by leasing to him the soil of the coppices in which he owned the trees. This lease, continuing the provisions for fencing, specifies the traditional method of reconciling deer and coppicing. Deer were to be let into the coppices from six years' growth after felling, rather than the nine years' after which the commoners' livestock were allowed in. Every time each wood was cut Barrington was to erect

eighte deare leapes of one rod [16½ ft] in leanghe and foure foote in height in euery seuerall inclosure [when the underwood was] in the full growth of six yeares for the deare ... onely to leape in and out And for noe other

120

Cattell whatsoeuer. And the said deare leapes ... to contynewe soe longe as the ... coppices shall continew inclosed. ...[172]

The deer were to be allowed to feed quietly in the coppices. Barrington was to provide browsewood for them when necessary (p. 124). He had also to make four gates to every coppice and to leave the keys at the Forest Lodge.[134]

A renewal of this lease in 1639, besides mentioning deerleaps and browsewood, lists five of the coppices (p. 109). The lease for the five coppices was to run respectively for 3, 5, 6, 7 and 8 years, presumably being the times which the coppice fences still had to stand before the nine-year removal. Barrington was probably felling a whole coppice each year.

In the next century, the two lords quarrelled less about the fence than about the earthwork that it stood on. It had for centuries been the custom for the owner or purchaser of any wood to maintain the relevant part of the boundary hedge and bank whenever it was felled. Sir Jacob Houblon and his predecessors had long enclosed their own coppices with 'an Hedge & Ditch',[165] yet when Barrington did so he protested that this infringed his ownership of the soil. In 1736 he briefed Counsel on a claim that Barrington's steward

> has ordered one Abraham Sapsford to digg a large Ditch round one of the Coppices ... on the Outside of the Hedge next the Forest who (tho' forbid ...) still persists in doing it and throws the Soil dug therefrom into the Forest which is a Detriment to the Deer Cattle etc. feeding ...

The ditch was

> 6 foot broad 6 foot deep and 200 foot long and [Sapsford had put] 500 Cart-loads of Earth upon other the Soil of Plaintiff ... and thereby rotted other his Grass ... to the value of £10.

Sapsford's version was that he was merely clearing out an old ditch:

> he did throw up a quantity of Mould and Dirt out of the Ditch which was made when part of the Quarter called Bushend was enclosed. NB. The time for keeping the enclosed Ground in was not expired and the Defendant did not break the Soil of the Plaintiff in any fresh place but only throw up the Dirt out of the Ditch which was made as aforesaid.

Sapsford must have been right. The coppice boundaries are massive woodbanks, dating from long before 1736, and the bank is every-where on the inside of the ditch and not the outside as Houblon claimed. Barrington apparently lost the case, and ever after politely

121

asked, and was politely given, permisson to ditch round his coppices.[165]

Presumably the upkeep of fences was a regular expense, but the only bill I have seen is for 1783, when the Forester charged £14 for 'Carting Bushes Stakes and Ethers for Repairing the coppice ffences', and labourers were paid £28.[173] Fences were evidently still being made in the Neolithic manner, of hurdlework of stakes driven at intervals and interwoven with long flexible rods called *ethers*.

Woodland grass　Not surprisingly, with all the inroads of cattle, sheep and deer on the coppices, the underwood was not continuous. The deer-keeper and another witnessed in 1612 that

> the Wood was not so thick ... but that there was some void ground between the Trees ... in places where the sweetest Grass did grow the ... Cattle did Eat it very near & bare before ye said Coppices were laid forth.[171]

Grass growing in recently-felled coppices was thought to be of value. In 1597 Edward Lord Morley leased the 'Herbage, Pasturage and ffeedinge' of his coppices. The lessee might put in horses, sheep, lambs, and also cattle of under $1\frac{1}{4}$ years old; he was to pay £15 a year and to repair the coppice fences.[157] We marvel that woodland grasses were worth so much: what now grows in coppices is *Deschampsia caespitosa*, with tough and serrated leaves like hacksaw blades. Probably the lessee's livestock revenged themselves by eating Lord Morley's ash and hazel.

Woodland grasses were quarrelled over. In 1612 Abell Hurley said that

> while it is Inclosed the Commoners & Sharers can have no benefit by the feeding therein Except it be by reaping the Grass & carrying it away in Baggs wch would be a great hindrance to them in neglect of Business of greater Weight. ... Except it be a poor Body that hath nothing else to do ... and he may perhaps may lye in a Copice reaping grass a whole day together. ...

This grass was said to be a benefit to 'some fewe of the porer sort of commoners' and to inhabitants not having common-rights.[122] The Hatfield love of petty dispute descended to bags of tough grass. In *c.* 1630 the Essex Justices reported to the Privy Council that

> we find that one Thomas Clark a wandering fellowe was harboured by ... Tho: Garratt & Katherin his wife & wholly by them Imployed to cutt Grase

in the Coppices of ... Sr Tho: [Barrington] ... to have from them for every bundle he should cutt 1d.

the said Clarke the same Morneing about halfe an hour before the said Coppice hedges were on fire tooke a firebrand out of Garratts house & went towards the said Coppice. . . . And that Garratt & his wife being required to quench the said fire they answered ... let them quench it that sett it on fire. . . .

Garratt & his wife had often expressed that if the said fforrest should be driven[a] (as it was conceived to have beene lately done by some officers for the kinge) that then the said Coppice should & would be sett on fire. . . . And Garratts wife had broken the said Coppice hedge & carryed the wood awaie. And ... there hath beene divers young trees spring wood & grasse cutt & taken out of the said Coppice.[174]

[a] That is, the commoners' animals on it rounded up to find any that were there illicitly.

In 1720 Turnor's agent wanted to know 'how many acres there are ... of mowing ground in the ridings' of each coppice.[163]

Deer

Poaching appears quite often in the earlier records. The 1446 grant says that anyone taking deer in the Forest without the Duke's permission is fined £10.[175] Edward Duke of Buckingham had repeated trouble with John Burrell and his friends hunting without permission.[112]

The 1612 inquiry mentions deer 'wounded with bowes and Doggs'. The keeper of the deer thought the compartmentation of the Forest was a help to poachers in catching deer 'with Buckstalls and ropes or Snares which may be set in Creepers thorough the Hedges. . . . (p. 100)[122, 171]

Deer were important all through the seventeenth century. Sir John Barrington occasionally exercised his right to take them.[176] In 1674 Thomas Bull of old Barrington Hall (by now reduced to a farmhouse) got into serious trouble for one which was 'accidently' killed in his yard.[177]

Keeping the deer alive in winter was difficult. Letting them into the coppices at six years' growth would have allowed them some sustenance from low underwood and the remaining coppicing plants; this, as we have seen, was reported in 1612. The 1639 commission claimed that there were nearly 400 deer and not enough room for them (p. 93).

The medieval custom of browsewood is mentioned in the 1624 and 1639 leases. Barrington was to cut 'reasonable browse wood' for Morley's deer, or to allow Lord Morley's men to cut it from his trees instead. Barrington's woodward was 'to haue an eye to the said browse wood' and to faggot it up when the deer had finished with it. In 1639 Barrington was allowed the option of providing two loads of hay instead.

In c. 1690 there were said to be about 600 deer on the Forest. The zenith of deer-keeping was reached in the next century. The 1730 report found 'abt. 800 out which may be killed every Season 30 brace of Bucks and as many Does'.[164] I do not know what to make of this estimate. Deer are difficult to count, especially in this terrain, and are usually underestimated (FD); on the other hand, if there really were 800, then 120 would have been too few to kill each year.

For this number of deer, the Forest would hardly have given sufficient pasture, even if there had been no other animals on it. It is not surprising to hear that

> Mr. Houblon is Obliged to put them into the Copices of the Wood that are kept Inclosed to be made fat, and the keeper Observes the Deer not to be so large as they were some years ago . . . owing to the want of Pasture.[178]

In 1781 there were

> 500 Deer ... if Mr Houblon had not been at the charge of giving them Hay most of the Winter they could not have been kept alive.[179]

In 1783 hay for feeding the deer was bought for £15, but some was made in the Forest. The Forester was paid 14s. for haymaking, and a further £1 14s. for 'Mowing Making & Carting Hay Rolling the Meadow ground in the Cottage Coppice'. 5s. 6d. was spent on 'Printed Bills of Deer being stolen'.[173]

An inquiry in 1838 found that Houblon

has increased his Stock of Deer to such a number as to leave little or no pasture for the Commoners but this is likewise an injury to himself as his Deer are in bad condition and he is obliged to fodder them at a considerable expence.[145]

All through the centuries the convention was kept up that deer were priceless, but on one unusual occasion a value is given. In 1805 the executors of the last Forester paid 5 guineas for a buck.[7] A deer was thus worth about four times as much as a sheep of roughly the same size.[96]

The Plains

Pasturage From the sixteenth century onwards there was trouble from the over-use of the Forest by too many animals. The manorial court, composed mainly of commoners themselves, could make by-laws to limit grazing; the by-laws for 1592 survive.[180] Courts tried to enforce the well-known *levant et couchant* principle, that the number of animals which each commoner might put on the common ought to be limited to what he could feed on his own farm over the winter. Thus, in 1574

Myhell Borling keepeth 2 bullocks in ye forest, ye which he did not keep in ye winter, nor ought to keep yem in ye forest, yerfore we amerce him at 20d. [not a deterrent fine].[180]

Another rule was that a commoner 'must take the herbage with ye mouthes of his owne cattell',[181] and not sublet his rights. Every so often, the commoners were supposed to help in holding a 'drift' of the Forest, at which illicitly grazed animals were rounded up and impounded.

Grazing 'offences' took up much of the time of manorial courts; for example a court in 1619 imposed fines for 23 bullocks, 3 cows, 10 mares and 16 colts.[182] Bulls were forbidden, and in 1662 Matthew Palmer was fined for grazing one.[183]

Pigs were troublesome in the seventeenth century. Avesage was still being charged in 1623–4 at the medieval rates of 2d., 1½d., or 1d. for a 'Hogg of Age', a 'Hogg of a Year old', a 'Piggot', or a 'Pig'.[124] In 1616 the court fined 'All those that of Right shold have paied Avisage for their hogges & have not' at 21*d*. a head.[184] In 1662 the court found

> that the forest is much rooted vpp with hoggs & we warne all thos that doe put hoggs on to the forrest that they be safetiently ringed vpon paine of twelf pence the hogge.

Two years later, Richard Hatley had built a 'hogscoate' – a shed for pigs – on the Forest near his house, and was fined 1*s*., with a 10*s*. fine if he did not pull it down.[124]

The 1639 commission found that the commoners were grazing up to 40 sheep each.

Later, the authority of the manor court weakened, and complaints of abuse of common-rights become more general. In 1675, according to Turnor, the Sharers and some other commoners

> doe overcharge the common and turn in Sheepe and hoggs and build hoggs coates upon the Soyle of the said fforrest and keepe their geese there and refuse to keepe up their ffences. ... Whereby the Deere being pinched in their feed are forced to struggle out of the fforest. ...

They also refused to help in the drift.[185]

In 1749 Houblon alleged that the farmers of Hatfield

> have of late years Oppressed the Common. ... Some of them, being Occupiers of ffarms of 40 or 50 £ per Annum or more, have put 80 Sheep or more on ye fforrest ... besides 5 or 6 Cows. ...

Nathaniel Humfrey, tenant of Barrington Hall, had put on 220–240 sheep, intead of the 140 allowed him by the 1576 agreement. The Sharers, too, who (Houblon claimed) were entitled only to '4 Head of Black Cattle' each,

> have for 40 or 50 years last past put on what Horses, Cows, Bullocks and Sheep they thought fit ... and the Number has Increased every Year for Several years past. ...[186]

Six of the commoners complained to Sir John Barrington in 1751:

> There is another Abuse, which we cannot but take Notice of ... the great Number of Asses (deemed Uncommonable Cattle) that are usually kept on the Forest, and not only Eat the Grass, but when that is short, they feed upon the Wood.

They even objected to 'the Excessive Number of Geese generally kept on the Forrest'.[187]

Assignment of grazing rights was a frequent abuse. In 1749 Barrington had let part of his quota to a Mr Dixon of Birchanger, who

> often puts in the fforrest all his Stock of Sheep and Lams to the Number of 140 or 160 at a time besides Cows and Bullocks.[188]

How much grazing went on is difficult to assess. It raises problems of definition that even contemporaries could not solve; for example, are animals to be counted that are on the Forest only for a short time? Nathaniel Humfrey, accused in 1753 of putting 'upwards of 300 Sheep' on the Forest, replied that he never put on more than 160, these only for about a month around May and only in the day-time, and that he seldom put animals on the Forest from September to May 'except casually on a wet day'.[189,145] It nevertheless looks as though in the eighteenth century everyone with an interest in the Forest was taking advantage of the weak organization to get as much as he could out of it – the Houblons heading the list with too many deer. The manorial court could have changed the rules but would not. Proposals were made to limit the number of animals, but the commoners never reached agreement.

By the nineteenth century the Forest reeve seems to have become inert: there was no drift between 1816 and 1836. Grazing, apart from deer, may have declined because the larger farmers thought it not worthwhile. In the 1830s there were 187 people claiming rights on the Forest, but on average only 51 exercised them in each year. However, many of these were small farmers turning on more live-stock than their farms could justify; a man with only eight acres of land was grazing 94 sheep and a horse.[190]

Pollards and scrubs   Pollards, as we have seen, are expressly mentioned in 1639. In 1730 they are recorded in Woodrow (the southern plain) as well as in the rest of the Forest.[164]

When Lord Morley acquired the Forest, his interest in boundaries led him to investigate

> all the presentments which I find yett in the Rolles from the beginning of the queenes time vntill this Daie touchinge the thornes or Bushes growinge in the foreste.

He lists a handful of persons fined for cutting and removing or selling bushes, thorns and windfall wood. The fines seem not to have been deterrent.[191]

The survey of *c.* 1625 ends with a note

> that the busshes of Sr ffrancis Barringtons side, are none of his, but the
> Commoners onely to mainetaine theire fences next vnto the fforrest.

The gravel-pit   Gravel is scarce in the immediate area, and even
the little deposits by the Shermore Brook were of value. As mineral
rights they belonged to the landowner:

> no one ever pretended to digg within this Chace even so much as a Load
> of Gravell or Clay . . . without the Owners Leave. . . .[192]

However, if the landowner dug any gravel he was liable to be fined
by the manor court for spoiling the pasture.

The gravel-pit had begun in a small way before 1610, and one
of the coppices was named after it. In the eighteenth century it
appeared in several of the Houblons' and Barringtons' favourite
lawsuits.

In 1783 Barrington was suing Sir Peter Parker of Bassingbourn
Hall, north of the Forest. Houblon had opened pits for sand and
gravel on his own side of the Forest; some he had used himself,
and some he had given to the highway authority to make up the
main road (Stane Street) to the north of the Forest. He had lately
given permission to Parker to take gravel for making a new road
to Bassingbourn. Parker had carted away 'several thousand Loads',
as well as topsoil 'for the use of a Plantation of Firs and Shrubs'.
Barrington, as lord of the manor, was aggrieved because in so doing
Parker's men had (so he claimed) destroyed 50 acres of grass, 50
acres of herbage, and hedges and fences amounting to 100 cartloads
of wood and 100 of underwood; the total damage amounted to £500.
The pit had been so enlarged that the Shermore Brook was running
nearly through the middle of it.[193] I do not know what to make
of this claim, since the gravel-pit is now definitely on the Barrington
side; possibly the evidence of Parker's pit is now hidden under the
delta of the brook.

By 1826 the highway surveyors for Hatfield were taking gravel
from this pit under a recent statute authorizing highway authorities
to dig road-metal from common-land without payment.[194]

The lake and Shell House   The lake is first mentioned in an accusation of 1754 as having been made 'several years' before, destroying the grazing.[195] Litigation naturally followed, and we learn more from a brief of 1758:

> Sir Jacob Houblon made a Dam or Head of Earth at the Bottom of a low Bogg and Rushly part of the ... fforest through which the ... Shermore Brooke runs and converted about 8 Acres of the ... fforest ... into a Pond and Stocked it with ffish (to the makeing whereof ... John Barrington Signified his Consent by Letter) ... did likewise Stubb the Trees and Wood in his own Coppice called ffairsted Quarter ... and built a small House there for himself and ffriends to drink Tea in and made a little Garden round it and cut several Walks in the said Coppice ... Thomas Claydon lives in the said House.[165]

Lady Alice Archer-Houblon, the family's historian, recounts genial picnics and hunting parties by the lake, to the sound of the peacocks kept by Mrs Claydon for the table. She represents the making of the lake as intended to create jobs.[140]

The lake was first formed by a simple dam, and is shown thus on the great map of 1757. But Jacob Houblon III was not content with a simple lake. I have seen 'A Plan for the Alteration of the Water adjoining to Cottage Coppice', dated 1757;[196] it looks like the work of a fashionable landscape designer, although it is too early to be part of Capability Brown's scheme for Hallingbury. The lake was to be given two curving arms, each with an island at the far end. The south-western arm of the lake was executed, as the 1772–4 map proves. The engineering was difficult and involved more than doubling the length of the dam. The arm and island still survive, though cut off from the main lake in 1979. The other arm (of which two alternative positions are sketched) would have extended up the Shermore Brook towards the gravel-pit; it was never made.

Tree-planting   From the middle ages onwards trees were commonly planted, but very rarely in woods or Forests. In 1504 Robert Noke was fined for planting divers ashes on his farm at Great Hallingbury.[197] A Hatfield example is a payment in 1638 'for watering the Oakes at Hatfield Heath', probably replacements for the famous oak there (p. 242).[198]

The making of the lake began the gradual conversion of Hatfield Forest into an ornamental annexe to Hallingbury Park. As the next stage in this 'beautification', trees were planted in the Forest for

129

the first time, and duly entered into the litigation. In 1754 Barrington was claiming that

Jacob Houblon the Elder has also Dug up . . . upon Woodrow Quarter great Quantities of Soil . . . and has planted a great Number of Trees thereon.[195]

The 1757 map shows Emblem's Coppice bisected by a walk, continuing as a formal avenue into the southern plain, together with what look like formal clumps and belts of trees in the extreme south of the Forest. The avenue was of elms, whose suckers are still alive now.

In 1759 a 'fresh plantation' of the 'cottage coppy' [Warren Coppice] was made.[140] Was this replanting a consequence of cattle damaging the wood, or was it part of the 'beautification' around the Shell House? The coppice is shown on the map of 1772–4 as an enclosure with two avenues and only scattered trees. By 1803 it was back into the coppicing rotation, but had not recovered as a wood: the woodcutting account in that year shows it producing only £9.34 worth of underwood per acre, little more than half the other coppices. The timber trees felled included beech and chestnut. Like many other woods that have been replanted, this coppice disappeared altogether another half-century later.

My only other reference is a trifling payment of 7s. 6d. to the Forester in 1783 for 'Planting in the Wood and Coppices'.[173]

Forest Boundaries

The perimeter fence   An important difference between the medieval and the later Forest is the attitude to its perimeter. In the middle ages a Forest was not a park, and the deer were not confined; they could come and go as they pleased, although if they left Hatfield to the north or west they lost the protection of Forest Law. The Forest gates were intended to confine domestic animals only. In other Forests it is definitely stated that neighbours had no right to fence deer off their land. At Hatfield the custom grew up that adjoining farmers had the right, and later the duty, to maintain deer-proof fences to confine the deer in the Forest. They were allocated thorns and underwood for this purpose.

1 The Forest in 1940, photographed by an unknown German pilot. Note the denser, long-established scrubs in the southern plains. There are small clouds over Collin's Coppice and the Warren.[222]

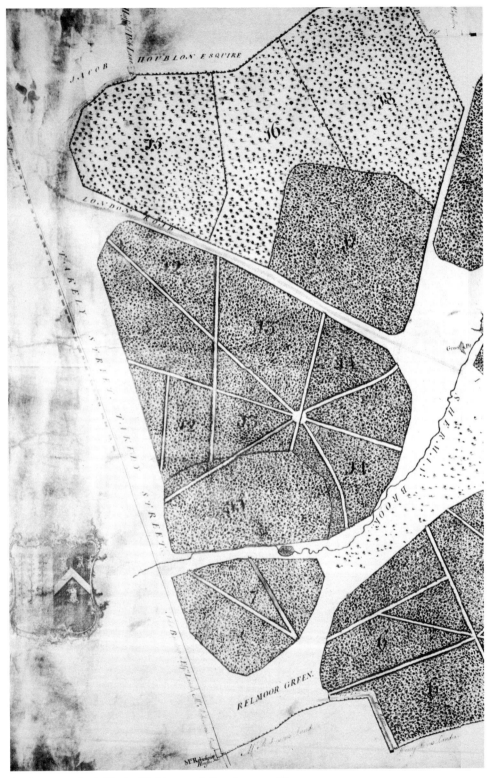

2 The Forest in 1757: the Hollingworth-Lander map.[151]

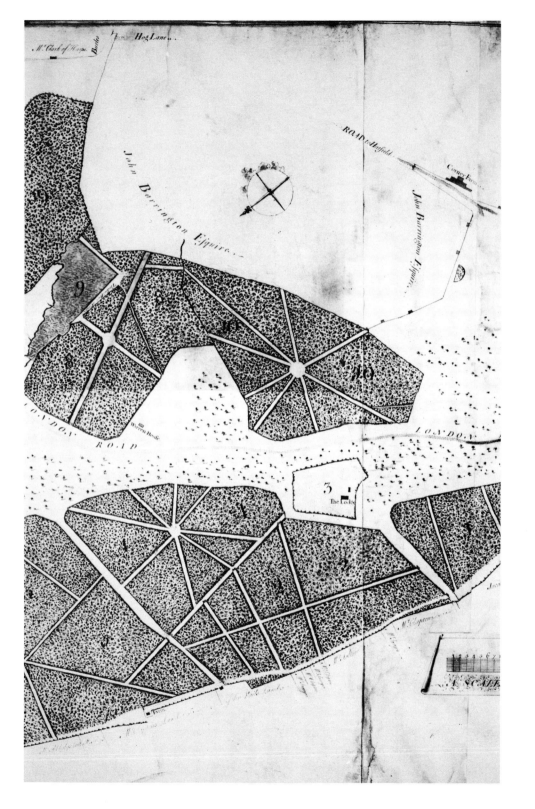

2 (*continued*) The Forest in 1757: the Hollingworth-Lander map.[151]

3 The Forest in 1940. Note the many irregular glades and open areas in the coppices. The scrubs are much less dense than now, but a young generation of hawthorn bushes has sprung up on the site of Doodle-Oak Coppice in the north-west. (The construction of Stansted Airport, to the north, has not yet begun.) *Luftwaffe aerial photograph, 31 August 1940*[222]

4 The Forest in 1970. The scrubs have become consolidated since 1940; their sharp edges show that they have not been expanding recently. Note the overgrowing of rides, the making of 'motorways' in the western coppices and Collin's, and the destruction (for replanting) of Emblem's Coppice. Outside the north-west corner of the Forest the Yemerlinoke earthworks have been destroyed. *Hunting Aerial Surveys, 9 October 1970*[301]

5 Woodland before coppicing: ash–maple, mainly from ancient stools, not cut for many decades. Lodge Coppice. *May 1979*

6 Wood newly coppiced, mainly of hazel. Spittlemore Coppice. The many young oaks have been left as timber trees. *February 1981*

7 What happened when fencing was not good enough. A bullock has got into Collin's Coppice and is devouring the regrowth of newly-coppiced ash. (This is no longer allowed to happen.) *June 1986*

8 Hazel as a great tree forming the canopy. Spittlemore Coppice. *February 1981*

9 East Anglian elm, near Canfield Hart outside the Forest. *June 1979*

10 East Anglian elm in the east of Spittlemore Coppice. *April 1974*

11 East Anglian elm, Emblem's Coppice (note young plantation on site of coppice). *May 1979*

12 Pollard Lineage elm, Bush-End Plain. The double base derives from its origin as a coppice stool in Middle Coppice. *February 1981*

13 The pair of giant pollard oaks in the scrub between Emblem's and Collin's Coppices.
June 1986

14 Ancient pollard oak on Bush-End Plain.
February 1981

15 Pollard beech in the southern scrubs.
February 1981

16 Ancient hawthorn by the Gravel-pit. *November 1987*

17 Pollard hornbeams on Bush-End Plain, about four years after re-pollarding. *July 1983*

18 (*Above*) Ancient coppice
stools (not pollards) of oak,
Lodge Coppice. *May 1979*

19 Giant pollard maple with
mistletoe, south-east of Forest
Lodge. *February 1981*

20 The Forest Lodge. The range with the central chimney is the oldest. *May 1979*

21 Oxlip, Dowsett's Coppice. *April 1984*

22 Marsh and spotted orchids on one of the Shermore Brook fens. *July 1983*

Already in 1568 a committee was set up by the manor court to investigate this 'ancient custom'.[191] The right as claimed in 1653 was for

Bushes Stakes & Edders ... according to their auntient Customes ... to make hedges ... to keepe wilde & tame Cattle within ye said fforrest. ...[199]

These materials would have been to make a dead 'hedge', or to reinforce a live one, up to the high standard needed to confine deer. 'Edders' are *ethers*, long flexible rods (p. 122).

From the 1610s onward, Lord Morley had been complaining that the commoners had been cheating him by this custom:

they often tymes keepe their hedges lowe and badd and sometymes pull up their hedges in the night time and lett out ... deare out of the saide fforrest and they come ... and cutt more wood and busshes to repair their hedges at their pleasures whereby great distruccion comes not only to his game and deer ... but allso by reason of their takynge ... the fuell of their hedges to burne in their owne houses. ...[125]

By 1675 Turnor was seeking to establish that the neighbouring tenants had an 'ancient' obligation to fence the Forest to keep in the deer. They refused to do so unless he supplied the materials, and said that three of the gates were his responsibility.[185]

Gates The 1592 by-laws list eleven gates, each connected to the Forest fence by posts, rails and pales. Woodrow and Bush-End Gates (Fig. 3) and four others on the Hatfield side were the commoners' responsibility to maintain with timber from the Forest. Lord Rich maintained the two gates on the main road and the one by Wall Wood; his tenants maintained Lyphatch and North Gates on the Hallingbury side.[180]

In 1662, when Lord Morley's affairs were in confusion, the manor court pursued him for not supplying timber for repairing the gates:

severall gats about the fforrest are oute of repaier by reason that we Cannot haue timber of the Lord morly ... it was denyed which is a great pregidis to the tennents and we warne the Lord morly to asigne [us] timber vppon the forrest to make vpp the gats according to the Costom: vpon paine of twenty pound.[124]

Well into the nineteenth century, bushes were still being used for repairing the fences, and there were still gates on the main road (then a turnpike) where it passed through the Forest.[169]

131

Wall Wood, Monk Wood and Woodside Green

These three formed a wood-pasture common with two coppices and a plain, a kind of miniature of Hatfield Forest, operated by the manors of Wallbury and Monkbury. Each wood belonged to one of the manors, but the common was shared. After 1592 both manors belonged to the owners of the Forest, but kept their separate institutions. The two woods, as we have seen, were distinct by the thirteenth century, and the system seems to date from before Great and Little Hallingbury were separated in Anglo-Saxon times; but details have not survived in writing until much later.

A court roll of 1518 mentions 'Walwodegrene' and one of its hatches.[197] The Monkbury courts of 1653 found it to be the custom

> that the auncient Tenants should have the bushes and herbage in the Lords woods and that the third part of the said woods should alwaies lye open and not be coppiced in.[200]

The practical working of this seems to have been settled long before, by dividing the wooded area approximately two-thirds and one-third. The smaller part formed the green, with pollard trees on it; the larger part was the lords' coppice-woods. In 1653 John Wheeler was ordered 'to make up his gate into Monkewood'.

The courts expressed the commoners' point of view. In the same year the 'Commission for the sale of lands and estates forfeited to the Common Wealth for Treason' descended upon Great Hallingbury, and found

> One Spring or Copice of wood commonly called Wallberry wood Conteyning by estimacion ffyfty Acres . . . ye Vnderwood is of about Three yeares growth & wee vallew ye same together wth ye Standers & Storers [timber trees] there left at 10s. per Acre [plus twice as much for the value of the land if it were arable].[201]

The zigzag eastern boundaries of the woods, which do not reach the parish boundary, probably result from grubbings-out at some unknown date. A map of c. 1800 shows almost the same state as today, except that there were still many trees all over Woodside Green.[78] The satellite wood Wallis's Spring was already detached from Monk Wood. A cottage lay, as now, between Wall and Monk Woods. The enclave of private land, with a house on it, between Woodside Green and Monk Wood was then two enclaves; this might have been a traditional place for the smithy, a public service which needed to be kept well away from other buildings lest they be burnt.

Coppicing of Wall and Monk Woods The valuation at the forced sale of the estate in 1665 includes 'The Copps wood of Walberry & Monckberry', worth £37 at 10*s*. per acre per annum.[133] The purchaser thought this too much: a note reads 'The Copsewoods are nowhere in Essex aboue A noble y acre', which agrees with my own experience for the time (a noble being 6*s*. 8*d*.). The area of 74 acres, however, is either underestimated or measured with a big acre; the woods now add up to 106 acres, and there is no sign that they were once smaller.

The Forest accounts for 1803–19 (Table 4) show that each year part of Wall or Monk Woods was felled, together with Thremhall Priory Wood or one of the small woods belonging to the Houblons in the vicinity. More of these other woods tended to be felled in years in which no coppice was cut in the Forest. As in the Forest, there was apparently an 18-year coppice cycle: in the 16 years for which records survive, the whole of Monk Wood and Wallis's Spring were felled once, and about two-thirds of Wall Wood. Timber trees did not come regularly from these woods: there are small entries for topwood of ash felled for use on the estate, but the only substantial felling of timber was in Wall Wood in 1819. The 16 acres of wood felled in that year produced £260 worth of underwood; the oak trees yielded 1002 cubic feet of timber which sold for £218, plus £80 in 'Topwood & Faggots' and £66 in bark.

Underwood prices from Wall and Monk Woods ranged between £0.81 and £1.22 per acre per year. Like the Forest woods, they were worth well above the Essex average, perhaps because there were few timber trees to shade the underwood.

Pollarding on Woodside Green Trees on the green, as on the Forest plains, belonged to the lord, not the commoners. The valuation of *c*. 1690, besides £37 per annum for the 'Coppice woods upon the Green', includes £13 for 'The Pollard trees on the green of which the lops and tops are felled once in 12 years.'[138] 'Faggots from Woodside Green' were sold in 1800 and 1803; the purchasers were slow in paying.[7]

An eighteenth-century tithe dispute mentions that the Woodside

Green pollards included ash, oak and hornbeam, from which charcoal had been made.[202]

Hunting and Shooting

Gamekeeping The seventeenth-century Barringtons were sporting men. Sir Thomas got a licence from Charles I 'to take partridges and pheasants with Netts and Setting dogges' on his own lands.[65] His son Sir John, who took up firearms, spent £2 on 'makeinge a settinge dogge' and 10s. on 'a spaniell to perch pheasants'. He fished with a tame cormorant. They both kept hawks and fed them on pigeons, partridges and dogs.[176,198]

My earliest gamekeeper is William Brice of Broxted, who served the Turnors and Houblon from 1673 to 1735.[135] In 1715 Dan Twamlow became keeper to Hatfield manor; his equipment might include

> Gunns, Bowes, Greyhounds, Setting Doggs, Lurchers, Doggs to kill Hares or Coneys, and all Ferretts, Trammels, Lowbells, Hayes, Notts, Harepipes, Snares or other Engines.[203]

The Houblons and Barringtons, of course, quarrelled about game. Jacob Houblon III claimed the sole shooting rights as owner of the soil, and also (wrongly) that as owner of the Forestal rights he was entitled to stop others from shooting at least the hare. John Shales Barrington claimed shooting rights as lord of the manor, and also under an ancient right of free warren:

> John Shales Barrington ... claims a right of killing Game ... & often Sends his Servants &c with Doggs & Guns on Mr Houblons Side of the Forrest who kill there Great Quantities of Hares and other Game which frightens the Deer out of the Forrest whereby they are Liable to be killed & is also a Great hindrance to their fatning & breeding Besides the destroying the Game which Mr Houblon is at a Great Expence to preserve. ...

The matter went right up to the Court of Common Pleas in 1736. Houblon was suing William Duncombe and Matthew Gray, Barrington's servants. He claimed that each

> with fforce & Arms of his own wrong broke & entred ... trod down consumed & spoiled the grass of the said Jacob ... with his ffeet in Walking And with Guns Charged with leaden Shott & Gunpowder ... shott at and killed the game, to wit twenty pheasants, forty partridges & ten hares.

In more detail, for example,

> Jan. 3 [1735] Matthew Gray came into Hatfield Chase with a Gun and severall Spanials he Shott a hare in Round Coppice.

Within 13 months he was seen to bag nine hares and four rabbits; he missed six hares, four pheasants, seven rabbits and a woodcock. By now rabbits were no longer in the Warren but in various coppices. Other quarry included snipe (still in the Forest today), blackbirds and 'Greybirds' [thrushes?].[135,204]

Houblon seems to have won, after squandering at least £250 on legal fees.

In later years the Forester acted as gamekeeper. In the 1800s the keep of dogs cost £2 2s. a year, and the dog tax up to £4 10s.[7]

Foxhunting Essex was one of the earliest hunting counties: in 1221 the king gave the Abbess of Barking, that sporting prelate, permission to chase the fox in Havering Park.[60]

Although the modern specialized foxhunt, disdaining hare and cat, is usually traced to the eighteenth century, there is earlier evidence at Hatfield. One Christmas in the early seventeenth century Sir Thomas Barrington 'went a fox hunting' with the hounds of Sir Richard Everard, a neighbour, using his new 'hunting whipp', and tipped the huntsman 5s.[198] Sir John Barrington took a fox alive; he spent 3d. 'in a drinke for the hounds, they being bitten with a mad dogge'; he also went to an otter hunt at Down Hall, at which the huntsman speared three otters.[176]

One of the oldest extant foxhunts is what is now the Puckeridge & Thurlow Hunt, which still visits Hatfield. In the nineteenth century, when the various hunts parcelled out England into their territories, Hatfield Forest became neutral ground between the Puckeridge and the Essex Hunts; and, once again, litigation arose out of this unusual status. The case went on from 1812 to 1854; John VII Archer Houblon was involved as Master of the Puckeridge.[205] At last the neutral status of the Forest was confirmed, and it is still used by both hunts.

Hatfield Forest was shared because it was too big and too wooded to be a good fox-covert from which to start a hunt. It was a source of foxes which might be driven out into other coverts and hunted later:

it was a great nursery and preserve of foxes, and then so strong and impracticable a woodland that there was no getting a fox away, and no chance of a run from it . . . it was necessary for the sport of both counties that it should be routed as much as possible.

The two hunts shared this task, which they regarded as a duty and not a pleasure.[206]

Hunt archives show that the Essex Hunt preferred the middle-sized woods around, such as Row Wood (still a favourite today), Man Wood and Canfield Hart. But both hunts sometimes managed to chase foxes out of Hatfield Forest. The quarry usually headed east, which was inconsiderate if the Puckeridge were after him. Some thrilling runs (and the occasional hair-raising accident) are chronicled.

Public Usage

A sign of coming events is to be found in 1826, when John Archer Houblon told his lawyer that

among the Shrubbage growing upon the Forest are an immense Quantity of Hazel Stubs . . . as soon as the Nuts begin to get ripe persons of all descriptions but consisting chiefly of the idle and disorderly Men and Women of bad Character from [Bishop's] Stortford . . . and the several neighbouring Villages have come . . . in large parties to gather the Nuts or under pretence of gathering Nuts to loiter about in Crowds disturbing the Deer and Game, breaking down the Trees . . . and in the Evening . . . take Beer and Spirits and drink in the Forest which affords them an opportunity for all sorts of Debauchery. . . . Sometimes as many as 500 persons have been there. . . . Other persons of a better description sometimes come to the Forest in small parties and then gather wood and make a Fire to boil water and drink and smoke under the Trees and although this is not so great an arrogance it is done without permission being asked and sets a bad example to the lower class of Trespassers.[194]

I regret to say that Houblon's reaction was to lock the coppice gates and to take advice about proceedings for trespass.

Personnel

The Barringtons were technically in charge of Hatfield Forest, but I doubt if they wielded axe or bill. In the 1520s they were appointing 'underfforsters or kepers' to do the work.[207] A Hatfield lease of 1548 includes the mysterious, evidently honorific, office of 'master leader of the game of the dere of all the seid fforest'.[208]

In the Morley period the head Forester was called a Ranger. In 1608 Lord Morley's son appointed Richard Man to this post; with it went the lodge and lodge close, a supply of firewood, an annuity of £20, and perquisites including permission to kill deer 'in the same sorte as other Rangers haue heretofore had there'. This too may have been a sinecure: Man lived in Lancashire, and was appointed 'in consideration of the faithful service to me heretofore donne and hereafter to be donne'.[209]

There was a working keeper of the deer. In 1612 Henry Gates was keeper, and Abell Hurley had preceded him.[171] In 1639 the corrupt Commissioners remembered to ask for some provision to be made for James Mayleycent,

who ... obteyned the Office of keepership about thirty yeares past upon a valuable consideration it being his only livelyhood for himself his aged Wife and many Children himself through painfull watching and Care ... exercising of his said Office is growne Lame and decriped.

A woodward is envisaged by the 1592 by-laws: not the Barringtons as hereditary woodwards, but a humbler personage elected by the commoners themselves. He was to supervise the grazing and to impound illicit animals, for which he was to be paid by results. He was to take underwood and timber from the Forest as needed by the commoners for repairing the Forest boundaries, gates, stiles and bridges. He was to fell 30 cartloads of wood each year for the manor-house, and 'to have 6 load more for his own paynes'.[180]

By the 1610s, as we have seen, the woodward had disappeared, for which the commoners blamed Lord Morley. We next find instead a reeve, whose duties were to supervise pasturage, brand or mark the animals, and collect fines for improper grazing. By 1750

... the Lords of the Mannor ... have ever since Elected a person to be Reeve or Overseer of the fforrest, whose Office has been to mark the Cattle ... for which there has been usually paid the ffee of Twopence for each Beast and 4d. for every Score of Sheep. And this Officer has sometimes made a Drift of the fforrest, but at no stated time of the year, to see that the Common was not overcharged. 'Tis said that formerly the cattle were not driven from the fforrest for this purpose, but of late years they have been driven to the pound belonging to the Mannor of Hatfield. This officer frequently has Neglected or Abused his office and for some years past Few if any Sheep . . . have been marked till after Sheering time. . . .[186]

There was a keeper of the gates, who was ordered to mend them in 1661.[124] Barrington had a coppice-keeper, who in 1665 was paid £12,[176] from which it would seem that supervising the north-eastern coppices was a full-time job for about eight months a year.

I have no record of any Forest court at Hatfield after the bogus one of 1634; but well into the eighteenth century the staff and some of the trappings of a medieval royal Forest were kept up. Daniel Gilbey, the keeper – of a noted Essex family – lived in the Forest Lodge and went about dressed in Lincoln green. He kept a man and a maid, six cows, three horses and four large hounds.[140]

The Smith family were the last Foresters. In 1786 Abdy Smith was paid £40 in wages, plus £5 5s. as 'Salary for looking after the Wood & Coppice ffences and paying Labourers'. In addition he earned various amounts for haymaking, fencing and odd jobs such as molecatching and 'Cutting Weeds in the Lodge Pond'. In that year he made £69, a fair stipend for a skilled man.[173] Twenty years later William Smith was still paid £40 a year (in depreciated money), plus 5 guineas in lieu of 'fees' – that is, his traditional perquisite of deer – and odd amounts for 'killing vermin' etc. After he died in 1805 his heir Edward was paid merely 5 guineas a year 'for care of woods' – a small part-time job.[7]

6 Survival of the Forest

About twelve months ago he learned that this Forest would probably be in the market, and he went several times to look round it. He came to the conclusion that he ought to make an effort to preserve it as a public space. I myself went with him once on a very hot day in July, and although we only walked about a mile through it, he was very much exhausted, but he said to me that he should like this to be 'the crowning effort of his life'.

... About Christmas Eve we were in a position to tell my father that we had an offer of part of it .... He told me that he had never spent a happier Christmas Day ... For the next few days the plan of the Forest never left his side and each day he told me his wishes about it and its future management. As regards the Forest, one thing he made clear to me, and that was, that I was not to stop at the sum he had handed over ....

Gerald Buxton on the last act of his father, Edward North Buxton, 1923–4[210]

The foresters' picture of the woods was so cherished and handed on that it gained an authority which set aside the evidence.
Colin Tubbs on the Ancient & Ornamental Woods of the New Forest, 1986
(NF)

The Enclosed Forest

The 1857 Enclosure Act destroyed a social fabric that had endured from the age of the longship to the age of railways. No more would the Forest know sheep or geese or donkeys or poor people collecting firewood. The Forest itself was truncated. Pieces of land were given as compensation to commoners and others with claims on the Forest; the seven remaining Sharers got from $\frac{1}{2}$ to $1\frac{1}{2}$ acres each. These allocations were set out round the margins, and as a result the Forest is now straight-edged and is no longer shaped like a Forest. (Woodside Green was not affected and still has common-rights.)

139

Matters could have been much worse. The normal fate of Forests, or any common-land, after enclosure was to be destroyed and made into ordinary farmland. Enfield Chase (Middlesex) had thus gone in 1777, Needwood Forest (Staffordshire) in 1801, most of Windsor Forest in 1817, and Neroche Forest (Somerset) in 1830. By the 1850s the idea was growing that this was unnecessary and antisocial; indeed much of the land 'reclaimed' was proving to be uncultivable. The destruction by special machines of most of Hainault Forest in 1851 was a public scandal; the modern conservation movement began with efforts to prevent a like fate for Epping Forest. The last Forest enclosures were of Wychwood (Oxfordshire) and of Hatfield, both in 1857. Wychwood was given the usual treatment and is now reduced to a largely unrecognizable fragment.

Hatfield Forest survives because the Houblons loved it. It was already their second park, the scene of light-hearted picnics and carriage drives and showing distinguished visitors the Shell House. John VII Archer Houblon understood the Forest well and knew how to maintain it. He kept up the grazing by cattle and deer; he continued to coppice the woods; and he was not too tidy-minded about preserving scrub and ancient hawthorns. He put magnificent fences, with cast-iron posts (p. 159), round some of the coppices. The words 'DEER PARK' on Ordnance Survey maps suggest that he tried to confine the deer, although I can find no trace of a deer-proof perimeter fence.

By the standard of modern conservation, we cannot approve of everything that Houblon did. He shared in the contemporary mania for drainage, and even before he enclosed the Forest he dug deep ditches through it at great expense,[140] doubtless ruining much of the wetlands in the plains. In the coppices, brick culverts and drains made of buried faggots sometimes come to light. In his time the Shermore Brook was straightened and its meanders lost. Like his contemporaries, he disapproved of pollards – he stopped cutting the old oaks – and loved to plant trees.

Most of the tree-planting in the Forest came after 1857. There are fashions among trees, and Houblon shared in the Victorian *penchant* for such exotica as black pine, horsechestnut and copper beech. In planting these, he unwittingly infringed the meaning and *genius loci* of the Forest and began to reduce it to the same level as everyone else's park. Horsechestnut, for instance, was once a tree of spectacular rarity and romance; I have had the thrill of finding it in a wild gorge on the marches of Albania which are its home. In Hatfield Forest, far from the land of Ali Pasha, it became an unthrilling tree with no special meaning. The horsechestnuts of the Forest, magnificent though they are of their kind, are out of place and hide the meaning of such historic features as the Warren. Fortunately the planting was mainly confined to the neighbourhood of the Shell House and Table Coppice.

Railways came with the making of the Bishop's Stortford, Dunmow and Braintree line, opened in 1869. This went through the medieval anti-highwayman trench along the north edge of the Forest (p. 92). The strip of land to the north was sold off, made into fields and eventually built on. The Forest thus lost its traditional frontage to the main road and its link with Takeley Street.

Two-and-a-third coppices were abandoned. By 1874 (the date of the first edition 25-inch Ordnance Survey, Fig. 20) Warren Coppice was converted to a plain with scattered trees, most of which were felled in the twentieth century. Its structure as a coppice was doubtless weakened by the eighteenth-century replanting, and lying behind the Shell House it was liable to be made the victim of beautification. Doodle-Oak Coppice disappeared at the same time. On the railway plans (1860–1) the other coppices are described as 'Pasture Wood and Timber', but this one as 'Pasture and Timber', the same description as the plains.[211] Many scattered trees remained until the 1920s. Part of Gravel-pit Coppice also was given up; here it was the underwood that survived and still stands – tree-rings show that it was last felled c.1855.

The Houblons were proud of their deer, and yearly presented bucks, half-bucks or haunches to their tenants and neighbours. For the first time in its history, Hatfield briefly had red deer – according to an unlikely-sounding story, all of them descended from one hind pursued into the Forest and lost by a hunt. A photograph of c.1905 shows six harts, a stag, a hind and a calf under the then youngish horsechestnuts on the Warren.[140]

John VII Archer Houblon, the hunting squire, died in 1891. His successors took to rearing pheasants, and the Forest lost its reputation as a fox covert.[212] The diaries of the young Lindsay Archer Houblon, who was to fight in the Boer War, tell a very different story from the rough shooting disputed in 1736. For example, on

Fig. 20 The Forest in 1874, from the 25-inch Ordnance Survey. The Ordnance Survey was at its best in the 1870s, and this particular sheet is perhaps the finest map it has ever produced. Note the exact depiction of individual pollards in the plains; the woodbanks; the irregular shapes of individual woodland rides; and the conifer symbols. Air photographs confirm the extreme accuracy

31 January 1900 a party of six shot 104 pheasants, 228 rabbits and five hares.[213]

The Buxtons

The fortunes of the Houblons were now in decline. They left Hall-ingbury in about 1909,[214] and retreated to the other family seat at Welford, Berkshire. Hallingbury Place was restored to a brief last glory under a tenant, Lockett Agnew,[215] but was pulled down in 1922 – a forerunner of the country-house demolitions that were to go on, in wave after wave, all over England for fifty years. It was a great gloomy small-windowed pile, a hybrid of Jacobean and Palladian architecture, ascribed to 1771; the kitchens and stables (which still stand) were inherited from the days of Lord Morley.[216]

The Forest shared this decline. Grazing was maintained, since nearly all the trees and bushes on the plains are either younger or much older than this period. So was woodcutting, as is proved by tree-ring counts in the coppices. But the two were, once again, not effectively separated. In a normal coppice-wood the stems in any one area have exactly the same number of annual rings. At Hatfield this is often not so: trunks growing side by side, or even from the same stool, differ by several years. Although many coppices were cut between 1900 and 1924, the exact year is sometimes difficult to determine. This means that, as we would expect of a decaying estate, the woods were still felled, but the Victorian fences were not mended: cattle and deer got in and ate the shoots, and regrowth was slow and patchy. Elm and ash, whose rings are the easiest to count, were the most palatable. In many areas the stools were killed altogether. This has resulted (Chapter 9) in large tracts of hawthorn and birch within the coppices, and a few open glades which still remain.

The Houblon estate was broken up and Hatfield Forest was put on the market in 1923. The sale catalogue lists the coppices and buildings and describes 'THE SHELL ROOM OR GROTTO'. It relates the misinformation then current about the Forest, such as that it had 'formed originally part of Epping Forest'. We learn that the deer-park had been discontinued.

I cannot say what would have happened to the Forest but for

the appearance of a steadfast and princely benefactor, Edward North Buxton. Buxton was a lifelong preserver of Forests. He was one of those who frustrated the destruction of Epping Forest by its land-owners in the 1870s; he refused to let the Commons Preservation Society compromise by saving only a tenth of it. He had written what is still the best book on that Forest.[217] He probably drew up the management plan in the Epping Forest Act of 1878 which, had it been read and acted upon, would have kept the historic character of the Forest intact. He was too late to prevent the grubbing-out of Hainault Forest, but he saw to it that what remained was preserved in 1903.[218] He was a council member of the National Trust; a man of substance, he had already given the Trust other properties including Paycocke's House, Coggeshall.

On hearing of the sale in October 1923, the 83-year-old Buxton went to inspect the Forest, and decided to buy it and give it to the National Trust. His telegram miscarried and the Forest was sold to a Mr Place and to timber merchants instead. But Buxton refused to be defeated, and on his death-bed on 1 January 1924 he completed the first part of the purchase and instructed his family about the remainder.[219] His sons Gerald and Anthony faithfully carried out these wishes and bought the rest of the Forest, except for Table Coppice which was contributed by Major Archer Houblon. By October 1924 the Trust had become the owner of the whole of the post-enclosure Forest. The Forest was ceremonially opened on 10 May 1924 by Lord Ullswater, vice-president of the National Trust. A report in *The Times* celebrates the Buxtons' generosity; the vener-able Ullswater is photographed talking to an old man who remem-bered the Forest before the Enclosure Act. (It was even proposed to re-name the Forest after Buxton, which he would have hated.)

Some of the timber trees in the Forest were redeemed by the Buxtons; others were kept by the timber merchants, who felled and removed them. A tally scribed on a railway gatepost by Street Cop-pice probably records the loads taken out. This felling in 1924 is mentioned as a tragedy in every subsequent account of Hatfield, and its shadow has fallen on the management of the forest ever since. Such a view is an exaggeration. It is clear from the oak stumps (which still remain) and the surviving trees that only timber trees and a few pollards were felled; all underwood and all hornbeams and maples were exempt. Many oaks, elms, ashes and beeches were

144

big trees in 1924 and yet were not felled. Standard oaks in the coppices were felled, but even these were not many, as the stumps prove. The timber merchants were not wicked asset-strippers: they were catching up with what had been abnormally little timber-felling in the previous hundred years.

Woodside Green (and the small Wright's Green and Mott's Green in Great Hallingbury) was given to the Trust by Major Houblon in 1935. Wall Wood was presented in 1946 by the Essex and Puckeridge Hunts, to whom it had been given by the Stacey family.

The National Trust

The National Trust for Places of Historic Interest and Natural Beauty dates from 1894. Its founders were Sir Robert Hunter of the Commons Preservation Society, Octavia Hill the housing reformer, and the versatile Canon Hardwicke Rawnsley. It was a private body intended to acquire threatened lands and buildings; but in 1907 it acquired a peculiar semi-public status through the National Trust Act. This Act enables the Trust to declare its properties inalienable, so that they cannot be sold or expropriated, and gives it a security of tenure not dependent on the whims of personalities or of governments.

The National Trust which was given Hatfield Forest in 1924 was not the mass-movement which it is today. It had fewer than 2000 members, and only some 30,000 acres of land, instead of the half-million acres which it has now. Although it had taken on some modest historic buildings, its main business was owning land, especially coastland. In this spirit it acquired Wicken Fen in 1899, Blakeney Point in 1912, and now Hatfield Forest. Not until after World War II did the National Trust undertake its huge present activities of conserving great houses, castles, gardens and historic industrial buildings.[220]

The early National Trust years To judge by its publications, the Trust was only vaguely aware of the meaning of what it had acquired. Hatfield was recognized as a royal Forest, but what Forests were, how they worked, what kind of Forest Hatfield was, and how this should affect management were questions that still lay in the future.

The Forest was regarded less as a unique historic landscape than as a place of public amenity and resort.

This period is poorly documented because of a fire among the Trust's local archives. The Forest was managed by a local committee including Theresa Buxton, the donor's sister.

Field evidence and surviving records indicate that for over thirty years the Trust was content to follow roughly the Houblons' style of management. Grazing was kept up, at times more intensively than before. Hunt archives of *c.* 1928 mention the many cattle on the Forest in winter as well as summer.[212] Scrub, however, increased in the plains, and there were periods with no grazing at all (Chapter 10). The Trust did not reinstate the coppice fences, and indeed sold some of the ironwork; it is clear from evidence on the ground, as well as hunting records, that cattle got into all the coppices. This change has had a more drastic effect on the woodland than the great felling of timber (p. 224). The debris of that felling was tidied away.

The coppices continued to be cut: for example, all 35 acres of Emblem's in 1939 (Fig. 21). The nature of coppicing was not well remembered: for example, a report of 1935 says 'Elm, maple, ash cut. Hazel left'. A ranger, an underkeeper and five labourers were employed; wood was transported on a two-horse sled. The operation made a substantial loss. The local committee disapproved of elms, against which 'a stern battle' was fought: it was held that 'the suckers go everywhere & kill the nice undergrowth of thorn etc.' In 1936 'signs of improved appearance' were reported in Collin's Coppice, especially in 'the monotonous patches which were formerly elm suckers'.

Gradually coppicing was attenuated into thinning, which was thought to be a good thing – it was hoped that 'forest trees especially oak and hornbeam' would be encouraged, and that 'a general increase in variety of undershrubs' would result. The object was to produce 'natural wild woodland of a beauty comparable to the un-spoiled portions of the Forest' by 'eradicating the legacy of an out-worn coppice attenuated, crowded and monotonous in its outline'.[221]

Deer and rabbits were regarded as a nuisance, except when they bit down young elms. Rabbits were no longer delicate beasts of the warren: in 1937 eleven hundred were snared in six weeks. Deer were shot sporadically, and it was even considered trying to exterminate them.

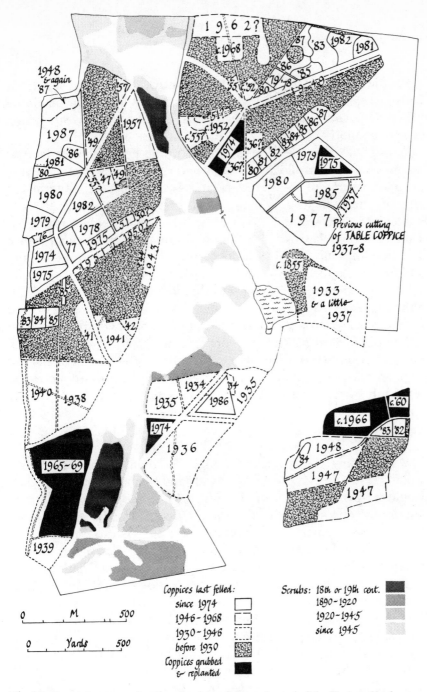

Fig. 21 Coppicing map, showing the date when each part of the Forest woods (or Wall Wood) was last felled. From National Trust archives and my own records (including tree-ring counts). I have not tried to draw the line between coppicing and thinning. In the plains, the ages of the various scrub areas are shown.

147

People had taken to driving cars and motorcycles round the Forest. Ruts in rides were levelled with horse harrows and with something called a 'slosher'. There were frequent Boy Scout and Girl Guide camps, and in 1937 a visit by the Army on manoeuvres.

World War II made little difference to the Forest. Twice in 1940 unknown German pilots flew over and took the earliest surviving air photographs of the Forest (Plates 1, 3). Stansted Mountfitchet airfield, made nearby, was to cast a long shadow ahead. Its only immediate effect was that (as often with ancient woods near airfields) Table Coppice was used for hiding installations from enemy eyes. The buildings have almost disappeared, but the hard roads remain, and traffic into the Forest still goes through this coppice.

The air photographs confirm that coppicing was in decline: although huge areas were covered, far too few trees were cut. For example the south-west quarter of Lodge Coppice, despite the great felling of 1924, and although 'coppiced' in the 1939–40 winter, still appears as almost continuous trees in August 1940. Thinning, instead of proper coppicing, would have aggravated the harm done to the regrowth by the livestock. In later years the acreages cut also declined.

The replanting controversy It might be thought that the Forest would be safe in National Trust hands and that its disputatious days would be over. Not so: on 20 July 1955 Anthony Buxton, son of the donor, denounced the Trust in a letter to *The Times* for having decided to lease part of Hatfield Forest to the Forestry Commission to replace with plantations. Buxton, who had succeeded his aunt on the local management committee, publicly resigned in protest.

The secretary and chief agent of the National Trust both replied, and a correspondence followed in *The Times* and other newspapers. The Trust claimed that the Forest was overgrown and impenetrable, and lacking in young trees; that this was wrong and could be remedied by replanting; that the Trust had no money to do so itself; and that either 86 or 150 acres of coppices (including Emblem's and Collin's) would be handed over to the Forestry Commission to plant with oak and larch, with the intention of ending with oak plantations. Other contributors included Maynard Greville, a near neighbour and regional chairman of the Royal Forestry Society, who

148

said that young trees would come naturally if the coppices were fenced.[223]

The controversy grew. The Forestry Commission, then at the top of its fortunes, was making a name for itself as a destroyer of ancient woodland and creator of conifer plantations. Buxton, though he supported the Commission in Norfolk, wanted to 'ensure that the Forestry Commission never sets a single foot on a single inch' of Hatfield. Contributors were sceptical of the Trust's assurances that oaks would be created here and that public access would be preserved. They denied that any action other than fencing was appropriate. The Trust was particularly opposed by Women's Institutes all over Essex; but the Ramblers' Association and Youth Hostels Association supported the Trust after being reassured about access. At a public meeting on a wet October day, 200 people debated for an hour and a half and voted for Buxton's proposal by two to one.

The Trust itself was divided. The proposal came from above: whether it originated within the Trust, or whether the Forestry Commission called upon the Trust to set what in forestry terms was a 'good' example, I cannot say. The national executive committee made the decision *nem. con.* The local committee acquiesced with regret, by only one vote.

In the face of this opposition, the original plan was shelved. Four years later, the National Trust succeeded in negotiating an 'Approved Woodlands Scheme' for the coppices and Wall Wood. The Trust would retain control, but would be subsidized by the Forestry Commission for managing the woods 'in accordance with the rules of good forestry'. Under the said rules, some 50 acres of ancient coppices were grubbed out and planted with oak, beech and various conifers: an action hardly different from the proposal denounced by Buxton. We shall follow the fate of these plantations in Chapter 9. In general, oak plantations have not resulted, and the only parts of the Forest now truly impenetrable – I have tried to penetrate and failed – are areas where they were attempted. In 1955 nobody thought to ask the deer.

Several other things were done in a similar spirit. Somewhat earlier the grassland was 'improved' – that is, converted from old pasture, full of different plants, to the monotonous sward of coarse grasses favoured by British agricultural opinion. Thistles and ragwort had already given trouble in the 1930s. Field evidence (Chapter 10) points to a phase of fertilizing and weedkilling in most of the plains in the 1950s, from which the Forest is slowly recovering. I am given to understand that after World War II the Ministry of Agriculture, which had powers to compel farmers to follow 'sound agricultural practice', leaned on the National Trust to do this.

The Forest was scheduled as a Site of Special Scientific Interest by the Nature Conservancy in 1956, on the strength of its dragonflies and butterflies. This designation came just too late to save the grasslands.

Although coppicing was abandoned as 'no longer an economic proposition', quite large monies were collected and spent on planting trees. Around 1963 seven small groves were planted in the plains, each of a different species. The sites look like a random selection, and so do the trees: horsechestnut, beech, hornbeam, Corsican pine etc.

Also in the 1960s came the idea of 'opening up' the woods, in which the eighteenth-century rides had been allowed to get overgrown. Instead of restoring these rides, great swathes were bulldozed through the coppices and made into grassland, each one with two deep ditches along its length. These glades were promptly called '*motorways*' by the local inhabitants. They have confused the identities of the coppices and injured their ancient earthworks.

Not all the changes were intentional. Mr John Fielding tells me of still finding a 'sea of rabbits' when he first knew the Forest. Rabbits were struck down by myxomatosis in 1954 and have never fully recovered. Like the rest of England, Essex used to have the red squirrel, which was partly native and partly introduced from the Continent. The grey squirrel, introduced from America, reached Hatfield about 1950. The red died out – the last certain sighting was in 1958.[224] This has greatly affected the ecology of hazel.

The last fifteen years   Since 1974, and increasingly in recent years, the traditions of the Forest have been rediscovered. Coppicing has been restored. It was discovered that success depended on fencing the coppiced areas promptly and completely after felling. For the first time since the Houblon period, there is now a permanent fence with cattle-grids round Table Coppice, and Takeley Quarter is also fenced. At the same time pollarding was resumed. A few of the Bush-End hornbeams, neglected for 60-odd years, were cut each year, and there is now a complete sequence of pollards in different stages of regrowth.

In the 1920s probably only a few thousand people visited the Forest each year. Visitors have proliferated lately; it is estimated that 120,000 people came in 1986, and on a summer Sunday there may be 3000 head in the Forest at one time. The National Trust has, with difficulty, been able to cope with these numbers, at the cost of some damage to the fabric of the Forest. Until 1980 cars were allowed to drive anywhere until they got bogged down. They are now confined to a car-park and to a hard road leading to the lake. Motor-cyclists no longer air their machines in Gravel-pit Coppice. The result is that most visitors go no further than the lake, where they give the Trust an income from fishing tickets and from buying refreshments and the goods that the Trust sells. Some go for short walks, and a few of the most energetic reach the southern plain, but even on the busiest day one can spend hours in the western coppices and not see a person.

On 16 October 1987 there was one of the great storms of history. The wind was not very exceptional and did only moderate damage to buildings, but it came when trees were in leaf and the ground weakened by weeks of heavy rain. In east and south-east England it did damage comparable to the strongest American hurricanes in parks, gardens and plantations. Ancient woodland was not much affected. In Hatfield, on the edge of the storm, damage was not specially unusual, and was chiefly to hornbeams and horsechestnuts. About 10 great hornbeam pollards collapsed or were uprooted, and many more would have gone but for the re-pollarding. Huge boughs were broken from the horsechestnuts. Fallen branches were strewn under the big oaks in the plains. In the woods, occasional ashes and other trees split (chiefly at narrow forks); standard hornbeams were uprooted (especially in Gravel-pit Coppice). Storm damage exceeded that of 24 March 1986 and 27 March 1987, but was about equal to that done by the gales of 3 January 1976 and 11 January 1978 put together.

The National Trust and Conservation

The National Trust has now become part of the history of Hatfield Forest, as are the Bruces and the Houblons. The time has come to review the last 63 years and to ask, as we did with Hatfield as a royal Forest, what difference its peculiar status has made.

The National Trust is responsible for almost the entire field of conservation, from the fen violet at Wicken Fen to the conservation of manuscripts in country-house archives. With the conservation of buildings and their contents, the Trust follows – indeed it often sets – the highest standards of scholarship, research and attention to detail. Unfortunately it has only recently been appreciated that some of the Trust's landed properties are of equal historic importance and that this demands equally high standards of management.

Wicken Fen, one of the earliest Trust properties, goes back to a time when such places were supposed to represent a world of Nature uncontaminated by human activities. The proper management of a nature reserve was thought to be to do nothing – to terminate the digging of peat and cutting of reed and sedge which had shaped the fen down the centuries. In consequence it ceased to be Wicken Fen and turned into a wood, from which it has been rescued by many years of effort.

Hatfield Forest was acquired later and escaped a similar fate. Until World War II the local committee, perhaps unconsciously, acted on the principle: *if a site is not fully understood, continue existing management practices unless they can definitely be shown to be harmful*. This is a wise and cautious basis for conservation, but in Hatfield was less than ideal. Fences were not restored: even in 1955 it was claimed that 'some members . . . remain strenuously opposed to fencing of any kind'. The committee confused thinning (a technique appropriate to *plantations*) with the coppicing of *woods*. Thinning would not have let in enough light to stimulate much growth of new trees and herbaceous plants, and the grazing animals would have devoured what was stimulated. The committee's mistakes were very understandable – many conservationists have made them since – although it is a pity that it took so long to discover that thinning plus not fencing was a particularly damaging combination for an ancient wood-pasture. It is as if the National Trust had been given an ancient, dilapidated building, and had maintained the corrugated-iron roof, mistaking this for a historic feature.

After the war the Trust fell under the influence of current fashions in agriculture and forestry. We now realize that the Trust should have refused to reduce its grassland to agricultural standards, even (had the worst come to the worst) using its legal immunity to resist any coercion by the Ministry of Agriculture. In the event, it seems not to have been appreciated that old grassland was worth fighting over. Conservationists of the time often went to the opposite extreme of error; it was said that the countryside is entirely an artefact, the mere creation of farmers and foresters in the past, and that the future even of special places like Forests lies in following the 'good estate management' practices of the time.

This philosophy informed the Trust's attitude to modern forestry. In the nineteenth century it was fully understood that 'natural woods' and plantations were different; many surveys record them separately (*TW*). By the 1950s the distinction had been forgotten; it was assumed that all woods were a mere artefact, planted at some date in the past and needing to be replanted from time to time. Even the National Trust did not allow woods to have a life of their own. Many were replanted, often with pride; thus the historic Frithsden Great Copse (Berkhamsted, Herts) became 'Queen Elizabeth Wood, planted 1952'. The Trust thought itself fortunate in persuading the Forestry Commission to agree to an Approved Woodlands Scheme under which broadleaved trees might be planted instead of the fashionable conifers. Too few people questioned whether trees should be planted at all.

Grubbing-out and planting in Hatfield were in accordance with what was, for a decade or two, generally regarded as conservation. Ever since 1924 the Trust's managers had been haunted by the thought that the Forest had lost its fine trees in the great felling. Thirty years on, this problem had in fact solved itself through natural regrowth. But nobody notices the slow increase of trees, and it was still supposed that the lost trees could be regained only by deliberate intervention.

The Trust claimed in 1955 that the Forest was 'untended and overgrown' and also lacking in young trees. The two claims are to some extent contradictory, but if either was true this would have resulted from the operations of the 1930s. In fact, there must have been plenty of young trees. The woods today are full of oaks, ashes and birches which in the 1950s would have been at the stage of turning from 'scrub' into 'trees'. Theresa Buxton commented on seedling oaks and hornbeams in the 1930s.

The Hatfield planting came when modern forestry was at the height of its reputation. Even conservationists could be persuaded that, where natural trees had failed to grow, planted trees would somehow be more successful; there was then no recent evidence to the contrary. The key phrase to the 1955 debate is 'Forests are not immortal'. This was claimed by the Secretary of the National Trust, and not challenged by his opponents. Both sides accepted this belief without stopping to think whether it could possibly be true of a Forest with a history like Hatfield's.

Even after thirty years the National Trust still hardly appreciated the *genius loci* of the Forest. Anthony Buxton, instructed by his father, clearly understood that an oak plantation, even if successful, would be a solecism in a medieval Forest – but he was outvoted. All the other correspondents regarded Hatfield only as a public recreation ground; they were only vaguely aware that it was a historic landscape at all.

Had the Hatfield planting been delayed for another ten years, it would probably have been avoided. The knowledge would have come that the woods are an integral part of the Forest's historic interest, and that replacing them with plantations is equivalent to demolishing an ancient stone building and replacing it with concrete blocks. Experience has now shown that, even on their own terms, the 'rules of sound forestry' are not as sound as they appeared in the 1960s. To make a plantation on the site of an ancient wood has, at most, a 50% chance of success. Anthony Buxton and the Women's Institutes have been vindicated.

The National Trust has been slow to understand and conserve the less simple kinds of semi-natural landscape. Much more forceful criticisms than mine have been made of its actions in other places.[225] But I hope and believe that fashion is now being replaced by real understanding, especially through the work of the Trust's Conservation Advisers. That hope rests very largely on the new management proposed for Hatfield Forest, to be discussed in Chapter 12.

7 Earthworks and the Earth's Surface

In Beggars-Hall Coppice on the Forest, in the Way to Stane-Street, is a small Spot of Ground called Porting-Hills, and Portingbury-Hills. At a little Distance from that, the Traces of a larger circular Entrenchment.

N. Salmon, *The history and antiquities of Essex*, 1740

Boundaries

Forest boundaries The edge of the physical Forest did not have an earthwork of its own, but was defined only by the hedges and ditches of the neighbouring fields. Although the Forest was curtailed in 1857, nearly all these hedges survive (Fig. 3). They are mixed hedges, not unlike the usual ancient hedges of Essex, but with very few pollard trees.

On its (pre-1857) northern edge the Forest is demarcated from the main road by a weak bank with a hawthorn hedge and remains of an iron railing. The road, which had previously been included in the Forest, came under the control of a turnpike trust in the late eighteenth century, and was fenced some decades later.[78, 155]

The post-1857 boundaries of the Forest are marked by straight, parallel-sided roads with hedges typical of the period: pure hawthorn, now invaded by the occasional ash or briar.

Woodbanks The coppices are demarcated from the plains and from each other by banks and ditches (Fig. 22). A typical such earthwork has a rounded profile, 23–29 feet in total width. Most of the woodbanks are irregularly sinuous or run in short straight lengths. The boundary between coppice and plain always has the ditch on the plain side.

155

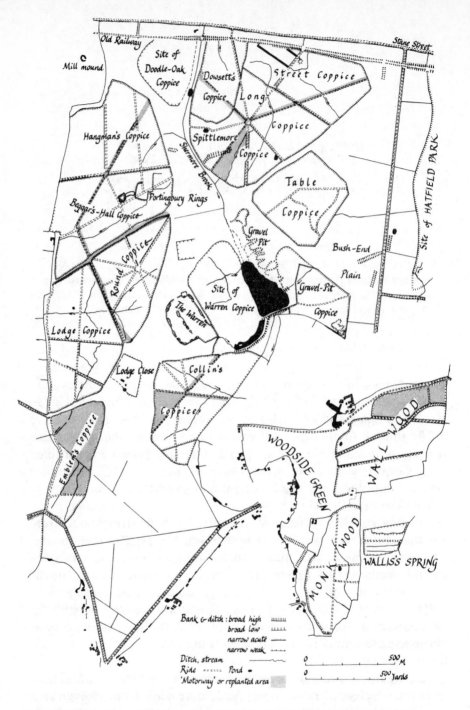

Fig. 22 Earthworks of Hatfield Forest (including lands lost to the Forest in 1857). Inset: Woodside Green and purlieu woods. Some alterations since 1950, and some small ditches and grips in the coppices, are omitted.

156

Woodbanks surround all the coppice-to-plain boundaries, including both sides of the tongues of plain between, for example, Round and Beggar's Hall or between Spittlemore and Table. Usually there is only a ditch where coppices abut on the edge of the Forest (e.g. the south side of Gravel-pit). Some of the coppice-to-coppice boundaries have banks in straight lines.

These, like all woodbanks, were to demarcate the coppices and to make it easier to fence out grazing animals. Forest Law forbade or discouraged the making of woodbanks; this provision, like much of Forest Law, seems to have been ignored. At Hatfield the system was clearly not planned as a whole, and the straight banks are probably later than the sinuous ones. In Takeley Quarter the outer bank would have come first. A curving bank was later constructed within it so that livestock could be kept out of Dowsett's but admitted to the rest of the wood. Later still, Street Coppice was separated by a straight bank; and even later, the remainder was divided into Long and Spittlemore – the only division which is not marked by a bank at all. Among the western coppices, the original Northwood, with its sinuous perimeter, was divided by a straight bank into Hangman's and Beggar's Hall.

The south end of Collin's Coppice has two banks, indicating that at some time it has been smaller. The younger bank is earlier than 1757. Gravel-pit Coppice was reduced in size after 1857; this produced a new, narrow woodbank typical of its period.

We have seen that the coppices are first documented in their present form in the early seventeenth century. Even the straight boundaries must be earlier than the 1654 list, which separates Northwood and Beggar's Hall. The sinuous woodbanks are typical of medieval wood boundaries. As we shall see, the present Forest Lodge (which may not be the earliest on the site) is a medieval building, and its position seems to be determined by sight-lines which depend on the coppices being where they are now. The woodbanks were probably made piecemeal in the fourteenth century or earlier, although the straight ones could be somewhat later.

Among the abandoned coppices, little now remains on the ground of the perimeters of Low Street, Middle or Bush-End. Warren and Doodle-Oak Coppices have remains of their banks. The outer bank of Gravel-pit is still visible. Some lengths of bank were lost to the railway. In the National Trust period, the making of 'motorways' thoughtlessly destroyed three-quarters of a mile of woodbanks and confused the meaning of the system.

Woodbanks outside the Forest Most of the neighbouring woods are surrounded by medieval banks and ditches. Wall Wood and Monk Wood have fine examples separating them from Woodside Green; on the east side these banks are incomplete owing to later encroachment on these woods for farmland. There were probably once pollards on the banks; a pollard was sold from Monk Wood in 1817.[170]

Birchanger Wood has not only a perimeter bank but internal woodbanks reflecting its division into five ownerships (Fig. 23). One of these massively-embanked sub-woods, Prior's Wood, belonged to St Valery's Priory, Takeley, until the Priory was dissolved in 1379; it was then given to New College, Oxford, which owned it for over 500 years. Prior's Wood, Takeley, and Prior's Wood, Widdington, have the same history[226] and the same embanking. The Takeley wood has also an internal woodbank, relic of some forgotten division of ownership.

Woodland was so valuable that even small woods were embanked. The three woods of Leaden Roding, separated by lanes, are together no bigger than Table Coppice, but each has a strong bank; they are unchanged in area since at least 1439.[227] Even Digby Wood in Birchanger, 8½ acres, has complex woodbanks.

A remarkable exception is Canfield Hart. Though an impeccably-documented ancient wood,[71] it has the weakest of earthworks; much of its perimeter is only a ditch.

Writtle Forest (Fig. 7) has a set of woodbanks like those of Hatfield. So did Rockingham Forest (Northants), Wychwood Forest (Oxfordshire), and probably most compartmented Forests.

Fences A woodbank was topped with a hedge or fence. Many medieval woods, including some of those named, have pollard trees on the boundary banks to reinforce the legal demarcation. Sometimes there are remains of the hedge itself.

In Hatfield (and Writtle), the pollards belong to the plains, only rarely to the woodbanks, and the original coppice fences have long rotted away. Around Table, Gravel-pit and Collin's Coppices there

158

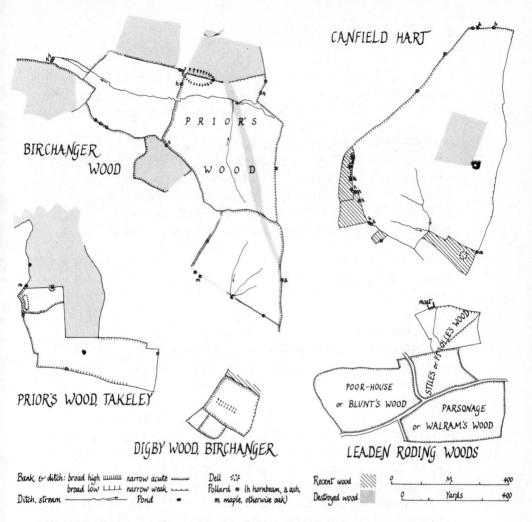

CANFIELD HART

BIRCHANGER WOOD

P R I O R'S

W O O D

PRIOR'S WOOD, TAKELEY

DIGBY WOOD, BIRCHANGER

moat

STILES or FINFOLE'S WOOD

POOR-HOUSE
or BLUNT'S WOOD

PARSONAGE
or WALRAM'S WOOD

LEADEN RODING WOODS

Bank & ditch: broad high ⊔⊔⊔⊔⊔ narrow acute ‒‒‒‒ Dell ∴∵ Recent wood ▨▨ 0 · · · M · · · 400
broad low ⊔⊔⊔⊔ narrow weak ‒ · ‒ Pollard ⊙ (h hornbeam, a ash, Destroyed wood ▨▨ 0 · · · Yards · · · 400
Ditch, stream ‒‒‒‒‒‒ Pond ● m maple, otherwise oak)

Fig. 23 Earthworks of some ancient woods near Hatfield Forest.

are remains of elaborate Victorian iron fences. The principal posts
are fluted iron pillars of two kinds, one cast by 'JOHN BOYD & Cᵒ
LONDON'. Each is fastened by four great screw-bolts to a massive
oak base in the ground; some of them are still firm today. The
original wires are solid wrought-iron rods. The fences are about
4 feet high, and could have kept out only cattle.

Hatfield Park The Park, as we have seen, goes back almost to
the earliest years of the Forest. Most of the sinuous outline (where
the medieval pale and hedge ran) still survives; it contrasts with

159

the mainly straight hedges by which the interior was subdivided in the sixteenth century. The park abuts on the Forest in the valley of the Pincey Brook; the boundary runs a little to one side so as to include the brook within the park.

The park is firmly divided from the Forest by a bank and ditch, 29 ft in total width, with the bank on the park side. This earthwork is best seen (though damaged by ploughing) at the south-west corner of the park, below Bush-End church; the corner is rounded for economy in fencing. Where it adjoined farmland the park boundary is only a slight earthwork with a mixed, but not remarkable hedge.

Ponds, Dells and Streams

Ponds and hollows are a most complex subject. The earth's natural surface had all the hollows left by the glaciers and other agencies, known and unknown, which shaped the land. To these have been added the pits, holes and ponds which men have made for innumerable reasons down the millennia. Although for centuries farmers have been levelling them out, those that remain are of many kinds: among field-ponds, for example, it is often difficult to say which are natural, which have been dug as ponds, and which are the result of digging minerals (*HC*).

Commons and ancient woods often have more numerous ponds than the rest of the landscape, for there have not been farmers to fill them in. The woods around the Forest have about one pond to thirty acres. Hatfield Forest has relatively few. The two ponds in Spittlemore Coppice are oval depressions with no trace of a mound where the contents might have been heaped up, nor of a track for carting them away. This is the commonest type of woodland pond, and appears to be natural. There is one such inside, and one outside, Wall Wood. The pond called Old Woman's Weaver has more of an artificial, squarish appearance.

Among mineral-pits, the Gravel-pit is described in Chapter 10. The south-east corner of Gravel-pit Coppice is full of small, steep-sided, apparently artificial pits. I cannot suggest why they were dug here: the subsoil is ordinary boulder-clay.

All over the coppices are little sinuous watercourses which converge on bigger watercourses in the valleys. These are probably natural streamlets, the ultimate branches of the original 'tree' of rivers and streams. They very seldom run in the present climate. They have been augmented by straighter ditches, dug probably in the Houblon period. The Shermore Brook was originally sinuous too, but was straightened in the 1850s.

Portingbury Rings

These earthworks lie in Beggar's Hall Coppice. First comes a roughly rectangular mound, about 100 by 70 feet, surrounded by a strong ditch 25–35 ft wide, now wet only in winter. The top of the mound is flat, with traces of hummocks and hollows, much confused by the anthills which abound. To this is attached a sausage-shaped mound, less strongly ditched round (Fig. 24). To the east run two zigzagging banks not forming a complete enclosure. Similar but weaker banks appear to continue across the Shermore Brook into Spittlemore Coppice, and there are traces of a three-sided earthwork in the plain between.

The earthworks are manifestly older than the coppice boundaries, to which they seem to be unrelated (although it is possible that they once extended further still but have been adapted as woodbanks and thus hidden). They have been known since Anglo-Saxon times; this is implied by the name ending in -bury, from beorh, the Old English word for a hillfort or other prehistoric earthwork. Most of the writings on them mention only the two mounds. The topographer Salmon, who first wrote about the Rings in 1740, mentions also a 'circular Entrenchment', probably the Warren.

Larry Luckett and the West Essex Archaeological Group dug three trenches through the mounds in 1964–5; what follows is derived from this excavation as published by Patricia Wilkinson and P.J. Huggins in 1978.[228] The finds were few, but sufficient to establish an Iron Age date, at least for the rectangular mound: four potsherds, a small flint blade, animal bone, burnt flint and charcoal. The ditch had been V-shaped and was originally dug about 6 ft deep into the boulder-clay. It is now partly filled by silting and by material slumped from the sides, but in the bottom there is some peat, presumably formed when the ditch was permanently wet and before the sides had begun to collapse into it. Huggins, having calculated the volumes

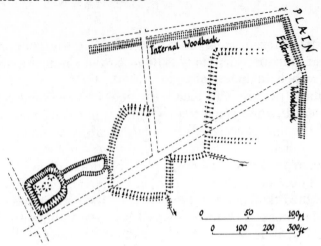

Fig. 24 Portingbury Hills in Beggar's Hall Coppice. Composite plan from air photograph, published accounts and my own measurements. Parallel broken lines are rides.

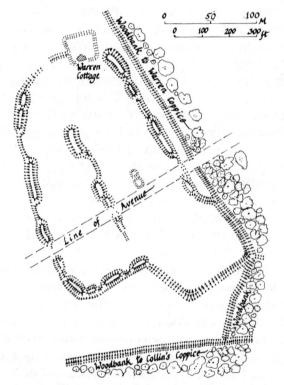

Fig. 25 Plan of the Warren earthworks. Surveyed by the author, with the help of Professor H. Art. Modern trees are omitted.

162

of soil involved, argues that the rectangular mound was not originally flat-topped but was surrounded by an earthen rampart, the sides of which were held up by timbers.

Until this structure is further excavated, its function can only be conjectured. It is too small to be a hillfort, nor is it in a defensible position. It could conceivably be a farmstead with minor defences and fields attached, on the scale of the *raths*, Iron Age farmsteads in Ireland. Whatever it was, it was probably not lived in for any long time, for it does not have the beds of nettles, living on accumulations of phosphate, that mark habitation sites in boulder-clay country (p. 193–4). The outer boundary banks appear to be unfinished.

The Warren

Pillow-mounds   In the midst of the Forest, in the angle between Collin's Coppice and the site of Warren Coppice, there is a cluster of mounds. Seventeen mounds are rectangular or sausage-shaped, with rounded or slightly flattened tops, having ditches round them. They vary in length from 49 to 155 feet; most of them are around 35 ft in width (to the middle of the ditches). They are between $2\frac{1}{2}$ and $4\frac{1}{2}$ ft high above the bottom of the ditch.

The place is called The Warren, and these are undoubtedly *pillow-mounds* made to be the homes of rabbits. They are now hidden incongruously among giant horsechestnuts, but the area is devoid of pollards or ancient thorns, and may have been treeless in the past.

The rabbit, introduced at about the same time as the fallow deer, was a Mediterranean beast which at first was ill-adapted to our climate and needed careful attention to keep it alive. Until recent times it was a valuable animal, properly appreciated for its meat and fur.[229] Pillow-mounds, which are a regular feature of warrens, may have been to make it easier for the rabbits to burrow, but possibly also helped in catching them when wanted.[230] We shall never know for certain: pillow-mounds were once commonplace, everyone knew what they were for, and nobody thought it necessary to tell posterity.

Pillow-mounds are often on Forests and other commons. Typically they are set out in rank and file like Army hutments, on well-drained ground; a good example are those below the King's Oak Inn in Epping Forest. Usually it was held that a landowner might introduce rabbits without diminishing the common-rights. At Hatfield the commoners took a less generous view with Lord Morley. There can be little doubt that these represent the 'Coney Burroughs' for which he was fined before the manorial court from 1639 onwards (p. 104). Many sets of pillow-mounds are of around this date,[230] although coney-keeping had declined from its medieval heyday. In the late 1680s, as we have seen, the warren was revived by Sir Edward Turnor, who introduced fresh rabbits, built the Warren Cottage (Chapter 8) and employed a warrener. Although the site is most unsuitable, it seems to have prospered for a short time; legal witnesses in 1735 said that it had been 'well stockd with Rabbits' but by then was extinct.

The underlying earthwork These are not quite typical pillow-mounds. They are bigger, higher, and less flat-topped than usual, and are set out in chains (Fig. 25) sharing a common outer ditch. The site is flat and wet; water collects like a moat round each mound, which rabbits would have hated.

Detailed measurement reveals that the pillow-mounds are adapted from an earlier earthwork. Lord Morley saved his men some trouble, at the cost of discomforting his rabbits. Lengths of unaltered earthwork remain between most of the mounds, and in the north and south there are long stretches without mounds. (Several other examples of earthworks converted into pillow mounds are known.[230])

The earthwork was a bank with external ditch, now about 26 ft in total width and 2 ft in total height. It enclosed an irregular area of 10 acres and carries thirteen pillow-mounds; a length of similar bank in the interior has been made into four mounds. (There are also two low square mounds which are not derived from an earlier bank.)

Each pillow-mound was made by driving two ditches through the bank to define the ends. The bank between them was heightened, partly by enlarging the existing outside ditch, and partly by digging a new ditch behind the mound. Usually the original ditch is the bigger.

What was the earlier earthwork? In profile it is not unlike a wood-bank, and it would be nice if it were, since this would make the

Warren the site of another coppice; there would then have been eighteen coppices and an eighteen-year felling cycle (p. 113). But this can hardly be. The area enclosed is much smaller than the other coppices. The earthwork leaves awkward gores between itself and the two neighbouring coppices, instead of joining neatly to their woodbanks as another coppice would have done.

The date and purpose of the Warren earthwork can only be settled by excavation. It is like the outworks of Portingbury Hills in its general size and profile, and especially in its right-angled bends for no apparent reason. For the moment it should be classed as another possible Iron Age site.

Street Coppice and Bush End Earthworks

In Street Coppice there are two great ditches which are perfectly straight and parallel; they are about 25 ft wide and 2–3 ft deep; the longer is 250 yards long. They are symmetrical and have no banks. They are usually full of water. At one end they are truncated by the edge of the wood and by the old railway; the longer ditch turns a right angle just before it is cut off. At the eastern end they terminate in an area of hummocks and hollows with nettles and elder, suggesting an old habitation; beyond these are irregular pools and streamlets. The woodbank between Street and Long Coppices, which runs parallel, might have been adapted out of a third member of the same system, although its profile is now very different.

Being straight and parallel, these ditches are probably an artefact, although it is hard to see what could have happened to the clay dug out of them. The longer ditch is noted, and mistaken for a ride, on the 1757 map (Plate 2). Since they do not conform to the layout of the Forest, nor to the 'Roman' road immediately to the north, I suggest a prehistoric structure of unknown purpose.

Linear hollows of similar size are scattered irregularly over the plain which was once Bush-End Coppice. Some of them are straight and some crooked.

Woodland Rides

Although lanes *between* woods are usually medieval, rides within them appear always to be later. Previously there had been winding tracks among the stools, such as still survive in Chalkney Wood. From about 1600 onwards, people began to drive straight rides through woods. These partly express the post-medieval obsession with straight lines, but have a practical use in giving a field of fire for sporting guns. In seventeenth-century France it became the fashion to carve up woods into geometrical diagrams of straight rides radiating from central points, as can be seen on a gigantic scale in the Forêt de Chantilly. These radiations are called *pattes d'oie*, goose-feet. The fashion spread to England and became a cliché of eighteenth-century landscape design, for example in Savernake Forest, Wiltshire.

The first evidence for the rides of Hatfield is the 1757 map. The system is shown almost exactly as it is today (except for the 'motorways'), with four *pattes d'oie* in Takeley Quarter, Round and Collin's Coppices, and near Portingbury Rings. It was not quite finished in 1757, and cannot be much older. The rides are clearly younger than the coppice boundaries, and the radiation in Takeley Quarter cuts incongruously and impractically across Dowsett's Coppice. Grids of rides (e.g. in Lodge Coppice) seem to come first, and the *pattes d'oie* later.

Coda: Was Hatfield Forest a Neolithic Observatory?

In about 1970, Mr Tim O'Brien made a series of discoveries. He found that the 'Leper Stone', a great stone that stands by the main road just north of Newport near Saffron Walden, lies exactly halfway, in a nearly straight line, between Wandlebury Ring (the well-known circular Iron Age hillfort near Cambridge) and an upright boulder beside Hatfield Priory. On the way the alignment passes through the middle of another hillfort called Littlebury Ring, the barrow called Mutlow where the medieval courts of Uttlesford Hundred were held, three other boulders and another earthern mound (Fig. 26). It also includes the intersection of the eight rides in the north-east of Hatfield Forest.[231]

So far this resembles a demonstration in ley-hunting, the art of finding antiquities that lie in straight lines on the map. The significance of these lines is disputed: some claim merely that prehistoric men had an obsession with alignments, others that leys had a practical

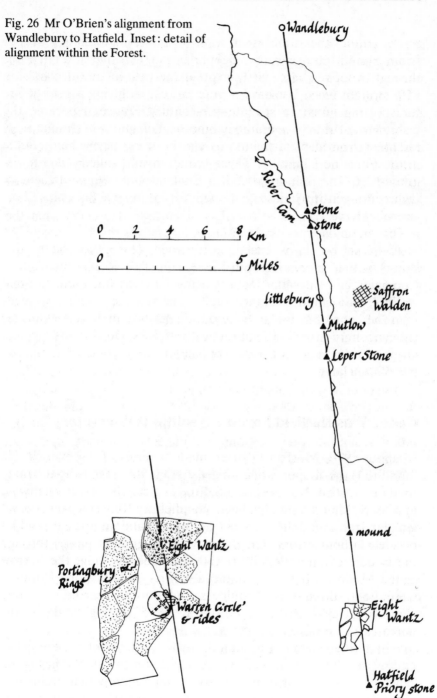

Fig. 26 Mr O'Brien's alignment from Wandlebury to Hatfield. Inset: detail of alignment within the Forest.

use in turning to good account the magic of the chthonic goddesses.[232] Ordinary archaeologists, noting that the things aligned show no tendency to be of the same period – if indeed they are antiquities at all – and that some of them are very large, usually regard the alignments as coincidental and ley-hunting as a pseudo-science.[233]

But Mr O'Brien is no mere ley-hunter: he made very careful measurements and allowed for the curvature of the earth. He demonstrated that the alignment between the various objects was not a straight line (a great circle) but a curve called a rhumb-line, well known to navigators at sea, which passes at exactly the same angle to each of the successive parallels of latitude. He claims that the stones, mounds, etc. are the survivors of a set of originally 27 markers, set out at exactly equal intervals along the rhumb-line. Others can be recognized but are not in their original positions; these include the boulders of conglomerate rock which now lie near the Shell House in the Forest.

For Mr O'Brien, the significance of the Wandlebury earthwork lies in various gaps in its outer bank, through which the rising sun and moon could be observed for calendrical purposes. He claims that Wandlebury is, in effect, a henge, and was constructed on elaborate astronomical alignments like those claimed for Stonehenge by the late Professor Alexander Thom.*[234] Earthworks did the duty of stones. The exact end of the rhumb-line is marked by a boulder buried within the Ring at a point, not the centre, which is significant in its internal geometry.

At the Hatfield end, O'Brien claims that the western arm of the Forest lake is all that remains of a huge earthen circle, even bigger than Wandlebury, also made as an observatory. This circle does not form the end of the alignment, but would have been tangent to it. He proposes that Portingbury Rings, although they make no pretence to be a circle, were a third observatory: the small hummocks are the remains of sighting-mounds whose alignments recorded astronomical measurements.

The purpose of all this geometry would have been nothing less than measuring the circumference of the earth. The people responsible had no sextants or other modern devices for measuring angles, but they were able to use the rhumb-line to compare the directions

---

* Thom did not support O'Brien's theory.

of midsummer sunrise at the latitudes of Wandlebury and of Hatfield. The direction of the rhumb-line enables this to be done by a simple geometrical construction not using a protractor. According to O'Brien, they would have got the size of the earth correct to within 1% – much better than Columbus knew it.

The apparent movements of the sun and moon change over the centuries, and these changes, well known to astronomers, can be used to provide a date for the observatory. O'Brien claims that the whole system, to have been of any use, would have to have been contructed between 2700 and 2200 BC. This puts it at the end of the Neolithic period.

This theory would give Hatfield Forest a monument, as old as Stonehenge, which might even have been 'the inspiration behind the development of Western Civilization'. The area would have to have been a plain stretching away to the eastern horizon: an environment more readily conceivable for Wandlebury than for Hatfield. Even the present trees would make sunrise observations impossible.

Could it be true? None of the objects aligned is, *prima facie*, older than the Bronze Age. The stones are undatable: they are big glacial erratic boulders of a kind not unusual in Eastern England, though O'Brien claims to have found traces of worked faces. Wandlebury looks like a conventional Iron Age hillfort, 2000 years too late to be of any use to O'Brien's theory, and this has been confirmed by a partial excavation.[235] The only rather unusual feature – which O'Brien does not stress – is its exactly circular shape. (Littlebury, the other hillfort on the line, is not circular.) O'Brien replies that Wandlebury was made as a henge and *adapted* into a hillfort. Perhaps this is not quite impossible. What is impossible is that the features which once had an astronomical meaning – the bank with its gap and the stone at the end of the rhumb-line – should have been preserved despite this transformation, long after that meaning had ceased to exist. They would also have had to survive later transformations of Wandlebury, such as making a landscape park in the eighteenth century. The same applies to all the other markers. In this part of England, innumerable antiquities of all kinds, down to the Roman period, are known from air photographs, but very few of them are still upstanding. How can so many boulders and mounds have survived, unaltered and unmoved, for 4500 years, when much larger and much later structures have vanished without trace?

O'Brien's objects have nothing in common except that they line up. The alignment is of great precision, and thus deserves to be taken more seriously than most ley-lines, but the precision itself is suspicious. O'Brien concludes that the rhumb-line was measured to an accuracy of one part in 30,000 and that its direction is accurate to within 5 seconds of arc. Such precision is far beyond the powers of people limited to wooden measuring-rods and the naked eye. (Anyone doubting this should read a car number-plate half a mile away, and then should make a measuring-stick ten feet long which, when used out of doors, will not vary by more than half the thickness of this page.) He goes to some lengths to show that the odds are enormously against the alignments being fortuitous, but his calculations are not entirely convincing: there must be very many directions into which a learned and ingenious scholar, given freedom to choose a suitable date, could read some astronomical meaning or other.

As a site for precise observation, the Wandlebury-Hatfield system seems ill-chosen. Measuring the base-line would have been complicated by steep hills and river-crossings, which could easily have been avoided by choosing another line. Wandlebury (in the absence of trees) is a possible site for observing the sunrise, but the Hatfield lake is not, since the ground rises to the east.

It might be hoped that Mr O'Brien's observations, even if his theory is mistaken, might tell us something about the prehistory of Hatfield. Alas, this is not so. His only feature here which is pre-historic at all is Portingbury Rings, where excavation, although on a small scale, has produced not a trace of anything earlier than the Iron Age. I have looked very carefully for remains of the 'henge' attached to the lake, and must conclude that it does not exist. The western arm of the lake is certainly not there on the great map of 1757, and the plan still exists for its construction a few years later (p. 129). It is formed by a dam of the usual eighteenth-century kind. There is no trace of any prolongation of this arm to form a complete circle. Such a circle, if it existed, ought to survive at least at the place where it would intersect the warren-banks. These, as we have seen, may be a genuine prehistoric earthwork, but are not noticed by O'Brien.

O'Brien attaches significance to two intersections of what he calls 'ancient forest tracks': the two rides which crossed Warren Coppice (Fig. 17) and which play a part in the internal geometry of the 'henge', and the eight rides whose meeting in Takeley Quarter is one of the 27 interval-points on the rhumb-line. These are not ancient: both of them are part of the formal system of rides which, as we have seen, dates from the first half of the eighteenth century. Rides in woods are unstable and get overgrown and lost unless often maintained; some of those in Takeley Quarter have nearly been lost in the last few decades. It is inconceivable that these features could have survived all the vicissitudes of 4500 years. Moreover, if these tracks had indeed been clearings in a forest – which O'Brien takes to mean a place covered with trees – then the trees would have obstructed both the surveying and the astronomical observations.

I therefore infer that O'Brien's theory has no archaeological basis and tells us nothing about Hatfield Forest. I am not an archaeologist, still less a conventional one, and am driven to these conclusions with reluctance. But it is easy to under-calculate the 'long arm of coincidence'. Alignments are all very well for investigating the functions of objects already dated in some other way. No alignment, however accurate, means anything by itself; to carry conviction there must be at least a little *positive* evidence that the features on it are of the date claimed for the alignment.

8 Forest Buildings

Presented that Lord Morley had not removed the house called The Coney Burroughs on the Forest of Hatfield.

Manor court roll, 1650[183]

Essex has one of the biggest concentrations of ancient timber buildings in the world. The great barn of William of Wykeham stands at Widdington, six miles north of the Forest; the Monks' Barn at Netteswellbury is seven miles south-west; and the double farmyard of Colville Hall, surrounded by buildings of the twelfth century onwards, lies four miles south-east. These are the mightiest and most wonderful, but lesser examples of the carpenter's craft are to be found by hundreds in the hamlets and scattered farms within ten miles of the Forest. Even to describe the buildings of Hatfield parish, though their timbers would often have grown in the Forest, is beyond the scope of this book. I shall confine myself to those on the Forest itself or directly connected with it.

Forest Lodge

This house in the midst of the Forest appears at first sight to be unusual only for its beauty and remoteness.* With two rooms upstairs and two down, around a massive brick chimney-stack, and with a jetty or overhang all along the front, it might be any one of scores of small houses all over eastern England. They date from the seventeenth century or the very end of the sixteenth, when the fashion for symmetry had descended to the houses of ordinary folk. In just

* Forest Lodge is a private house and is **not** open to the public.

172

this style are also the earliest surviving houses of New England.[236] As with many such houses, the original appears to have been extended to the south by a timber-framed rear wing, and to the west by what was built as a small boarded barn (Plate 20).

Appearances are deceptive. The Lodge is older and more complex than it looks; the symmetry disappears inside. Fortunately for the historian, alterations to timber-framed buildings cannot be concealed. When an original timber is removed, the mortices by which it was attached to other timbers remain, and from them we can reconstruct the missing part. When a later timber is added, it is difficult to integrate it properly into the existing frame, and it is joined instead by an easily-detected makeshift.

The earliest part is the western half of the main building, including the small middle bay containing the chimney (Fig. 27). Upstairs this consisted of one big room with an arched tie-beam across the ceiling. Downstairs there were two small rooms; mortices for the partition between them remain in the main ceiling-beam. These rooms ended eastwards, in front of where the chimney now is, in another partition; its mortices indicate a central post with a doorway on either side. The main ceiling-beam ran on beyond the central post. It would not have been possible to build, still less to use, the chimney when the frame was complete; the chimney is therefore a later alteration.

This half of the building, with its solid and well-carpentered frame, contrasts with the eastern half, which is more clumsily built and differs in its decorative details. The junction between the two is vague and irregular. I infer that the original house was partly destroyed and the present eastern bay is a patching-up of what remained.

Can we reconstruct any more of the original Lodge? The western half, as described, is typical of the 'service end' of a medieval hall-house – the usual dwelling of country-folk from the thirteenth to the fifteenth century, of which there are countless examples in Essex. It consisted of a buttery and pantry (rooms for storing drink and food) with a bedroom above. The rest of such a house would have comprised a great hall open to the roof, usually heated by a central fire in the middle of the floor. At the other end there would be a parlour with another bedroom above it. The front and back doors would have faced each other at the service end of the hall; they were connected by a 'screens passage'. The Lodge, thus reconstructed, would have been much longer than the present, apparently

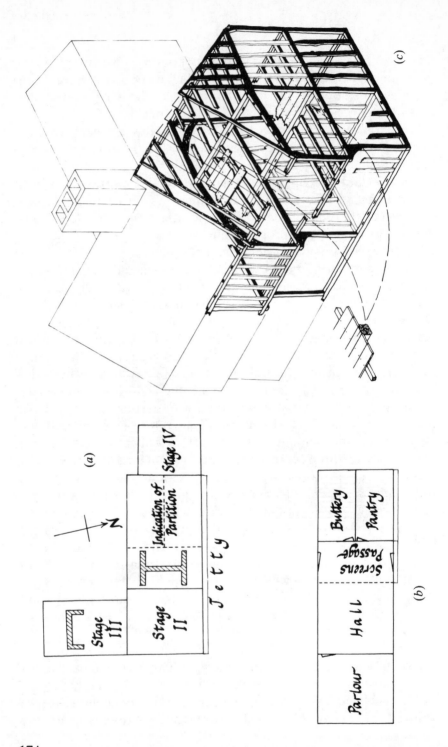

174

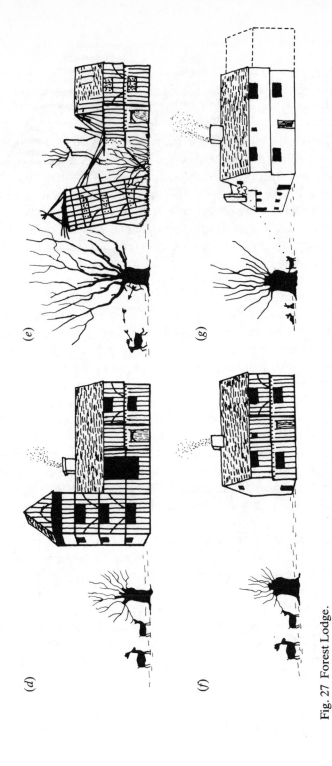

Fig. 27 Forest Lodge.

(a) Sketch-plan of present Lodge. The main building (without Stages III or IV) measures 33 × 17 ft. Chimneys are shaded.

(b) Reconstructed plan of medieval hall-house (part of which forms Stage I of the present Lodge).

(c) Surviving original part of present Lodge. Timbers shown by thin lines only are inferred, the originals being missing or covered up. Many timbers are omitted to avoid confusing important detail. Inset: detail of floor-construction.

(d)–(g) Suggested history of the Lodge: (d) As originally built; (e) End of Stage I; (f) Stage II; (g) Stage III (IV in broken line).

175

seventeenth-century, house. What survives is the buttery and pantry with the screens passage and a fragment of the hall. The bedroom, as in some houses of this type, extended over the screens passage.

The Lodge is sited at the point from which as much as possible of the Forest could be seen. The sight-lines between the coppices, though now much blocked by trees, are evident on the map (Fig. 28). In many parks I have found that the park lodge was placed at the best viewpoint (*AW*). The exact sight-lines converge on a point outside the present building, where the original parlour would have stood. This suggests that instead of the parlour, or on top of it, there was a *standing* or observation tower.

Standings were a normal feature of parks and sometimes Forests. The best-known and most elaborate is 'Queen Elizabeth's Hunting Lodge' in Epping Forest.[237] There were at least two other standings in Epping Forest. Several buildings interpreted as park standings have been discovered in Essex in recent years. A standing – not to be confused with a hunting lodge – acted as a grandstand for distinguished visitors to watch ceremonial hunts. This may be an unlikely function in Hatfield Forest, but the Foresters would also have found it useful to overlook the scrubs and underwood when keeping an everyday eye on things.

The Lodge was a plain and workaday building with little ornament. Its size, considering it as a hall-house, suggests a middle-class dwelling; there would have been dozens like it in Hatfield, although several smaller sizes of hall-house are known. The roof, much of which appears to be original, shows no trace of soot-blackening from the usual central hearth; there must therefore have been a chimney, or at least a timber-framed smoke-hood, somewhere other than at present. The bedroom was not open to the roof, as in most medieval houses, but from the start had a ceiling which formed a floor to a (probably windowless) loft above. The ceiling rose in the middle as though it were a low-pitched roof. Its original oak boards still survive (as do those of the bedroom floor); as in many medieval floors, one board is omitted in the middle where the lengthwise central beam forms part of the floor surface.

Transformations The Lodge is thus a unique survival: as far as I know, it is the only medieval Forest lodge of which any particle

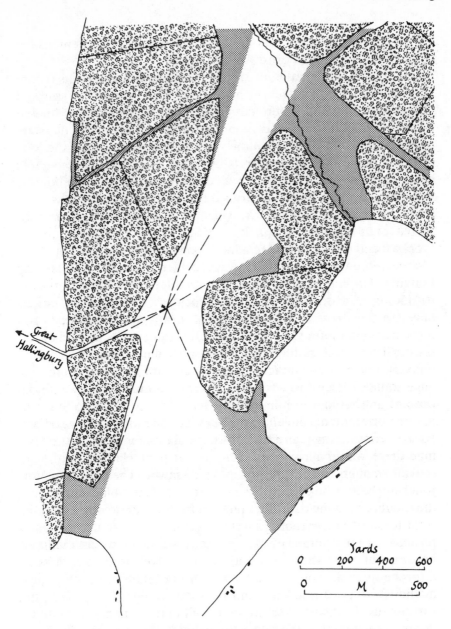

Fig. 28 How the Forest Lodge is sited at the best point for overlooking the plains. The sight-lines converge at a point a few feet outside the present east end of the Lodge. Areas of plain not visible from this point are shaded. The coppices are shown as they were before 1700. The scrubs (of unknown extent, but then much less than now) are omitted.

remains above ground. (New Lodge, Epping Forest, was demolished soon after the Epping Forest Act in 1878.)

If we call this original building Stage I, then Stage II was its reconstruction to form the present main building – reduced in size and outwardly (though not perfectly) symmetrical. The roof was taken down and rebuilt: original carpenters' numbers can be seen on many of the rafters, but they are in the wrong sequence. Both of the lofts were made into habitable garrets by inserting windows in the gable ends; the newer loft has a flat, not cambered, floor with elm boards. The chimney was probably inserted at the same time. It is built in 'thin' bricks, $2\frac{1}{4}$ inches thick, which were current before the mid-seventeenth century. Originally it had two flues, but one upstair fireplace and a third flue were added soon after, in the same bricks.

Next (Stage III) a back range was added to make an L-shaped building. The frame of this range is not integrated with that of Stage II, and is in a different style of carpentry, with squarish panels between the timbers. Its chimney fits into a space provided, and must be contemporary. Probably at the same time, the whole of the outside of the building, which would originally have had exposed timbers, was plastered over and decorated with pargetting in rectangular panels (part of which still survives). A few originally external timbers still remain visible at the back of Stage II where Stage III has protected them. Finally (Stage IV) the boarded western end was added; this is a very late frame of pine, dated by maps to the mid-nineteenth century.

We can guess at the dates of these stages by considering the fortunes of the Forestal lords. Stage I implies someone putting capital into maintaining the deer, building a substantial house for a working Forester, but not spending lavishly on ornament. Then there has to follow a long period of dereliction in which more than half the house fell down, followed by a reconstruction on a smaller scale than the original, and then a later addition (Stage III). Stage I was medieval in its construction and in what survives of the plan, but two details – the loft over the bedroom and the apparent absence of a central hearth – imply a date at the end of the Middle Ages. Stage II, with its attempt at symmetry, thin-brick chimney, but probably exposed timbers, has an air of about 1600. Stage III, with heavy timbers exposed on the inside only, belongs later in the seventeenth century.

The original Lodge might be the work of one of the Dukes of Buckingham or of Henry VIII. Henry is known to have made three parks in Essex. Of his short-lived park in Epping Forest all that remains is the Great Standing, finished probably in 1543, now mis-named 'Queen Elizabeth's Hunting Lodge'; it is a costly building, much more modern in its carpentry than the Hatfield Lodge, and doubtless intended for state occasions. In the royal accounts for making Nazeingwood Park in 1542, a new lodge and a new standing together cost £13 15s. 0½d., an amount which would have bought only a flimsy building.[238] Hatfield would have come somewhere between these extremes. If it was the work of Henry, however, this leaves hardly enough time for it to fall down before Stage II.

It is best to attribute the original Lodge to one of the Dukes of Buckingham. It could have been built when Duke Humphrey took over the Forestal rights in 1446, but this may be too early a date for a house that is not soot-blackened. A more likely builder is Duke Edward in the 1510s or 1520s. After he lost his head, Hatfield would have been too remote for a royal park, and the Lodge might well have been left to rot for seventy years under the king and the Rich family. A modest rebuilding would be consistent with the Morleys in their earlier and happier days around 1600. Stage III would then have been added by Sir Edward Turnor when he revived the Forestal rights around 1670. Stage IV would have been built by John VII Archer Houblon as part of the Victorian emparking.

Materials Ancient buildings preserve the actual trees of the woods and hedges of past centuries. From the timbers we can work out how many timber trees went into a building, their species, diameters and ages, the height at which they started to branch, and the environment in which they grew. It is difficult to do this with modern structures because carpenters now treat trees as if they were plastic: they begin by felling a few big trees and sawing them up into lifeless rectangular beams and flat planks. The medieval carpenter chose many small trees of suitable sizes to make the various rafters, joists, posts, etc. Every beam represents the whole, or a large part, of one tree, and often has impressed upon it the rounded surface and crooked shape in which God made the tree. Sometimes wattle-and-daub is preserved and enables us to reconstruct the underwood, although in Forest Lodge oak laths were used instead.

179

All the timbers now visible are oak, except for the elm floorboards in the loft of Stage II. Most of the timbers of Stage I each represent a whole tree, or half a tree sawn lengthwise. The trees were quite small, being mostly about 7 in. in diameter at the base and never more than a foot, except for those that provided the floorboards (which are 12 in. wide and ¾ in. thick).

The original Forest Lodge, though built (presumably) with timber out of a Forest, was not different from other houses of the period. The trees which went into it were identical to those of ordinary coppice-woods at the time. Most of them would have been of less than 50 years' growth; the present oaks that have grown up in the Forest woods since 1924 are already too big. Not enough of the original fabric survives to make an exact enumeration possible, but the analogy of other buildings elsewhere suggests something like this.[239]

The carpenter would have gone into the coppices to choose about 250 oaks, varying in diameter from 6 in. to 18 in., but mostly of the smaller sizes. A few of the biggest would have been used for a central truss over the hall (which does not survive) and for sawing into floorboards over a sawpit. About twenty specially knot-free logs would have been set aside to be rent into laths for filling the panels and hanging the roof-tiles. The rest would have been used for the ordinary components. They would have been roughly squared up, but without entirely effacing the shape of the original tree. This was apparently done with an axe – a few axe-cuts survive on rafters – and finished with an adze. Some of the beams were sawn lengthwise into two. They would then have been ready for cutting to length, digging out the mortices, and cutting the tenons. The various sections of the building would be laid out flat on the ground and then reared into position in a sequence worked out in advance.

Outbuildings and Lodge Close Attached to the Lodge are outbuildings of the Houblon era. They include a specially-built butchery with pulleys in the roof for hanging carcases of deer.

The present gardens and paddocks lie within a much larger enclosure, some 7 acres in all, most of which is now open to the Forest. It is surrounded by a bank and ditch. This 'Lodge Pasture' is shown on the 1757 map and continued separate throughout the Houblon period. It had been made much earlier: the 'Lodge Close' is mentioned in the rangership grant of 1608.[209] There is a pond which seems originally to have been shared between the close and the Forest.

Warren Cottage

This is a mysterious house. It is hidden away just inside the Warren earthwork; its beauty and character have been so damaged or concealed by later additions that it has not hitherto been recognized as an antiquity. What remains are the outer walls and roof; the window and door openings are modern.*

The house (omitting modern additions) is tiny, 26 feet by $12\frac{1}{2}$ inside. There may have been only one room up and one down, though some division is possible. At the rear there is a staircase turret. At one end is a full-sized chimney with a walk-in fireplace 7 by 3 feet; this is spanned (as usual) by an oak beam resting at each end on an elm sill built into the brickwork.

The house is built of brick, and of no common brickwork, but of a hard dark-red brick with ornamental blue headers forming in places a diagonal pattern.

The roof (Fig. 29) has heavy wall-plates resting on the walls. From these rise 19 couple of rafters to meet at the apex. Halfway up the rafters on each side are horizontal side-purlins, braced apart by one original collar in the middle. At each end a cambered tie-beam unnecessarily joins the two wall-plates. The rafters are prolonged by sprockets, timbers nailed to their outer faces and projecting over the eaves; these are original and prove that the roof (like most roofs in Essex) has always been tiled. The timbers, except the wall-plates and tie-beams, are from very small oaks, just like those of Forest Lodge. The rafters measure $5\frac{1}{2}$ by $3\frac{1}{2}$ inches at the base, and most of them are each from a small oak-tree 7–8 in. in diameter, tapering above. Each purlin is from a similar oak but is 28 ft long and tapers from 8 in. diameter at the base to $5\frac{1}{2}$ in. at the top; the tree was only just long enough.

The datable features are conflicting. The patterned brickwork

---

* The cottage and its garden are private. This account was written in 1987, when further alterations were about to begin.

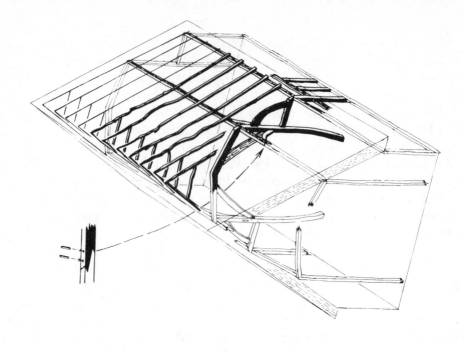

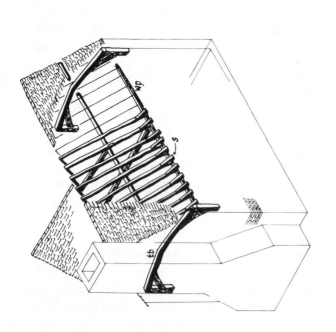

Fig. 29 Warren Cottage, showing roof-frames with tie-beams (*tb*), wall-plates (*wp*), sprockets (*s*).

Fig. 30 Forest Cottage, showing original timbers. Conventions as for Fig. 27c. Inset: detail of scarf-joint.

could be Tudor, but is usually in great houses and colleges; the external chimney is also characteristic of great buildings. The staircase turret should be late sixteenth century. The bricks are 2½ in. thick, a little thinner than modern bricks, and could well be mid-seventeenth century; however, the inside of the walls, where visible, somehow contrives to have 2⅛-inch bricks, which would be earlier. The cambered tie-beams are in the medieval manner, but the rest of the roof could be seventeenth or eighteenth century. The small oaks indicate medieval woodland practice.

The house has not been reduced from a bigger one: its patterned brickwork continues over the outside of the chimney, which must always have been external and visible. Nor can it originally have been timber-framed and later under-built in brick; if it were, then the wall-plate would have mortices and pegs at regular intervals for the studs of the wall.

As we have seen, from 1639 onwards Lord Morley was fined for 'making Coney Burroughs and erecting a Cottage'. We might conclude that this was the present cottage, though in some respects it would have been old-fashioned even for the 1630s. However, other documents survive which date it securely, and later still.

The Turnor valuation dated *c.*1690 (p. 105) mentions:

> The fforrest ... a Conny warren with a very good new brick house and the stock of Connies ....[138]

Among the Houblon records of lawsuits over shooting and gravel-digging we have the evidence of the man who made the bricks, and the man who carted them:

> Richard Wyborough of Little Hallingbury Woodward to Sr. Edwd. Turner and Brickmaker remembers Hatfield Chace 50 Years ... says he remembers the Warren House being built for he made the Bricks which was above 40 years since ....

> Daniel Robinson of Hatfield remembers the Chase 60 years ... there was a Warren house built by Sir Edward Turner about 46 Years since and that he filled the Waggon with bricks ....[135]

The date is 1734–5; the house was therefore built in the late 1680s.

Why was brick, and such beautiful brickwork, used for a mere warrener's cottage? Warreners were once important people: Thetford Warren lodge, in the Breckland, is almost a castle, but that was a very great warren and much earlier. Bricks had been made locally for two centuries, but were used for chimneys and great houses. Almost everyone for miles around the Forest lived in timber-framed houses, except for Turnor and the Barringtons. The roof of Warren Cottage, with its heavy wall-plate and redundant tie-beams, looks like the work of a carpenter who had never roofed a brick house before. Why did Sir Edward bring fine bricks and a special bricklayer for such a small and remote house? Was he defying Barrington and the commoners to pull it down?

The Shell House

The little tea-room of the Houblons is one of the prettiest fancies of the Grotesque phase of English Baroque. It dates from the 1740s (p. 129); the 'Frontispiece of the Shell House' appears as a vignette on the Hollingworth-Lander map and is still exactly the same 230 years later. (It is disfigured by cement repairs, and the back has been rebuilt and altered.) One of the two oaks outside, to which lanterns used to be fixed for feasts,[140] still stands.

The façade is faced with flint, tastefully varied with blue glassy slag from some furnace. In it are set shells from warm seas: scallops, cones, wentletraps, murices, a big cowrie, and the occasional branch of coral. A bird made of oyster-shells adorns the keystone. Inside the ceiling is decorated with more delicate kinds of shell-work.

Boundary Houses

All round the Forest are medieval and Tudor buildings, which fronted on to the Forest and thus define its extent (Fig. 3). All of them were still fronting the Forest in 1857, but the only one that now does so is Beggar's Hall, which is Elizabethan. The half-village of Takeley Street is a row of such houses, the homes of the Sharers, many of them disguised by later brick façades. One small medieval hall-house has been sliced in two, revealing in the present end-wall the timber frame with its crown-post that used to span the middle of the hall.[240]

At Bush End there is a group of medieval and seventeenth-century houses around a green that projected from the Forest. One of these

184

has been adapted from a mysterious structure attributed to the fourteenth century: a small, square, but very high two-storey building with several windows. Mr David Stenning, who discovered this building, proposes that it was a standing. It commands a good view of the east of the Forest – but a view then obstructed by woodland – and would have overlooked the south of Hatfield Park; but the main façade seems to have faced south, away from both Forest and Park. (The best place for a standing in the Park would be on the site of the present Park Farm.)

Forest Cottage Hidden away at the former edge of Woodrow Green is the oldest of the boundary-houses, another of Mr Stenning's discoveries.* It belongs to the earliest type of English house, the *aisled hall*, built round two rows of internal posts like a church. This kind of building goes back into the mists of prehistory; as a dwelling it died out in the fourteenth century, though aisled barns continued to be built much later.

Forest Cottage (Fig. 30) consists of two unequal bays with one pair of posts; one of the posts survives, with its complex braces to other parts of the frame. There may have been a third bay. The roof is very steep, one of the few ancient roofs in Essex which have always been thatched. The house was open to the thatch and was heated by a central hearth; the rafters are still soot-blackened. It may originally have been a one-room house, or there may have been some kind of cross-wing. Later it was divided into two rooms upstairs and two down. The carpentry details – notably the manner of joining timbers end-to-end and the absence of a *jowl* or swelled head to the post – suggest a late thirteenth-century date. The house was almost certainly lived in by somebody who owed labour services in the 1328 survey.

This venerable house is of great meaning because of its tiny size: at 25 ft long and 19 ft wide, it is probably the smallest aisled hall known. We used to suppose that the only extant medieval houses were those of 'People who Mattered', the relatively well-to-do, and that the homes of humble folk do not survive until much later. A number of recent discoveries disprove this theory. In reality, even the smallest 'peasants', of whom the owner of Forest Cottage would

* Forest Cottage is a private house.

185

have been one, lived in houses which were scaled-down versions of their betters' and which still occasionally survive. The early Barringtons lived in a much grander aisled hall which still stands, after many vicissitudes, as the core of the present Little Barrington Hall.

The timbers of Forest Cottage presumably came from the Forest. They show that at this early date there was an abundant supply of even smaller oaks than those that went into Forest Lodge. Each of the rafters (originally numbering about thirty) is the whole of an oak-tree no more than four inches thick. The main timbers are cut from very short and crooked oaks, and bear the marks of a pit-saw, worked by two men in a pit. The arcade-plates – timbers running the length of the house – although only 25 ft long, are joined midway. The visible principal post is markedly crooked. It is usual in humble houses for some of the timber not to be oak: one of the braces here is probably aspen, which as we have seen is recorded in the medieval Forest.

Even such a workaday little house as this is part of the High Gothic world of beautiful carpentry and architecture. There is nothing hasty, experimental or merely utilitarian about it. It is a work of art and ingenuity, in which the crooked timbers are made into architectural features.

9 The Woods

The almost total absence of Birch trees and Bracken . . . is attributable to the heavy soil . . . .

Hatfield Forest, 1925[241]

[Birch is now the fifth commonest tree in the Forest]

For most of its history Hatfield Forest has been rather more than half woodland (Table 1). The formal division between coppices and plains began in the middle ages or before (p. 77). This chapter is about the twelve coppices that remain. Most of Emblem's and parts of Collin's and Spittlemore were spoilt in the replanting period (Chapter 6), but I shall continue to count them as woodland. Woodland and trees in the plains will be discussed in later chapters.

As explained in Chapter 1, a normal wood consists of underwood, that is coppice stools and suckers, with a scatter of timber trees. Underwood species vary from one type of woodland to another; timber trees are mainly oak, although ash has been important in this Forest. Centuries of woodmen have had little direct (though some indirect) influence on the composition of the wood; in contrast, the structure of the wood is almost entirely of their creation, by their deciding which trees to treat as timber and which as underwood, and how often to cut them.

The history of normal (non-Forest) woods is played out by trees, woodmen and the environment. Because Hatfield is a Forest, there is a fourth group of actors in this theatre, namely the livestock. In non-compartmental Forests such as Epping, deer and cattle wander about and eat whatever plants and young trees they please. In Hatfield the woods were supposed to be fenced half the time.

187

Nevertheless, the likes and dislikes of the various animals have been a powerful influence both on the composition of the woods – deer are more effective than woodmen in determining what tree grows where – and on their structure.

Much of the woodland has been coppiced in the last twenty years and gives a good impression of its traditional state. Most of it has not been touched since at least the 1940s and is now grown up tall. The coppices, as their name implies, are full of coppice stools – trees of species such as ash, maple, hazel and hornbeam, which display their history in having several trunks growing from a massive, often gnarled base. The standard oaks scattered through the woods are for the most part a young generation grown up at the time of the last coppicing, or the last but one, and still no taller than the overgrown underwood. The previous generation of timber oaks cannot have been very numerous. Many of the oak stumps now to be seen are those cut in the great felling of 1924, but the more rotten ones probably date from *c*. 1900.

Flora of the Woods

The *flora* of a wood is the list of species present; the study of *vegetation* takes into account the abundance of trees and other plants, the numbers of individuals, and their relationships to each other.

The total number of flowering-plants and fern species recorded for Hatfield Forest is 406. Of these, 265 (roughly two-thirds) occur in the woods; many of these grow in the plains also. This latter list includes 36 native trees and shrubs, 17 exotic trees and shrubs, and nine introduced herbs. If Wall Wood and Monk Wood are included, a further 8 species are added.

This number of plant species in 490 acres of woodland is comparable to other ancient woods. Bigger woods tend to have more species, but not invariably nor proportionally: as a very rough rule, a wood of ten times the area has twice the flora. The woods of Hatfield Forest, taken together, are comparable with Hempstead Wood, a large ancient wood in N.W.Essex, with 164 species recorded in 173 acres. They are not as outstandingly rich as the Bradfield Woods, Suffolk (about 350 species in originally 323 acres) or Buff Wood, Cambridgeshire (195 native species in 40 acres). They are much richer than the woods of most Forests such as the New Forest.

The richer of the individual coppices is comparable with other woods outside the Forest. Beggar's Hall has 129 species recorded in 59 acres, which is very similar to West Wood, Great Sampford – though Prior's Wood, Takeley, has almost the same number of species in 20 acres. Table and Gravel-pit Coppices are the poorest.

Ancient-woodland plants   Many plants are characteristic of ancient woodland.[242] Oxlip *Primula elatior*, for example, grows in almost every ancient wood in north-west Essex and is often abundant, but rarely occurs in ancient hedges and is very reluctant to spread into newly-formed woodland. In Essex there are some fifty such species, including *Paris*, woodland hawthorn *Crataegus laevigata*, and to a lesser degree bluebell and dog's-mercury (*AW*).

In the woods of the Forest as a whole, 25 ancient-woodland plants have been recorded. Taking the area into account, this brings the Forest into line with most of the woods of known antiquity in N.W.Essex. The richest coppice in such plants is Collin's.

Notable woodland plants   The remarkable orchid *Epipactis purpurata*, coloured violet all over, lurks in the densest shade of the coppices; it is a south-eastern plant and is very rare in Essex. Its sister *E.helleborine* is also rare in Essex and occurs here.

Some of the coppices, especially Long, have the curious *Paris quadrifolia*, with its four or five leaves and central flower; it is a clonal plant and occurs in circular patches. Goldilocks *Ranunculus auricomus* flourishes in several coppices and in Wall and Monk Woods.

There are some remarkable absences. Wood-anemone has doubtfully ever been seen in the Forest, though it occurs in Wall and Monk Woods and is very abundant in Birchanger Wood. Bluebell is abundant in these three woods but is very local in the Forest. Ramsons *Allium ursinum* is missing, although in places the soils should be right for it. *Lotus uliginosus* is usually the common bird's-foot trefoil in woods, but here is known only in the Delta. The bell-flower *Campanula trachelium* and the grass *Milium effusum* are not recorded; wood forget-me-not *Myosotis sylvatica* and the grass *Melica uniflora* have been seen only once. Grazing impoverishes the woodland flora, but it is hard to see why these particular plants should be exterminated: animals rarely touch anemone or bluebell. Grazing may better explain why pignut *Conopodium majus*, a plant of ancient woodland and also ancient meadow, is rare in the Forest.

Oxlip and primrose   Hatfield Forest has not only primrose and cowslip but also oxlip, that shy and beautiful inhabitant of ancient woods in eastern England. Oxlip (Plate 21) has an umbel of flowers on a long cowslip-like stalk, but the flowers are large, pale, and hang to one side; they have a wonderful greengage-like scent quite unlike primrose and cowslip.

Oxlip is a plant of woods (and a very few ancient meadows) within a sharply-defined area from Hatfield Forest through Essex and Suffolk to Stowmarket, and a second area around Hayley Wood in Cambridgeshire. It is very reluctant to invade newly-formed woodland even where this extends an existing oxlip wood. It makes up for this local distribution by great abundance. There are now probably more oxlip plants than primroses or cowslips in Eastern England; in a good year (as in Hayley Wood in 1987) hundreds of thousands flower together. But it is a rather elusive plant, and the earliest botanist to notice it was John Ray in Cambridgeshire in 1660.

Oxlips in Hatfield Forest are few, and Miller Christy, the lifelong searcher for the plant, failed to notice them for his distribution map in 1884,[243] though he included them on later versions. They are mainly in and near Dowsett's Coppice, with about 300 plants (in 1983), extending into Street and Long Coppices. There is another population in Hangman's Coppice. There used to be a very few plants in the north-east of Collin's Coppice, but I have seen only hybrids since 1973. The 30 or so plants in the east of Wall Wood are the southernmost oxlips in Britain.

Woodland Soils

Woodland soils are not a random selection from soils in general. Woods survive on soils of little use for anything else, according to medieval and earlier ideas of land capability. In Essex they tend to be on flat hilltops that are difficult to drain, or on specially infertile soils. (Fertility is now bought in a sack, but until 150 years ago it was a valuable inherent property of the soil.) Woodland soils have differed from farmland from the start, but they also develop differently. Woods are not ploughed, limed or fertilized; and the various trees and other plants influence soils in different ways.

In a Forest there is the further difference between the soils of woods and plains, and the effect of animals moving from one to the other.

Boulder-clay and loess The old belief that soils are formed by weathering of the underlying rocks is only half true for England. The bedrock under the Forest is London Clay, but this is too far down to have the slightest effect on soils. (It does, however, reach the surface in a valley in Birchanger Wood.) The Forest is covered with some 50 feet of Boulder-clay, over which prehistoric dust-storms deposited a foot or two of loess (p. 21). Much of the loess has been washed away, and the remainder has been mixed into the boulder-clay by worms and moles.

Boulder-clay can be seen in newly-dug ditches and on the roots of uprooted trees. It is a stiff, grey or orange clay, full of chalk pebbles and larger boulders of chalk and other rocks; it is alkaline. Loess, where it can be seen as such (e.g. at Groton Wood, Suffolk), is a fine, compact yellow powder. In this area it is weakly acid.

These soils are clayey, 'heavy', and ill-drained, although the loess makes a difference. The Forest calls for gum-boots for most of the year, but the soil does not stick to boots as really heavy soils do. A typical woodland soil passes gradually from almost unaltered Boulder-clay, four feet down or so, to the top foot which is mixed with a good deal of loess. The topsoil is acid, partly because of the loess, but also because millennia of fallen leaves have rotted and released organic acids. These acids have dissolved away all the chalk pebbles down to a definite depth.

Soil properties The most important single measurement of a soil is the pH, a measure of acidity. English soils range in pH from 3.0 (the most acid) to 8.0 (the most alkaline). To avoid the complexities of surface acidification, all my pH measurements are from a depth of 15 cm. Unaltered Boulder-clay from beneath the Forest has pH 7.5.

The texture of a soil is measured by the proportion by weight of sand, silt and clay. For this analysis 'sand' is particles between

0.106 and 0.500 mm in diameter. 'Silt' is particles from 0.020 to 0.063 mm, most of which constitutes loess. 'Clay' is particles smaller than 0.002 mm; it measures the contribution of Boulder-clay.

A typical topsoil in the coppices is a little more than one-third clay and a little less than one-third silt; the remainder is material of other sizes. Like most woodland soils, these vary. At one extreme, in the valley in Collin's Coppice, a sample has 42% clay and 18% silt; here most of the loess has evidently been washed away. In contrast, on the plateau of Wall Wood there is 24% clay and 43% silt. Sand, as we shall see, contributes to the grassland soils, but in the woods rarely exceeds 12%.

Most Forest woodland soils are weakly acid, pH 5.5 to 6.7, but there is a very wide range and variation can be sudden. In a valley in Lodge Coppice the pH rises to 7.3; on the plateau of Street Coppice I have recorded 3.7, but 50 yards away the pH is 6.8. In general the siltier soils are more acid than the clays.

Drainage   Clay soils are impermeable to water, so that excess rain has to flow away over the surface. If there is little slope, as on the flat hilltops of the Forest, the water is ponded back by the slightest irregularity. The soil pore spaces become waterlogged, so that oxygen cannot diffuse to reach plant roots. Iron and manganese compounds in the soil become reduced to the ferrous and manganous state, which is toxic to many plants.[244] The result is known by the Russian word *gley*; such soils can be recognized by their mottled, often orange and grey, appearance. Lack of drainage is bad for all agricultural crops, but many wild plants are adapted to it in different ways.

Waterlogging is the normal state of the Forest woodland soils and is part of their character. The trees seldom root more than three feet deep, and the plants are adapted to resist wetness. High ground, as in the north of Takeley Quarter, is flooded in most springs. Slight slopes and shallow valleys shed the water and determine the degree of waterlogging.

In places waterlogging may be offset by *flushing*. Because the soils are variable, and some are less impermeable than others, water can trickle sideways along the junctions of different materials. As it flows past burrows and old root-holes, it can pick up oxygen from the air and transport it to other places.

Waterlogging affects the degree of surface acidity. In well-drained soils, worms and moles mix the layers and offset surface acidification. They cannot burrow in waterlogged soils, which therefore tend to be more acid at the surface.

Humus When dead leaves (and also bud-scales, catkins, caterpillar frass etc.) fall to the ground, one of two things happens. Either they pile up on the soil surface from year to year, gradually rotting down into humus by the attacks of fungi and mites to form a layer of leaf-mould. Or they are seized at night by earthworms, dragged into burrows, and consumed below the surface; the humus does not form a separate layer but is mixed into the soil. Earthworm soils and leafmould soils are called by the Danish names *mull* and *mor*.

Whether mull or mor is formed depends on soil, trees and worms. Earthworms, as Charles Darwin showed,[245] are as fastidious as goats: they take the soft leaves of elm and hazel first, and leave the tough bitter leaves of oak and chestnut till last. Most of Hatfield Forest has not very acid soils, in which worms are numerous and take most of what is offered to them, although oak-leaves are left until the spring. The soils are mull, with a crumbly structure and no definite humus layer.

On acid soils leaf-eating worms are discouraged; leaves pile up to form mor, especially if the trees offend the worms' tastes. In the Forest, soils occasionally are more acid than pH 4.4, below which hornbeam – a moderately unpalatable tree – forms mor (*AW*); patches of Street Coppice have leaf-mould 3 in. thick. Mor is more prevalent on the acid soils of Wall and Monk Woods, but only under hornbeam. In south and east Essex, where woodland soils often fall below pH 4.0, mor is common, and is sometimes found even beneath palatable trees such as ash and elm.

Phosphate The mineral in shortest supply in ancient woodland is usually phosphorus. Woods were short of phosphate to begin with – otherwise they would not still be woodland – and every crop of faggots or poles has removed some of what there was. Stinging-nettles tell us where phosphorus still lies: they are greedy for phosphate, and their roots are inefficient at getting it.[246] Nettles are plants of places where phosphate ends up, such as gardens and churchyards;

193

they grow in woodland only where phosphorus has accumulated for some reason.

A Forest is different. Deer and cattle do most of their feeding in the plains but deposit some of their dung in the woods. They move phosphorus from grassland to woodland. Probably for this reason, nettles are not uncommon in the coppices.

Relation to other soils   The Soil Survey classifies soils into named Series on the basis of their texture, structure and degree of waterlogging down the profile. The plateau soils in the Forest are woodland variants of the Ragdale Series, gleyed clay loam over clay. Less acid patches on the plateau belong to the Hanslope Series. The shallow clayey valleys have examples of Takeley Series soils.[247]

Kinds of Woodland (Fig. 31)

Woods of ash, maple and hazel   These are the ordinary trees of the Forest woods; between them they cover about two-thirds of the wooded area. All three are generally in the form of underwood, although ash and maple are often maiden trees dating from the last coppicing, or occasionally timber trees. Many examples disprove the belief among writers that maple is only a 'small tree' and hazel a mere shrub. There are magnificent canopy-forming hazels in long-uncoppiced parts of the woods (Plate 8), and hazel does not flower if it is shaded by taller trees.

Ash, maple and hazel can be mixed in almost any proportion. They form a complicated patchwork. These woods have standard oak trees; they are often mixed with birch and hawthorn, of which more later, and with many other trees and shrubs; occasionally there are patches (clones, p. 11) of aspen, wild cherry or blackthorn. In long-uncoppiced woodland, spindle and dogwood grow into sizeable trees; clematis – with cable-like stems as thick as a man's arm – climbs to the treetops.

Ash—maple—hazel woods are the usual ancient woodland of the English Midlands and parts of East Anglia and Essex. Variants have been described by myself at Hayley Wood, and by Dr George Peterken under the names 'wet ash—maple wood', 'wet maple wood', and 'acid pedunculate-oak—hazel—ash wood' (*WCM*). Hatfield is unusual in the abundance of maple; if we include pollards in the plains, it may be the most notable maple locality in all Britain.

Maple is an ancient inhabitant of the Forest (p. 91). There are many giant stools, some of which (such as one 13 ft in diameter in Lodge Coppice) go back at least to the days of Robert the Bruce. There are also young stools and maiden trees: maple has replaced itself freely from seed down to the last coppicing. Maple is likewise abundant in all the woods within a few miles of the Forest, except where hornbeam is dominant; but in none of those woods is maple clearly commoner than ash as until recently it was here. The clay soils of Hatfield encourage maple, which of all English trees is preeminently the species of heavy clays (*AW*). However, the difference is not great, and within the Forest the maple areas tend not to be obviously the most clayey. As we shall see, the special abundance of maple at Hatfield is partly to be explained otherwise.

Ash is now nearly as abundant as hazel or maple, but the size of the stools proves that it has much increased in the last 150 years. Ancient stools (e.g. one 8 ft across in Beggar's Hall Coppice) are not common; most of the stools are no more than a few coppicings old, and areas of ash (e.g. in Round Coppice) may consist entirely of maiden trees springing up at the last coppicing. Such an increase of ash has happened in many woods at different times in the last 100 years, and no general explanation can be offered (*HC*); here, however, the predominance of young stools can be accounted for, as we shall see, by Hatfield being a Forest.

Hornbeam-wood　Ash, maple and hazel are distributed more or less at random, but hornbeam is a ***gregarious*** tree: it grows as patches of hornbeam-wood among areas that lack hornbeam. When well-grown it is dark and densely-shading, and little else grows among or beneath it.

In the Forest, hornbeam is not quite so gregarious as it often is, but there are areas of nearly pure hornbeam in Long, Street and Gravel-pit Coppices, as well as in Wall and Monk Woods. Cherry sometimes accompanies it. To judge by the large number of pollards, it would have been the dominant tree also in the eastern coppices now made into plains. It is here a tree of high ground away from streams and valleys.

Hornbeam is nearly always a coppice stool (up to 8 ft in diameter),

Ash-Maple-Hazel woods	Mixed Ashwood	A
	Ash-Hazel	Ah
	Mixed Hazel-wood	h
	Maple-Hazel	Mh
	Maple-wood	M
Hornbeam-woods	Maple-Hornbeam	MH
	Hornbeam-Ash	HA
	Pure Hornbeam	H
Lineage Elmwood		E
Coppice Oak		
Plateau Alderwood		
Chestnut		Ch
Sycamore		S

0 M 500
0 Yards 500

Invasive & Clonal Trees:
Elm (suckering kinds)
Hawthorn
Birch
Aspen

Natural Glades

or a pollard in the plains, but there are a few standard trees. A mighty spreading hornbeam, one of the most magnificent in England, stood in Long Coppice; it was revealed to view in a 'motorway' clearing in the 1960s, but hurt by that brusque treatment (and the ditches severing its roots) it languished and died.

Hornbeam is the commonest woodland (seldom hedgerow) tree throughout south Essex, Hertfordshire and the London area. It is generally on clayey soils with more loess, and sometimes sand, than those of Hatfield Forest. It occurs in all the woods around, usually in greater abundance than here; some fine examples can be seen in Birchanger Wood. Compared with other hornbeam-woods, ours are less acidic than most; they belong to the Hornbeam—Ash and Maple—Hornbeam variants (*A W*). Maple—Hornbeam is a rare type of woodland – on the whole maple prefers heavier, less acid soils than hornbeam – and Hatfield has one of the best examples of it.

Birch and hawthorn   These are abundant, birch especially in the western and hawthorn in the northern coppices. Birch sometimes forms patches of pure birchwood and sometimes is mixed with other species, especially ash. It consists of maiden trees, either of timber size or smaller; in much of the Forest two generations of birch can be discerned. An example are the fine birches around Portingbury Rings. Hawthorn commonly occurs as areas of dense dark thorn-trees, with the occasional youngish oak. It too can be mixed with other underwood. Although birch and hawthorn can be coppice stools, they are very seldom so at Hatfield, where the birches and hedgerow thorns have come from seed.

Of the two species of birch (Fig. 4), silver birch is (as usual) the less common in all the coppices except in Hangman's and Beggar's Hall, where the two are about equal. Of the two hawthorns,

Fig. 31 Types of woodland in the coppices of Hatfield Forest and in Wall and Monk Woods. Tree communities are defined in terms of the underwood, timber trees being largely incidental (*A W*). Letters in the plains indicate where there are pollard ashes, maples, hornbeams and (Lineage) elms. Some of the elm clones are in abeyance through the combined action of Elm Disease and deer. The map was begun in 1973 and includes small areas since lost to plantation. The distribution of coppice oak and of pollards is mapped in general terms and does not show individual trees. Pollards are (in part) after H. Lamb.

hedgerow hawthorn (unusually for ancient woodland) is by far the commoner; the woodland species is rare except in the north of the Forest.

Oakwood A romantic, and nearly unique, feature of the Forest are the huge coppice stools of oak, hollowed and gnarled into Arthur-Rackham-esque shapes, some of them nearly as tall as pollards (Plate 18). In the western coppices they can be so many as to dominate the woodland (Fig. 31). They are all ancient stools, sometimes more than 9 ft across, and have been cut many times; they are not to be confused with casual regrowth from the stumps of timber trees.

Oak is the most versatile of English trees, and has developed an association with various human activities. It occurs on almost all soils and in all types of woodland, but in ancient woodland usually only as a *timber* tree. Ancient oakwood – in which oak is dominant to such an extent that woodmen have had to treat it as underwood as well as timber – is a specialized type of woodland, on poor soils or in difficult climates where few native trees other than oak will grow. It is the common ancient woodland of west Britain, from west Cornwall to Inverness, but in the English lowlands *ancient* oakwood is restricted to very infertile soils. In Essex most oakwood is either recent (as on many commons) or artificial, the result of replacing ancient woodland by oak plantation; ancient oakwoods are confined to a few very gravelly hilltops, so dry and infertile that even birch grows with difficulty (*SEE*).

The Hatfield Forest oakwoods do not resemble western oakwoods or their Essex outliers. Although the latter have ancient coppice stools, these are not like the tall monsters of Hatfield. The oaks root deep into rock fissures or gravels, very unlike the wet clays of the Forest. They are accompanied by birch, bracken and bluebell, not the maple, mercury, primrose, twayblade and even stinging-nettle which we have here. Hatfield is a unique example of ancient oakwood on a comparatively fertile clay soil where maplewood would be expected. The oaks are pedunculate oak, *Quercus robur*, the ordinary oak of farmland and scattered through other types of woodland; they are not the sessile oak, *Q. petraea*, the special oak of most other oakwoods both in the west and in Essex.

Why the oak stools are cut so high is not clear. High stools are a style of coppicing particular species, chiefly lime and ash, in certain woods. With Turkey-oak in Tuscany the stools get gradually higher at each cutting.[248] Sessile-oak coppice in Highland Britain usually has low stools.

Plateau Alderwood   Hidden in the north of the Forest, at the west end of Street Coppice, is a patch of about four acres of alderwood – of alder stools up to about 3 ft in diameter – mingling at the edges with hornbeam and hazel. The ground here is a perfectly flat plateau. There are a few more alder stools on sloping ground in Spittlemore Coppice.

Alderwood in such a place is almost as unusual as the oakwood. Alder is common in most of England on the banks of rivers and streams: for example, on the edge of the Forest below the lake, where alders have been irrigated by leaks in the dam. Alderwoods spring up on former fenland. Within *ancient* woods, alder is normally confined to the bottoms of steep valleys. Essex examples include Chalkney Wood in Earl's Colne and Barrow Spring in Writtle Forest. Alder does not grow in ordinary wet clayey woods. It is a plant of wet but *flushed* places; where the water is stagnant we get aspen instead.

Alder, as here, on level ground on the highest point of the Forest is a rarity, but is not unprecedented. The finest of all plateau alderwoods is in the Bradfield Woods, where there are about 100 acres with alder on the highest ground for miles around, at the point where the three main river catchments of west Suffolk meet. There is more alderwood at Swanton Novers, on almost the highest point in Norfolk. Smaller patches of plateau alderwood are very thinly scattered in similar places among the ancient woods of eastern England, including the Colchester woods and the limewoods near Braintree. All these woods are on high flat ground and have preserved surface layers of sand and loess over a clay subsoil. The junctions of these different materials promote flushing, and therefore oxygenation, of the soil.

Elms and Elm Invasion

The elms of the Forest   Elms are a uniquely elaborate genus of trees, especially in Essex: 'nowhere else in England, nowhere else in Europe, is so complex an assemblage of elms to be found'.[249]

They are peculiar in several ways. Most elms are clonal, perpetuating themselves by suckers. Like dandelions and hawkweeds, they have largely given up sex as a means of reproduction, and consequently exist in an infinite variety of different forms. They are intimately linked to human affairs, though mostly in connection with farmland and settlements rather than Forests. Of all trees, elms are the most palatable to deer and farm animals. From time to time they are devastated by disease.

One species, **wych-elm**, *Ulmus glabra*, is a 'normal' tree which sprouts from the stump when cut down and commonly grows from seed. It is the common elm of Scotland but is rather rare in Essex; here I have found it only in Street Coppice. Most other elms send up suckers from the roots (Fig. 5) which grow into trees and replace the parent tree, should it be cut down or die of Elm Disease, with a clone of identical copies of itself. Although elms produce plenty of seed, seedlings are delicate and very rarely survive. When a seedling does survive it starts a new clone, which is often different from its parents and perpetuates its distinctive characteristics for ever.

Suckering elms are divided into three groups, the **English elms** (*Ulmus procera* group), **East Anglian elms** (*U. minor* group), and **Cornish elms** (*U. stricta* group) (*AW; HC*). The last do not concern us. English elms are the traditional elms of the Midlands, south England, and south Essex to within a few miles of Hatfield. I have noted a few clones scattered over the Forest. These elms (which now survive only as suckers) have rather small, very broad, always rough leaves which bear little pimple-galls made by a mite called *Eriophyes campestricola*.

East Anglian elms are the traditional elms of East Anglia, the N.E. Midlands and north Essex. They include most of the thirty-odd elm clones within the Forest itself and those of the hamlets and hedges around. Their name is Legion. Within this one group of elms are innumerable 'species' as different from each other in appearance as any deciduous trees can be; some are spread over an area of several miles, but in other places a single parish, or part of a parish, may have its own unique elm (Plates 9–11). The late R.H. Richens made a study of Essex elms, although even his painstaking analysis only began to do them justice.[250]

One of the most distinctive East Anglian elms in the Forest is

200

the clone in the east of Spittlemore Coppice, which when full-grown is a massively rugged tree with down-arching boughs and great bosses on the bark – a black-poplar-like elm. Similar elms stand half-a-mile west of Hatfield town. In the south of the same coppice is a clone of utterly different East Anglian elms with narrowly-ascending branches and a narrow crown, almost like a Lombardy poplar. Different again are those on the east side of Emblem's Coppice, slender with sharply-angular branches like a false-acacia. Near the Forest are the elegant elms by Canfield Hart, with slender boughs and graceful twigs sweeping over to one side; the mighty elms of Great Hallingbury, with straight but leaning trunks nearly 100 ft high and short massive branches; and the weeping elms near Anvil Cross, with big branches forking near the base and twigs hanging down from the top of the tree. All these, being East Anglian elms, have narrow leaves with long stalks and very asymmetric bases, and the leaves of big trees are smooth. The leaves differ in their detailed proportions, and were used by Richens to discriminate between kinds of elm in a more measured and precise way than is possible from the appearance of the tree, which is difficult to put exactly into words or figures.

Although most Forest elms are typically East Anglian, some clones show some of the characters (large rough leaves with short stalks) of wych-elm; these may well be hybrids. One clone in Street Coppice I attribute to the English—wych hybrid group. There are occasional representatives of yet another set of elms, the *Lineage Elm* group; these resemble East Anglian elms and are gregarious but do not (or only slightly) sucker. Lineage Elms, unlike the other groups, are mainly woodland elms; they are common only in north Essex and south Suffolk (*AW*).

Elm invasion Suckering elms are aggressive: they spread into neglected gardens or farmland and turn them into elmwood. Such small elm-groves are characteristic of Essex: Bushy Leys Grove, so called on the 1587 map of Hatfield, still exists and is of East Anglian elm. Elms very successfully exploit the periodic neglect which plagues human affairs. They exploit men in a different way when they invade existing woodland. An elm clone in a wood produces suckers which survive in shade beyond the limits of the big trees. When the wood is next cut down, these forerunners grow up with the underwood, overtop it, and extend the front of the clone (Fig. 32).

Elms form clones in all the Forest woods (Fig. 31). The success of each clone depends on the properties of the particular elm (how far ahead it sends its forerunner suckers and how fast they grow) and also on what the competing trees are and how strongly they fight for their lives. In general, elm invasions prosper most in woods on clay soils and against the opposition of hazel, which is easily subdued.[251] This is broadly true of the Forest. The strongest invasion is in the north-west of Lodge Coppice, with tall, closely-set, very shady elms which allow little else to grow under them; here a very aggressive sort of elm meets only hazel and the occasional oak stool. Elms do not often win against hornbeam, and are less common in Gravel-pit Coppice and Monk Wood where hornbeam is widely dominant. In the east of Street Coppice a specially aggressive elm has successfully fought the dense hornbeams.

How long have elms been invading Hatfield Forest, and how did they begin? There is no long written history of elm in the Forest, which means that it could not have been abundant *as a timber tree*; it could easily have been here as underwood, of which the species are not recorded. In the 1800s elm was a rare timber tree (p. 118).

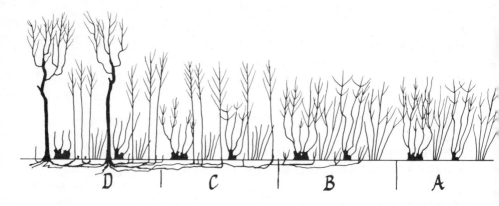

Fig. 32 How an elm invasion progresses, shown by a section through the advancing edge of the clone. A: underwood of ash, maple and hazel. B: the same with forerunner suckers of elm. C: after one coppicing, with elms growing through and overtopping the underwood. D: fully-developed elmwood with standard elms over elm underwood.

In the 1930s the management committee was aware of elm invasion and disapproved of it, elm not being regarded as a 'forest tree'.

In general, in this area, there is a thin scatter of medieval references to elm as a *non-woodland* tree. The timber, however, is the second commonest after oak in medieval buildings, and I have often identified it as being of the same group of elms as the traditional elms still characteristic of the locality. I concur with Richens's conclusion that the distribution of the various kinds of elm has not changed much since the middle ages. Elms were probably more abundant in hedges and farmland in medieval north Essex than the written records would suggest, though the absence of mentions in Hatfield parish (where hedgerow trees are well recorded) is unexpected. In *woodland*, elms were probably less abundant then than now; they seem not to be mentioned at all in Essex woods before the seventeenth century.

The biggest elm clones in Hatfield Forest have a radius of about 150 yards; by comparison with Hayley Wood (Cambs) this suggests an age of about 300 years (*HW*). Although this can only be an informed guess, since elms spread at widely differing rates, elm invasion in the Forest, as in many of the nearby woods, seems to be mainly post-medieval and much of it quite recent. Why it did not start much earlier – indeed why there should be any non-elm woodland left in N.W. Essex – is a mystery.

Invasion can start where a hedge of suckering elm abuts against a wood: elms spread out from the end of the hedge into the wood. Alternatively, people's habits of encouraging elms around settlements can start invasions, for example where a farmstead (active or deserted) lies next to a wood. Neither of these two sources of elm invasion has much scope in Hatfield, because few of the woods in the Forest adjoin hedges or settlements. A clone in Beggar's Hall Coppice, however, may have spread from the adjacent farm. Few if any elm clones in the woods originated from planted elms: tree-planters' elms are of particular kinds following a definite sequence of fashions (e.g. Dutch Elm in the 1700s, Huntingdon Elm in the 1900s), and the coppice elms are not of these kinds (*AW*).

I conclude that most Hatfield Forest elms are new clones which have started from seedlings. I have once or twice seen East Anglian elm seedlings; their survival depends on unusual luck with the weather, and in a Forest would be doubly difficult because of grazing.

Most of the clones appear to have started on boundaries. An example is the woodbank of Collin's Coppice, from which elms have suckered outwards into the plain and inward into the wood. Until recently the limits of the former Warren Coppice were marked out by its boundary elms, which remained after the loss of the coppice. The internal boundary between Dowsett's, Spittlemore and Long is lined with a row of small elm clones. An elm seedling would be less unlikely to survive in a damp woodbank-ditch where the coppice fence gave it some protection from browsing.

Elm Disease Much of what I have just said is now difficult to observe because of the ravages of 'Dutch' Elm Disease. The present epidemic began in Gloucestershire in about 1965 and a few years later on the lower Thames. It spread with devastating speed through the English Elms of south Essex, and reached the Forest in about 1972 (*HC*). Had the Forest elms been English, all the big trees would have been dead by 1976, but East Anglian elms are more resistant, and at the time of writing (1987) at least a quarter of the big elms are still alive. Suckers survive, and it is unlikely that any clone has been exterminated.

The disease – the name refers to its having been studied first by Dutch mycologists – is caused by the microscopic fungus *Cerato-cystis ulmi*, which lives in the water-conducting vessels of the wood and hijacks the tree's hormone system so as to make it kill itself. The fungus is carried from tree to tree by two species of elm bark-beetle. Most readers will know the decorative pattern of tunnels made by elm bark-beetle grubs burrowing under the bark of a newly-dead elm. The grubs pupate under the bark. When the beetles emerge they are contaminated with spores of the fungus; they fly off to nibble the crotches of twigs of living trees, and in nibbling they can inject the fungus into a new tree. The fungus depends on the beetle, but the beetle does not depend on the fungus, although it proliferates whenever the fungus provides it with fresh elm corpses.

Elm Disease is not specially British – the French epidemic now in progress is independent of ours – nor is it new. I have investigated its history elsewhere (*AW*; *HC*). There was a well-documented epidemic in the 1930s and 1940s, which was severe in Quendon, seven miles from the Forest[252]. The disease ravaged much of England and France from 1820 to 1860. In the Forest, I have found the characteristic streaks in the annual rings of trees that have recovered from the disease, which show that it was present at least from 1926 to 1955. 'Elm disease' appears in a report of 1935.[221] Some of the great elms near Round Coppice, felled in 1974, dated from 1795 and thus had survived two previous epidemics.

Elm Disease has probably been present throughout history. Among the medieval evidence are the soot-blackened timbers of a medieval house at Shudy Camps, 15 miles from the Forest, which include small elm poles full of medieval bark-beetle burrows; some of these run in a direction which proves that the tree died while standing. Disease is the only convincing explanation for the Elm Decline, a sudden decrease of elm, and not of other trees, which goes with the beginning of the Neolithic period throughout western Europe.

This disease runs in epidemics. From time to time a new and virulent form of the fungus appears, kills many elms, and after thirty years or so mysteriously loses its virulence and is forgotten. The behaviour of Elm Disease probably involves at least four organisms: the tree, the bark-beetle, the fungus, and maybe a virus that parasitizes the fungus. All of these interact with each other, and at least the elms and the fungus are exceedingly variable; so, despite much research, it is hardly surprising that the disease is only partly understood.

We cannot tell what difference Elm Disease has made to the Forest. It may explain why elms have not invaded still more widely. The recent disappearance of the big elms has affected the woodland ecology surprisingly little: most of the clones were not strongly dominant, and the gaps were filled by the better growth of neighbouring trees.

To judge by the past, the present epidemic should be getting near its end. A possible symptom of this is that the disease is now less mortal; since 1983 affected trees have often recovered (for example round the west edge of Collin's Coppice, and in the north of Hangman's). This was noted towards the end of the previous epidemic.[252] We can cautiously hope that the surviving suckers will re-create an astonishing variety of different elms to delight and instruct another human generation. Suckers, however, are now at a disadvantage because of the amount of grazing.

Herbaceous Vegetation and Undershrubs

This section is about the ground vegetation of *shaded* woodland; later I review the effects of coppicing. Herbaceous plants form a series of types of vegetation in much the same way as do the trees. Although in general there is some tendency for particular herb communities to grow beneath particular trees, in Hatfield the two are largely independent.

In most of the woods the predominant plant is dog's-mercury *Mercurialis perennis*. This is the familiar dominant species throughout ancient woodland where the soil is moderately well drained and not too acid; it forms a monotonous green carpet which can exclude more interesting plants.

In wet areas, such as the flat interiors of Hangman's Coppice and Takeley Quarter, the place of mercury is taken by the rough tufted grass *Deschampsia caespitosa*. This is less aggressive, and violets, primroses and other herbs can grow among it. Mercury appears wherever the soil is slightly less waterlogged, for example on woodbanks; it is most important for the conservation of woods that drainage should *not* be increased.

Brambles are not generally abundant here, but predominate in areas of more acid soil or slightly less shade. Shaded acid soils commonly have abundant wood-sorrel, for example in Long Coppice and the west of Wall Wood. Primrose is locally dominant under elm in Wall Wood.

Stinging-nettle is widely abundant, which is unusual in ancient woodland, and is dominant in much of Table Wood. Generations of livestock, feeding in the plains and dunging in the coppices, have evidently fertilized the latter with phosphate to the point at which nettles can grow.

Woodland grassland Ever since wildwood times there have been small open areas within woods (p. 23). These may be the origin of the peculiar kinds of old grassland now found in rides, glades and the marginal lanes of woods.

In Hatfield Forest, although the rides have suffered from too much shade or from conversion to 'motorways', there are several grassy glades. For more than a century a clearing has been maintained around Portingbury Rings. This has 'woodland grassland' plants such as cuckoo-flower and gromwell *Lithospermum officinale*, besides grassland species such as cowslip and woodland species such as barren strawberry *Potentilla sterilis* and St John's-wort *Hypericum tetrapterum*. More surprising is the exotic giant hogweed *Heracleum mantegazzianum*.

There are half-a-dozen smaller glades dating, as we shall see, from damage to the woods after 1924. Some of these have woodland grassland plants such as valerian *Valeriana officinalis*. An area in Hangman's Coppice is virtually a fen, with gipsywort *Lycopus europaeus* and big patches of the club-rush *Eleocharis palustris*.

Browsing

Deer and farm animals eat tree leaves, and often prefer them to grass. I have watched a poplar blow down in a summer gale, and a herd of bullocks prick up their ears at the crash and gallop off to devour the leaves. There is plenty of experience from Hayley Wood and other woods now infested with deer. In Hatfield Forest itself the recent practice of coppicing woods and not immediately fencing them has repeatedly demonstrated what cattle do to young underwood. Elm and ash are usually at the top of the menu; then come hawthorn (despite the thorns) and sallow; next are hazel and birch; maple and hornbeam are not highly regarded; and oak and aspen, which taste nasty, are definitely disliked. These are general preferences, and are not quite the same for different animals: for instance fallow deer prefer ash to hazel, but muntjac prefer the opposite; cattle are specially fond of sallow; pigs can devastate elm by gnawing the bark; sheep can eat aspen.

Browsing animals determine what a wood consists of. In all woods, trees compete with each other for space, and animals favour any tree that they dislike by eating its competitors. At Hayley Wood, for example, fallow deer have destroyed the stools and have turned an ashwood into an aspen-wood in a few years after coppicing. Even where the trees are too big to be killed, deer and other animals can wander round eating all the leaves within reach; the result is a wood with an empty bottom, in which the foliage abruptly ceases at a ***browse-line***, depending on the height of the animals.

The fallow deer of Hayley, varying between 40 and 70 head, spend most of their time in a wood of 100 acres (excluding fenced areas), but range over some 2000 acres outside the wood, including 350 acres of other woodland, Hayley, even where not recently coppiced, shows signs of severe deer attack: a conspicuous browse-line; oxlip and other favourite plants missing from wide areas; lack of low cover for birds. Farm animals, where they have access to woods, cause yet more severe damage. Many woods in South Wales, to which sheep have access, have lost all their woodland plants (except on cliffs) and are reduced to trees plus sparse grass.

In Hatfield Forest, deer damage is not now quite as severe as in Hayley Wood: the browse-line is hardly evident, and herbaceous plants (except oxlip) are not much attacked. Young underwood, though often damaged, is seldom killed. In the 1970s, when cattle had access to all the woods, there was a browse-line in many parts. I estimate that fallow deer alone – having access to plains or farm crops as well as woods – will produce severe damage of the Hayley kind when there is more than one deer to three acres of woodland.

Coppicing

Coppicing is an integral part of Hatfield's existence as a compartmented Forest. It is not only of historic importance. In woods in general, herbaceous plant communities have been shaped by cycles of years of light followed by years of shade, going back in succession to beyond the memory of records. Plants such as primrose and wood violets do better in such a regime than under continuous shade or continuous light. The massed flowering of primroses or oxlips, in the second spring after felling, is one of the grandest sights of English woodland, and in the years when coppicing was unfashionable was all too seldom seen.

Small birds crowd their territories into the dense thickets of young underwood. The nightingale, which prefers five to eight years' growth, disappeared from the Forest in the mid-1960s but came back when coppicing was resumed.[253] Coppiced areas encourage many insects: for example, hoverflies which feed on the nectar of summer-flowering plants, and fritillary butterflies whose caterpillars require abundant violets. In Hatfield Forest, grass-snakes favour the warm glades between the growing stools.

Regrowth and browsing Although in the 1930s coppicing was allowed to decline into thinning, the National Trust has now come to appreciate its importance. Since 1974, three to ten acres of underwood have been felled each year (Fig. 21).* Usually each panel has been fenced with three strands of barbed wire about 3 feet high. In 1974, Table Coppice was permanently fenced with four feet of barbed wire, and later Takeley Quarter has been fenced as a whole. The fences keep out cattle, but deer easily leap them.

In a typical wood that is not browsed, sallow grows some 10 feet – two inches a day – in the first summer after coppicing; hazel 5 ft; maple and ash 4 ft; hornbeam 3 ft. Table Coppice 1977 grew at these rates; deer got in, but browsed little except elm suckers (which, however, put on $1\frac{1}{2}$ ft).

Fencing is all-important. Beggar's Hall 1974 was left unfenced; cattle ate the regrowth, and the area is still a brambly glade, apart from a few hazel and elm shoots which have struggled through the brambles. Part of this panel was fenced after a year, and regrowth thereafter was almost normal. A late or incomplete fence is ineffective. If the fence is not finished when cattle are on the Forest, they instantly make for the gaps and devour the young shoots. In Collin's 1986, a few days' delay in completing the fence lost a year's regrowth (Plate 7).

Where cattle-fencing is effective, regrowth depends on deer. Occasionally (Beggar's Hall 1975) all underwood grows, but usually at least ash is damaged or destroyed. Hornbeam, maple and hazel usually survive, though they may be bitten at the tips. Aspen is eaten with reluctance. Browsing declined in 1984, after a third of the deer had been shot, but their numbers have now recovered. In badly deer-browsed areas (e.g. Street Coppice and Wall Wood) regrowth is still very patchy after several years; grassy glades have formed in which the deer congregate and prevent tree growth.

Coppicing plants The operation of coppicing gives plants much more light, especially in summer; it has other effects such as discouraging dog's-mercury, which competes with other plants (*AW*). In a normal wood, herbs and undershrubs respond in four ways. *Spring-*

---

* Coppicing is done in winter. I designate each panel by the coppice name and the year: thus 'Table 1977' means the part of Table Coppice felled in 1976–7.

flowering perennials, such as primrose, are there all the time but flower profusely only in the years after felling. **Summer-flowering perennials**, such as meadowsweet, are there all the time but are induced to grow tall and to flower. **Buried-seed plants**, such as St John's-worts, die out in the years of shade but wait until the next felling as long-lived seed.[254] **Mobile plants**, such as willowherbs, have seeds which blow around the wood from one coppiced area to another.

Coppicing plants in Hatfield Forest are not the same as in non-Forest woods. Many spring-flowering perennials are uncommon (e.g. oxlip, primrose) or absent (anemone). There is, however, often a good display of cuckoo-flower *Cardamine pratensis* in coppiced areas, and ground-ivy *Glechoma hederacea* may flower in profusion. Goldilocks *Ranunculus auricomus* responds here, which I have not seen it doing elsewhere. Summer-flowering perennials are also not abundant, although there are a large number of species: for instance meadowsweet, enchanter's nightshade *Circaea lutetiana*, and sanicle. There are some mobile species such as willowherbs and marsh thistle *Cirsium palustre*.

Most coppicing plants here belong to the buried-seed category: for example figworts *Scrophularia nodosa* and *aquatica*, St John's-worts *Hypericum hirsutum*, *perforatum* and *tetrapterum*, and centaury *Centaurium erythraea*. Surprising plants to find in woodland are mullein *Verbascum thapsus*, woolly thistle *Cirsium eriophorum* and dyer's rocket *Reseda luteola*. After a few years, a coppiced area is usually dominated by the tough grass *Deschampsia caespitosa*, which was a recognized woodland product in the past (p. 123). Less wet areas may be overrun by brambles. Both are probably buried-seed plants, though they can persist as perennials. Very wet areas are dominated by rushes, chiefly *Juncus conglomeratus*, which also come up from seed.

Coppicing plants are not always what they were, for example:

> in struggling through the woods the ladies quickly gained evidence of the profusion of the Hound's-tongue . . . in the hundreds of hispid 'nuts' clinging to their dresses.
>
> *Essex Naturalist, 1890*

Hound's-tongue *Cynoglossum officinale* is most surprising as a woodland plant. It has been recorded many times since, but has gradually decreased on the Forest and is now rare in the woods.

Woodland ponds, apparently sterile in shade (though probably rich in specialized micro-organisms), come to life when coppiced over. The pond in Spittlemore Coppice 1982 suddenly filled with spearwort *Ranunculus flammula*, water-plantain *Alisma lanceolatum* and other aquatics, presumably from seed lying dormant since the 1920s if not before.

Conclusions Despite all vicissitudes, the coppice stools, even if sparse, retain their vigour. In 1977 Table Coppice was in poor condition: it had been replanted twice and had been for many decades a favourite resort of cattle. After felling the stools, though rather sparse, have grown surprisingly well.

Our ancestors were right to insist on fencing newly-coppiced areas. The National Trust has re-learnt the hard way that success in coppicing depends on attention to detail in fencing and on coming to terms with deer. This is now being made part of the new management proposals. Keeping down the numbers is not a complete substitute: a smaller number of deer may spend longer in the coppices and do the same damage. Living with deer is a general problem in the modern countryside.

Does it matter if underwood is damaged? Some of the coppice panels look threadbare compared with, say, the Bradfield Woods in Suffolk; but this has often happened in the past – it is part of being a Forest. Deer slow the growth of the wood, but this is not necessarily bad: slow growth is rarely an embarrassment in managing a coppice. Where growth is delayed the coppice stays longer in the thicket stage which is the best bird habitat; warblers, for example, sometimes persist into the eighth year. Complete failure is due to cattle getting in; in only a few areas have deer done unacceptable damage at Hatfield. Coppices recover, provided that they are cut on a long rotation – at least the eighteen years traditional in Hatfield Forest.

Woodland Insects

The insects of the Forest are much less well known than the plants. The most notable habitat is not the woods but the ancient trees in the plains (Chapter 11). The woods, however, used to be an excellent place for butterflies. Up to the 1950s there was a national rarity,

211

the Large Tortoiseshell *Nymphalis polychloros*. The White Admiral *Ladoga camilla* was seen up to 1955. There are similar old records of four fritillaries: High Brown *Argynnis adippe*, Dark Green *A. aglaja*, Silver-Washed *A. paphia*, and Pearl-Bordered *Boloria euphrosyne*.[255] All these butterflies have declined nationally, and it is not always clear why. The caterpillars of the four fritillaries, however, all feed on violets, and in the years when coppicing lapsed there may not have been enough violets to sustain them. There are plenty of violets now, but once gone the butterflies do not easily return. (One has been reintroduced.)

The Purple Hairstreak *Quercusia quercus*, which goes with oaks, and the White-Letter Hairstreak *Strymonidia w-album*, an elm-feeder, appear still to be present. The Speckled Wood *Pararge aegeria*, which goes with woodland grassland, has recently returned.[256]

The moths include a number that are rare and specialized. *Eupithecia inturbata* (Maple Pug) has a caterpillar that feeds on maple flowers. *E. trisignaria* (Triple-Spotted Pug) devours the ripening fruits of angelica and hogweed. *Archiearis notha* (Light-Orange Underwing) and *Tethea or* (Poplar Lutestring) are aspen-feeders.[257] *Nemapogon wolffiella* feeds in dead wood and fungi.[258] The very rare fly *Empis volucris* appears to be associated with ancient woodland.[259]

Planted Trees in Coppices

An existing wood is the worst place to plant trees. The new trees, their roots inevitably injured in the transplanting, have to compete with existing trees or their regrowth. In a place like Hatfield, deer relish their tops and honey-fungus gnaws at their roots. But for two centuries people, defying common-sense, have persistently tried to make woods into plantations.

Plantations can fail in more than one way. The original trees may refuse to die and their regrowth may overtop and kill the planted trees. Or the original and planted trees may both perish and the site be taken over by self-sown ash or sallow. The many Essex woods in which recent replanting has not prospered include the Bendysh Woods (Radwinter), Chalkney Wood (Earl's Colne) and Hempstead

Wood. Probably the National Trust, by taking more care of its re-plantings, has given them a greater chance of success; to that extent, Trust ownership has been less favourable to the survival of original woodland than the Forestry Commission or the average private owner.

In Hatfield some plantings were clearly for ornament, specimen exotic trees intended as conspicuous features in the landscape. Others were probably commercial in intent, following the fashion for modern forestry since 1800 and the loss of the distinction between woods and plantations.

The earliest record is the 'fresh plantation' of Warren Coppice in 1759 (p. 130). Writers on the Forest have repeatedly claimed that trees were normally planted in newly-felled coppices, but of this I can find no evidence. Any attempt at planting would certainly have been denounced by one or other of the parties in the Forest and thus put on record. Planted trees, if still alive, would instantly have been devoured by the deer when they were admitted to the coppice after six years.

Warren Coppice was permanently weakened by the planting. By 1803 it had partially recovered (p. 131), but between 1857 and 1874 it ceased to be a wood. A successful replanting destroys the coppice stools and with them a wood's power of self-renewal. If the wood is then exposed to grazing, it easily disappears when the planted trees die or are felled or blown down; there are many examples in South Wales. Although I have no record of a planting in Doodle-Oak Coppice, it might also explain why that coppice disappeared.

The lesson was not learnt, and there was another wave of planting after the Enclosure. Most plantations include at least some conifers, and conifer symbols on 25-inch maps are a good, though not a complete, record. Ordance Surveys of 1874 and after show conifers thickly scattered through Table and Dowsett's Coppice, and in parts of Spittlemore and Gravel-pit (Fig. 20).

Older planted trees today   We now see only scattered survivors from what were once much more numerous plantings. These are nearly all exotics and thus easily recognizable. In many woods (but seldom at Hatfield) native trees were planted as well; for example there are areas of oaks all of the same age and all cast in the same genetic mould, unlike wild oaks which are very variable. Over the years

213

I have counted the annual rings of planted trees as they were felled, and can date the main periods of planting.

It is unlikely that any of the 1759 trees of Warren Coppice survive. The present big oaks were once the standard trees of the coppice, and date from between 1670 and 1740. A few trees remain from avenues in the coppice, but these are later: a big beech which died in the 1960s proved to date from *c*. 1773; several black pines survived into my time, two of which dated from *c*. 1788. (I dated one of the great elms round the edge to 1804, but these were probably not planted.)

Of post-1857 plantings, the chief survivors are in Gravel-pit Coppice: Scots pines of *c*. 1863, and maybe some oaks of similar age. Most of the other trees seem to have failed. The army of planted trees in Dowsett's Coppice has now vanished, but for one last Scots pine and a few decayed beeches, and the wood has recovered its structure as though they had never been. Also of this date is the ring of black pines and larches, originally eight, at Eight Wantz.

Planted trees of the later nineteenth century are more widespread. In every coppice except Hangman's single exotics stand by rides, evidently intended as specimen trees. They include sycamore, Scots and black pine, and the inevitable horsechestnut. A few box in Spittlemore are the only example of a class of trees associated with gamekeeping. Table Coppice is almost an arboretum, with twelve species of planted trees, including many sycamores and sweet-chestnuts and some oaks. These appear to be younger, a replacement for the post-1857 conifers which have disappeared; a typical larch dated from 1900. Remains of an early rabbit-fence were still visible in 1974. Although twice planted, this coppice still has most of its underwood; the planted trees are treated as standards.

In general these planted trees reflect ordinary Victorian fashion (though it is surprising to find no hybrid lime). The black pines are noble trees and conjure up memories of wild Balkan wood-pastures. In Table Coppice there are two species of greater surprise. There is a swamp cypress, which copes surprisingly well with the climate and the heavy soils, so different from the steamy peatlands of the Great Dismal Swamp in Carolina. On the edge of the wood are the dark umbrella crowns of four stone pines – the real *Pinus pinea*, far from its native sand-dunes in Spain and Italy. This tree from the warmest Mediterranean not only withstands the chill summers and fierce winters of Essex, but produces its huge cones with edible (and fertile) seeds.

Recent plantations   In 1959–64 four acres in the north-east of Wall Wood were planted with rows of larch, Sitka spruce, Douglas fir, *Thuja*, beech and oak. Presumably the conifers were intended to nurse a 'final crop' of beech and oak. The existing trees were reluctant to die, and much effort was put into getting rid of them. There now (1987) survives, in part, a plantation of beech and some of the conifers. In the rest of the area, which is very wet and full of deer, mainly oak survives, but only sparsely.

The next assault was on Emblem's Coppice. In 1965–9 three-quarters of it was felled and planted with oak and larch. The under-wood was killed, but the planted trees grew very slowly, especially in waterlogged areas. Most of them have survived, but the larches have outgrown the oaks which are very spindly. It will just be possible to realize the intention of removing the larch and ending with a plantation of oak only.

In about 1966 a further area of Wall Wood was replanted, making a third of the wood in all. Deep ditches were dug to increase drainage, and larch, Scots pine, *Thuja*, beech and oak were planted. The con-ifers survive; they have done moderately well and have been thinned.

Next the bulldozer appears. In 1974 one sector of Collin's Coppice was grubbed out and planted with a mixture of oak and larch, with a row of hornbeam and cherry round the edges. The existing trees still needed to be killed by mowing and weedkilling. The area has since been left untouched for many years. Much of it is a thicket of tall spindly larch, tangled with bramble and overrun with clematis; the rest has been claimed by the deer, and here it is the oaks that survive, though very bitten-down. The cherries have done better. In 1974–5 part of Spittlemore Coppice had this treatment. More of the oaks survive, but the larches are overcrowded and many have blown over. Finally, in 1975, about 1½ acres of Table Coppice were bulldozed and planted with cherry, oak and hornbeam. These soon vanished down the throats of deer, except that a few of the horn-beams may survive in a bitten state.

Although these plantations were presented as being for amenity,[260] it is hard to distinguish them from commercial plantations of the time, except that broadleaves were planted as well as conifers. Of the six plantations, three are partly successful in that they may yield a little timber. In only one (the third) is there any hope that the timber will justify the labour spent on inducing it to grow, let alone the damage to ancient woodland.

Let it not be thought that the National Trust has mismanaged or unduly neglected its plantations. On the contrary, it has taken more trouble with them than could be expected of the ordinary landowner, and yet has not succeeded. Small plantations normally fall into neglect, and the failure rate here is no worse than usual. It is sad that fifty acres of ancient woodland should have been sacrificed in repeating mistakes made a century before. Had the Victorians put the fate of their plantations on record, they might have saved their successors from the same failure.

The Meaning of the Woods: What Difference Did it Make that Hatfield was a Forest?

Hatfield's being a Forest made a great difference to its management history. The woods were felled on a longer rotation than usual, and in theory each of them was exposed to deer for two-thirds of the time and to farm animals for half the time. In practice livestock often got in when they were not supposed to. The long-term effects can be explored by comparing Hatfield with the surrounding 'ordinary' woods (Fig. 6); these were not (or little) exposed to browsing, and were felled more frequently than in the Forest. Wall Wood and Monk Wood were (in theory) attacked by deer but not farm animals.

Hatfield and English woodland   Ancient woods vary from one part of Britain to another in a way which goes back to wildwood times (Chapter 2): each region has a number of kinds of woodland which differ from those of other regions. Wooded Forests, although they have much in common with each other, are adaptations of their regional woodland: Epping and Writtle Forests are clearly related to the hornbeam-woods of south Essex.

In England the great division is between the mountain oakwoods of the Highland Zone (Pennines, Lake District, Welsh Border, Devon and Cornwall) and the more varied woodland of the Lowland

216

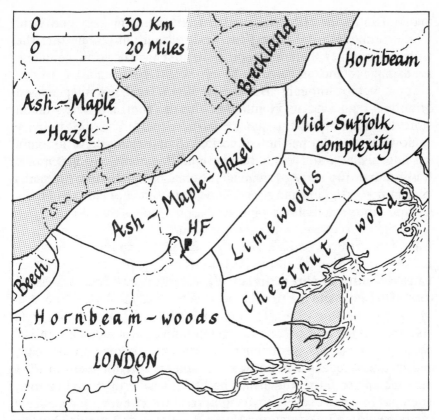

Fig. 33 Woodland regions in and around Essex. The map shows the predominant character of the *ancient* woodland in each region. Shaded areas have no ancient woods. HF = Hatfield Forest.

Zone. Hatfield, although belonging generally to the latter, has an echo of the Highland Zone in its oakwoods – although the resemblance, as we have seen, is not a detailed one.

The Lowland Zone can be subdivided into about twenty woodland regions, of which three meet at Garnett's Wood, six miles east of the Forest: the ash-maple-hazel woods of the East Midlands; the limewoods of mid-north Essex and south Suffolk; and the hornbeamwoods of the London region (Fig. 33). The Forest woods, like most of those immediately around, are of ash, maple, and hazel, much invaded by elm. Although all ancient woods are different, Hatfield Forest is part of a great region of such woods including Hayley Wood

217

and Monks' Wood (Huntingdonshire) and stretching into south Norfolk, Northamptonshire, and past Oxford right into Somerset. The frequent hornbeam, however, tells us that we are getting towards south Essex; and as close as Monk Wood we encounter a large area of solid hornbeam. Birchanger Wood, with its steep slopes, gravelly hilltop, and boggy golden-saxifrage valley, is a typical South Essex hornbeam-wood.

North Essex limewoods are a most complex mosaic of different kinds of woodland, usually having lime dominant on hilltops and hornbeam on slopes. Although all the ancient woods from Garnett's eastward are of this kind, there is no trace of lime in Hatfield Forest or in any of the neighbouring woods.

Effects on trees of being a Forest   The great abundance of maple is likely to be due, at least in part, to browsing. In Hatfield, Hayley and elsewhere, maple does relatively well out of moderate browsing: it is less eaten and more easily recovers than most trees. Several other Forests run to maple. For example in Rockingham Forest (Northants) surveys of 1564–5, enumerating the underwood in 187 coppices, give hawthorn and maple as by far the commonest species, much exceeding ash and hazel, and maple is still abundant in what remains of the Forest woods now.[261] It is also abundant in what is left of Salcey Forest (Northants), Wychwood Forest (Oxon) and Neroche Forest (Somerset). Maple is as characteristic of Forests on less acid soils as oak and beech of those on very acid soils.

We might expect ash to do badly at Hatfield, since cattle and deer love it and kill stools by repeated browsing. This is doubtless why there are few ancient stools: most of the coppices have been browsed at some time or other after felling, and once is enough. But, as Hayley shows, the matter is not so simple. Ash *seedlings* spring up even in a browsed wood, and are not so easily killed. Bitten again and again, they persist in a crippled state for many years, and once deer are excluded they grow up into trees, taking only 3–4 years to reach a height at which they can no longer be damaged. *Intermittent* browsing, therefore, is not necessarily bad for ash, but makes it into a shorter-lived tree with faster turnover. Fluctuating grazing would explain why there are historical records of ash down the centuries, and why it is abundant today but mostly in the form of small stools.

Why is there ancient oakwood here? Oak does well in wood-pasture, partly because it is a 'pioneer' species invading non-woodland sites, especially grassland; it withstands grazing better than it withstands shade. It is distasteful, and has a huge seed which makes a seedling with a big tap-root. If the top should be bitten off it has reserves with which to make a new top. Oak therefore does well in neglected grassland and bushy patches at the edges of glades. Any grassy wood-pasture, such as the plains of Hatfield Forest, grows oaks if grazing is relaxed for a few years. This applies to the pedunculate, but not the sessile, species of oak; wood-pastures therefore tend to have pedunculate oak even where (as in Epping Forest) the soils ought to grow sessile oak (*AW*).

At Hatfield, from time to time cattle have got into the coppices and destroyed the stools (Chapter 5). Severe damage would make glades within the coppices, lasting for some years and getting overgrown when cattle were again excluded. Sometimes, as in the present century, these would overgrow to hawthorn, ash or birch, but after a good acorn year they might become thickets of young oak trees. At the next coppicing, although the woodmen preferred to treat oak as timber, they would have had to coppice some of it for lack of other underwood species.

The great and bizarre oak stools in Hatfield Forest may therefore be the result of not fencing the coppices effectively. This explains why, unlike most oak coppice, they are of pedunculate rather than sessile oak. Although they are not all of the same age, we may even suggest a particular reason for many of them. They are almost confined to the western coppices, the property of Lord Morley & Mounteagle. May they not be a monument to the failure of that downtrodden lord to bully the commoners in the days of Charles I?

The history of hawthorn may have a similar explanation. It is recorded down the centuries at Hatfield, though usually the records do not distinguish between coppices and plains. Thorn-woods have been common in the countryside from Anglo-Saxon times onwards – the word *spinney*, a wood of thorns, has passed into the language – but most of these were evidently new woodland springing up on abandoned farmland (*AW*). Abundant thorns in *ancient* woods are characteristic of Forests, as, for example, in sixteenth-century Rockingham Forest. It is therefore likely that when animals trespassed in the Hatfield coppices and destroyed stools hawthorn was one of

219

the trees to colonize the resulting glades. This would explain why hawthorn is much commoner in the Forest than in any of the surrounding woods, and why most of it should be of the hedgerow species: woodland hawthorn does not colonize glades.

Lime does not like Forests. For example, it is present in all the woods round the Forest of Dean but not in the physical Forest itself. In what was to be Epping Forest it died out at about the time that the wood-pasture system is likely to have arisen.[262] In the New Forest and the Forêt de Fontainebleau (south of Paris) lime persisted long enough to have given rise to place-names (*Lynd*hurst, La *Till*aie). This strongly indicates that in Forests lime is easily destroyed by grazing. I have never seen it happen, but Mr Cyril Powick (of Shrawley, in the Worcestershire limewoods) and Dr C.D. Pigott assure me that cattle destroy quite big limes by tearing off the bark. However, native lime is absent not only from Hatfield Forest but from all the surrounding woods up to Garnett's Wood. Why there should be so much lime around Braintree, and virtually none in all south or north-west Essex, is a mystery; grazing may have had to do with it, but at a time well before Hatfield became a Forest.

Why is there so much elm?   Elm, being extremely palatable, should not be a Forest tree, and Hatfield is exceptional in having so much. There is practically no elm in Epping or Hainault Forests, and this can hardly be due to unfavourable soils, for the farmland just outside is full of elm. In these Forests, with no compartmentation, cattle and deer could devour elm whenever they pleased. Writtle Forest also has very little elm; although it is a compartmented Forest like Hatfield, the acid soils and abundant hornbeam discourage elm invasion. For other Forests comparable to Hatfield, we turn to Salcey (Northants), Wychwood (Oxon) and Grovely (Wilts). These were compartmental Forests, and (like Hatfield) are on heavy, not too acid soils with plenty of hazel and maple; yet their present ruins show little sign of elm invasion.

Compared, not with other Forests, but with its neighbouring woods, Hatfield has at least as much elm invasion as would be expected from its area. For example, Canfield Hart has more invasive elm, but Row Wood, Quendon and Dunmow High Woods rather less, and East-End and Birchanger Woods about the same. However, the non-invasive Lineage elms, locally dominant in Canfield Hart, Birchanger, and other local woods, are much less common in Hatfield Forest.

Elms illustrate the complex relations between men and trees. Richens took the view that wych-elm is the only elm native to England; all other species are the result of people, ever since the Bronze Age, sending to the Continent for their favourite elms and planting them round their homesteads.[249] This is an exciting theory – it would back-date the nurseryman's practice by 2000 years – but in my opinion is far-fetched: it is based on a long chain of reasoning in which some of the links depend on weak evidence (*HC*). It now appears, from identifications of fossil pollen, that at least one other group of elms besides wych-elm has been present throughout prehistory.[263] A reasonable view is that East Anglian, and prehaps also English, elms are native and grew mainly on flood-plains and in valley bottoms. Prehistoric men destroyed these low-lying woods, but gave elms an alternative habitat as farmstead and hedgerow trees. They no doubt selected particular kinds and encouraged (intentionally or not) those that sucker strongly. In the farmed countryside elms were given opportunities to evolve new kinds by hybridization and mutation. Each local kind of elm, once established, would sucker and perpetuate itself for ever.

As elms increased in farmland (despite setbacks from Dutch Elm Disease), woodmanship gave them opportunities to invade new kinds of woodland. Woodbank ditches were places in which seedlings could live and start new clones, and coppicing enabled these to spread. For centuries elms have thus invaded ordinary woods, but not woods in Forests, because young elms were eaten by deer and cattle.

Hatfield Forest is not too unfavourable to elm invasion: it is one of the few Forests in the territory of East Anglian elms, which are more invasive than English; it has calcareous soils and weakly-competing trees; and its compartmental system provided woodbanks and gave intermittent protection from browsing. Nevertheless, long-established elms such as the Lineage group are rare. Only in recent centuries have elms flourished. I infer that from about 1700 onwards the coppice boundaries were more effectively maintained and gave elms a chance to invade.

Changes since 1924

Many things have happened in recent decades over which the National Trust has had no control, such as Elm Disease. The arrival of grey squirrels seems to have put an end to nutting as a social occasion (p. 137): they take all the hazel-nuts when still unripe. There are plenty of big old hazel stools but almost no young ones; the long-term future of hazel is problematic.

Mr John Fielding tells me that the grass *Deschampsia* has much increased since myxomatosis killed the rabbits which ate it. If it was an abundant coppicing plant in the seventeenth century (p. 123), that was before wild rabbits were numerous.

The rise of hawthorn and birch   From the long history of hawthorn in the Forest we might expect to find many old thorns *in the woods*. In fact most hawthorn areas are all of the same age and quite recent: those in the north of Lodge Coppice, which I have ring-counted to the mid-1930s, are typical. Evidently hawthorn largely disappeared from the woods in the nineteenth century, and was suddenly encouraged in the early National Trust years.

From the same period date many of the birches. As far as I know there are no historic records of birch in the Forest. The only evidence in the area is the place-name Birchanger, which is ambiguous. Domesday Book calls it *Bilichangra*, which cannot be derived from birch, and spellings such as *Beelchehanger* continue all through the middle ages. However, variants such as *Birecengre*, which appear to refer to the tree, begin in the twelfth century.[264] Probably the presence of birch suggested the corruption to 'Birch-hanger' (from *hangra*, a steep wood) of a place-name which had originally meant something else.

Birch has changed its ecology in recent decades. Down the centuries it was an uncommon tree, noted for its beauty and valued for brooms and as a teaching aid. Ecologists traditionally regard it as a tree of sandy soils and as a pioneer, the first tree to grow in places which eventually become oakwood. Now it grows almost everywhere, including soils even heavier than in Hatfield Forest, and is permanent; when they die, birches are replaced by more birch.

Several circumstances in the last hundred years have favoured birch. Derelict railway and industrial land, dried-out fens, and heaths no longer grazed (as in Epping Forest) have given birch vacant sites on light soils into which to expand in its traditional way. It has been allowed to spread into existing woods by the nineteenth-century practice of encouraging too many oaks, whose shade weakens or kills the underwood; when the oaks come to be felled birch often fills the gaps. Foresters kill the stools of existing woods and plant conifers; the planted trees die or are felled, and birch replaces them. This was done by the Victorians and repeated in the 1950s and 1960s, and on both occasions has added to the stock of birch. Oak, which would have been birch's chief competitor, has lost its former ability to grow from seed in existing woods (perhaps through the introduction of the oak mildew fungus from America (*AW*)). Birch grows perfectly well on heavy soils, but evidently has difficulty in getting started; for a birch seedling to live may require some special spot such as a worm-cast and unusual luck with the weather. When birch was rare, it was unlikely that when an occasion arose there would be a birch seed to take advantage of it. Now that birch is common, its little fruits are blown to almost every corner of England and instantly take advantage of every suitable spot (*AW*).

Birch in our area probably began in Birchanger Wood, where there are light soils on which it could have grown for centuries. Much of that wood was coniferized in the mid-nineteenth century; and although the original underwood has largely recovered and the planted trees have disappeared, they have been replaced by great areas of birchwood. These birches (by now well into their second generation) have been a nucleus from which fruits would have blown out to colonize other woods.

The next to be invaded was East-End Wood, on rather heavy soils. Birches were evidently let in by an attempted replanting in the late nineteenth century and have increased at every subsequent coppicing. Birch has got into wood after wood in north-west Essex, often as the unintended product of Forestry Commission coniferization.

What was it in Hatfield Forest that let in birch and revived hawthorn? The 1940 air photographs were taken when the present birches and thorns were young. In that year the Forest woods had a moth-eaten look, with wide irregular glades and what look like areas of grassland and bushes within the coppices. Most of these patches are now wooded with hawthorn and birch, though small

223

glades exist even today. The Forest was then evidently recovering from something that had badly damaged its woodland.

We are tempted to equate this with the great felling of timber in 1924. This would be the explanation if parts of the woods had consisted of nothing but oaks, with no underwood to fill the gaps after felling. Had this happened we would still find the stumps under the hawthorns and birches. But there are not enough stumps: the Houblons had not made the common mistake of their contemporaries, of having so many oaks that the underwood was killed. The felling of 1924 was not unusual in the Forest's history; it would ordinarily have been forgotten in a few years, and cannot explain the present glades or the birch and thorn areas.

Only grazing, not felling alone, could have done the damage photographed in 1940. The coppice fences were probably very effective after 1857, but as the Houblon family left Hallingbury Place they may not have been kept up. Even if still stockproof in 1924 they would then have been breached by the felling contractors. Foxhunting archives of 1926–8 describe the woods as 'thick and impenetrable' after the felling, but add that many cattle were kept on the Forest in winter as well as summer and got into all the coppices.[212] The National Trust, misunderstanding the Forest's traditions, failed to restore the fences and thinned the underwood instead of coppicing properly. The regrowth was weak and was exposed to cattle; hence the glades. Years of little grazing allowed thorn and birch to spring up in the glades, as well as thorns in the plains. In the Trust's reports of the 1930s the increase of hawthorn is welcomed. Cattle and deer have continued to get into the coppices over the years, so that the remaining glades have shrunk very slowly and some of them are still open.

The changes I have just reconstructed – broken-down fences, a big felling, excessive grazing, slow recovery – will have happened before in the Forest's history. The reader may compare the effects on the woods of landowning by the National Trust (in its first half-century) with Lord Morley in the seventeenth century (Chapter 5). The chief difference is that there has probably not been a birch invasion before.

10 The Plains

In that part of [Epping] forest between Laytonestone and Woodford, and indeed in all forest thickets, it will be seen that each mass of thorns or brushwood contains one or more young trees, to which it acts as nurse and protector; these trees require no other defence against the numerous herds of cattle, and they grow to a prodigious size.

Humphry Repton, *An Enquiry into the Changes of Taste in Landscape Gardening*, 1806[265]

About one-third of the plains of Hatfield Forest is taken up by scrubs. The remainder, some 280 acres, is grassland with scattered trees, many of them ancient, plus the lake, fens and small plantations. The plains are historic features and just as important as the old woods. Over half the Forest's flora, and well over half the rare species, are to be found in them. It was for the plains that the Forest was first scheduled a Site of Special Scientific Interest in 1956.

Most of the plains have existed for at least 400 years, but some are on the sites of the five lost coppices. Their irregular shape, with tongues of plain penetrating between coppices, is a reminder of the roads and tracks which ran across the Forest – a feature of Forests and not of woods. (When a road traverses a wood, it divides it into two woods, with a woodbank on either side: London Road, dividing Spittlemore and Table Coppices, is an example.)

The soils of the plains are not just a continuation of those in the woods. Boulder-clay sometimes comes nearly to the surface, with little sign of an acid upper layer. Along the Shermore Brook, probably on both sides, there are stretches of sand and gravel; small fens arise where water seeps out of the junctions between sand and clay. In the main body of the grassland, the soils differ from those of the coppices in their development under grass instead of trees.

Grasslands and Fens

When grassland is grazed or mown continuously for centuries, it develops into a turf of many species of grass and sedge, filled with orchids and many other wild flowers. This is classic 'semi-natural' vegetation: natural in that the plants are wild and have not been sown; artificial in that it was formed and is maintained by civilization, and reverts to woodland if not used. It varies according to soil type, whether dry or wet, whether level or sloping and in which direction, and whether pasture (grazed) or meadow (mown).

Such grasslands, of many kinds, were once the normal vegetation of thousands of square miles; over much of England, nearly every farm had access to some. The first assault on them came with the agricultural revolution of the late eighteenth century, which ploughed up and destroyed nearly all the northern chalk downland from Essex to Yorkshire. By 1860 the Cambridge Professor of Botany denounced

> the rapacity of the modern agriculturist, who too frequently looks upon the native plants of the country as weeds, and its antiquities as deformities.[266]

More old grassland was destroyed in later times of agricultural prosperity by being ploughed up, or in times of agricultural adversity by being allowed to turn into woodland. Even so, many of us can remember these beautiful plant communities when they were still relatively commonplace.

Since World War II it has been the fashion to search out and destroy the remaining old grasslands by applying weedkiller or fertilizer. Both treatments quickly and permanently convert distinctive pastures into commonplace ones. Out of the rich mixtures of plants, one or two strong-growing species are favoured, get the upper hand, and suppress the others. The result is *improved grassland* as we in Britain understand it: a sward of coarse grasses, with clovers and perhaps a few buttercups and thistles. Even this is now not very common: most agricultural grassland is sown with varieties of rye-grass, timothy or clover, ploughed up every few years, and is no less an arable crop than barley or sugar-beet.

The destruction of old grassland is not a necessary part of twentieth-century enlightenment: in the Alps, 'improvement' is understood differently, and beautiful mixed meadows and pastures are the rule and not the exception. We might hope that Hatfield Forest, having belonged to the National Trust since before the British style of 'improvement' reached its nadir, might have conserved its grasslands. Alas, this is only partly true: the Trust appears to have been persuaded into following the fashion. In the early 1950s the Alps were far away, and the Trust would not have understood its actions fully. Records of what exactly was done seem to be lost. Ploughing would have created small earthworks round all the numerous obstacles, and of these there is no sign. Tradition tells of spraying with an early hormone weedkiller in the hope of controlling ragwort, and of harrowing to flatten anthills. A few applications of fertilizer and lime could easily have done damage which forty years have not undone. Fortunately, the grassland was not 'improved' very thoroughly, and bits of inaccessible terrain escaped, including all the fens.

The general grassland   The Forest is an example of 'neutral' grassland, where the soil is neither alkaline nor noticeably acid. Neutral grassland, especially on level ground, is very easy to 'improve', and survives in its original state only rarely, where it happens to be protected by common-rights or an independent-minded owner.

At first sight the plains appear to be dull: a sward dominated by the three grasses *Dactylis glomerata* (cocksfoot), *Lolium perenne* (ryegrass) and *Cynosurus cristatus* (dog's-tail), with red and white clover, frequent daisies and buttercups, and patches of creeping thistle. This is an example of what Derek Wells, the grassland expert, calls 'Ordinary Dry Meadows', the least distinctive of the fourteen types of neutral grassland.[267] This combination of plants is very characteristic of half-hearted 'improvement' of more natural grassland.

Most parts of the Forest have at least some more distinctive grasses and herbaceous plants as well. A usual assemblage includes Lady's bedstraw *Galium verum*, sorrel *Rumex acetosa*, the sedge *Carex flacca*, and the grass *Poa pratensis*. These four are typical of Wells's 'Loam Pastures', the old grassland of silty, well-drained soils. Not all of the plains are of this character. As can be seen in spring, patches of cuckoo-flower *Cardamine pratensis* are widely scattered; this plant is distinctive of well-established grassland (and woodland) on clayey, winter-wet sites. Other Forest plants with the same property are the grasses *Hordeum secalinum* and *Helictotrichon pubescens*. A few uncommon species survive in grassland: there is a report of Easter-ledges *Polygonum bistorta*.

From the past there are records of plants, most of them now rare if they can be found at all, that indicate other types of soil. Many of these go with chalky soil, or even with chalk downland: for example pyramidal orchid *Anacamptis pyramidalis*, bee orchid *Ophrys apifera*, picnic-thistle *Cirsium acaule*, the milkwort *Polygala vulgaris*, and catmint *Nepeta cataria*. A smaller number of plants indicate acid soils: for example the milkwort *P. serpyllifolia* and the heathland grass *Sieglingia decumbens*. Plants of dry places (e.g. the grass *Koeleria cristata*) outnumber indicators of wet grassland (e.g. strawberry clover *Trifolium fragiferum*).

From this I infer that the complex soils of Hatfield Forest, which are now best expressed in the woodland vegetation, extend also into the plains, and would, if properly managed, produce a beautiful series of different types of grassland, with various combinations of wet and dry; gravelly, silty or sandy; and acid, neutral or alkaline. Gravel-pits and fens, which now seem very different from the rest of the plains, once formed the two extremes of a continuous range of plant communities. We learn something of the nature of these grasslands from pre-1940 plant records. 'Improvement' turned most of the area into a monotonous and nondescript neutral grassland. Distinctive and uncommon plants survived, if at all, in odd corners and glades among the scrubs which were difficult to reach. Anthills, which indicate where the 'improvement' stopped, are still to be found in such nooks.

Forty years on, the old grassland is beginning to reassert itself. The grasses that demand most fertility, such as ryegrass and cocksfoot, are dying out. Some plants of old grassland, such as sorrel, Lady's bedstraw, woodrush and bird's-foot trefoil, have come back from their refuges – especially in the western plains where there were many nooks in which they could lurk. Pyramidal orchid has recently reappeared. Unfortunately not all such plants can recover lost ground. Over the years the less mobile species have been overtaken by the slow expansion of the scrub which has shaded and killed them.

The grassland soils in general are relatively alkaline, perhaps because they have been limed according to agricultural convention. For example, I have found pH 7.4 on Takeley Hill, in an area still of monotonous cocksfoot grass. Natural grasslands, in corners among bushes, may have acid soils (down to pH 4.3): grasses acidify the soil to a lesser degree than trees.

Some grassland plants are missing from Hatfield for reasons that are not so clearly a result of its post-war history. The long history of grazing, rather than mowing, is doubtless the reason why the Forest lacks oxeye *Leucanthemum vulgare* and has little oat-grass *Arrhenatherum elatius*. These are familiar plants on road and railway verges, but animals destroy them. This may be why *Trifolium ochro-leucon*, the pale yellow clover which is a speciality of this part of Essex, has only twice been noted on the Forest. I cannot say why the Forest lacks hay-rattle *Rhinanthus minor*, meadow saxifrage *Saxifraga granulata*, or frog orchid *Orchis morio*, three plants which before 'improvement' were quite common in old grassland. Cowslip is uncommon in the plains, and is usually to be found in nooks among thorns; most of the Forest's cowslip is in the woods, although it is not normally a woodland plant, and the best colony (in 1987) is in a part of Emblem's Coppice where replanting failed. Although cowslip easily succumbs to 'improvement', it is one of the first plants to come back.

The plains should be the most notable part of the Forest for butter-flies. They offer a now rare combination of the specific plants on which caterpillars feed, together with the shelter of pollards and scrubs. Butterflies, alas, are much less notable than they used to be. The uncommon grassland species Dingy Skipper *Erynnis tages*, Grizzled Skipper *Pyrgus malvae*, and Green Hairstreak *Callophrys rubi* have not been seen for thiry years. The Essex Skipper *Thymeli-cus lineola*, a speciality of this area, is still present. Among rare moths, *Eustrotia uncula* (Silver Hook) used to be present in marshy places. There is a recent record of *Rheumaptera cervinalis* (Scarce Tissue), surprising since its larva feeds on barberry – maybe a culti-vated *Berberis* in someone's garden.[256] Grassland butterflies and moths have generally declined in England, and I fear that, as in many other places, 'improvement' destroyed the food-plants. How-ever, the Forest still has glow-worms, an insect of unimproved grass-land which feeds on snails.[268]

The pasture of the Forest, although less well preserved than the woods, is a precious survival of a type of grassland that is rarely preserved at all. After thirty years of sympathetic management and fairly heavy grazing it is well on the way to recovery from 'improvement'. Whether it will ever recover all its beauty and meaning is doubtful. I expect that some of the less common grasses, clovers and sedges will increase, and maybe bee orchid will come back; but I doubt whether we shall see again catmint, which has become rare all over England.

The gravel-pit   Gravel-digging went on for over 200 years, but for such a litigious activity (Chapter 5) there is surprisingly little to show today. Shallow pits, no more than 15 feet deep, cover the slopes above the Shermore Brook from Gravel-pit Coppice to the London Road. Probably they began next to the coppice, already so called by 1639, and reached their greatest extent in the 1820s. They may have extended under the present delta of the Shermore Brook. Some areas are of sandy gravel and some of nearly pure sand.

The total area of pit was at least ten acres, but part of this has been buried by the growth of the delta or planted with pines by the Houblons. Much was lost to scrub or 'improved' grassland. There now remains about one acre of distinctive grassland on dry slopes at the north end of the pit, which were probably too steep to be 'improved'.

The turf here is short and sparse, and where the soil is thin the grasses are often annual, for example *Aira caryophyllea*, *Bromus thominii* and *Vulpia bromoides*. Annual herbs include parsley-piert (*Aphanes* sp.), the little chickweed *Moenchia erecta*, and formerly that curious plant *Montia fontana*. Low-growing perennials include harebell *Campanula rotundifolia*, wild thyme *Thymus drucei*, mouse-ear hawkweed *Hieracium pilosella*, the little sorrel *Rumex tenui-folius*, dog violet *Viola canina*, and the little buttercup *Ranunculus parviflorus*. Unlike the general grasslands, this includes several mosses such as *Polytrichum piliferum* and the remarkable *Rhodo-bryum roseum*, besides the liverworts *Calypogeia fissa* and *Cephalo-ziella starkei*. Here are to be found the only lichens in the Forest that grow on the ground, *Cladonia furcata* and *C. rangiformis*.

This is a beautiful miniature grassland of which most of the species are an inch or two high. They all, especially the mosses and lichens, have very little power to withstand shade; they will grow only in places where for some reason taller plants are kept out. It is the only patch of such vegetation in Essex; several of the species, such as *Moenchia* and *Rhodobryum*, are known nowhere else in the county. (Because many species are both rare and small they have no vernacular names.)

This plant community is closely akin to the 'grass-heaths' of the Suffolk Breckland, with dry shallow infertile soils and a short turf cropped by rabbits and sheep. They illustrate the ecological principle that the greatest variety of plants is to be found in rather harsh environments, where no one species gets the upper hand as it often does in places where growth is easier. Most of the Hatfield gravel-pit plants are to be found in the classic Breckland 'grass-heath' of Lakenheath Warren. At Lakenheath the soil is extremely variable, and there are seven different kinds of grass-heath.[269] Something alike evidently happens at Hatfield, where I have found the soil to vary from pH 4.9 to 7.8 within a few yards. (Although most sands are acidic, part of the sand here reaches pH 7.8, as alkaline as anything in the Forest; possibly it is percolated by water coming from boulder-clay.) Chalkland plants, such as the hawkweed and the little sedge *Carex caryophyllea*, can be found a few yards from plants of acid soils such as the *Rumex* and the *Polytrichum*. The well-developed anthills provide little environments of their own, and species such as *Cladonia rangiformis* grow on them.

Outliers of grass-heath can be seen in other places, such as the Sandlings of east Suffolk; but why should the only Essex 'Breckland' be here? What keeps out taller vegetation is the dry gravelly infertile soils, the steep south-west-facing slopes which are warmer and more droughty still, together with a history of severe grazing.

Was this plant community created by digging the pit? We might expect that a few species might have got here, by one method of dispersal or another, since the pit was worked, but there has hardly been enough time for a whole suite of grass-heath plants, many of them rather rare, to appear on this small spot. Probably they are a relict of a time when grazing was very severe, and especially when there were sheep on the Forest. Until the nineteenth century the slopes of the Shermore Brook may have been lined with short sheep-grazed turf with anthills, a possible habitat for Breckland plants on a much larger scale. Since 1857 this habitat has shrunk through reduced grazing, growth of bushes, and fertilizing. It now survives only on the pit, and we are lucky that it survives at all. Had the 'improvers' been a little more diligent in getting into hummocky terrain, or had bushes extended into the pit, the special plants would have vanished.

The main pit is managed as a nature reserve with the collaboration of Essex Naturalists' Trust. It is now fenced off from the rest of the Forest; this is perhaps a pity, since it discourages cattle and picnickers, both of whom (in moderation) favour the special plants by causing minor disturbance.

The lake and its delta The principal fen in the Forest, known as the Marsh, is where the Shermore Brook enters the lake. The lake when first made was bigger than it is now (Plate 2), and may have been enlarged by gravel-digging. The Brook drains arable land with some loess in the soils; whenever there is a spate it brings down silt which settles in the lake to form a delta. The delta now acts, to some degree, as a replacement for the 'low Bogg and Rushly ground' submerged when the lake was made. For many years it has been managed as a nature reserve through Essex Naturalists' Trust.

For the first 170 years the lake filled up only slowly, perhaps partly with peat, but later it has silted more rapidly. This was probably aggravated by disturbance upstream in the making of Stansted Airport (1942–3 and 1954–6), and by the destruction, soon after, of Taylor's Wood – which had covered about a third of the catchment – and the ploughing of its silty soils. In biological terms the shrinkage of the lake is no great loss, but it matters to the National Trust, for much of the Forest's revenue comes from visitors paying to fish. In 1959–60 the lake was dredged and the spoil spread in front of the Shell House (an area which still has very impoverished grassland).[270] This remedy was only temporary, and in 1980 the dam was heightened, raising the water-level by about three feet. This alteration was much criticized: it killed a number of fine oaks, by cutting off the western arm of the lake it spoilt an eighteenth-century landscape feature, and it drowned a sedge-bed in which the very local moth *Biselachista serricornis* lived. It too will not be a permanent solution. However, the effect on the delta vegetation was not as great as had been feared. There has been some benefit by discouraging the young trees which were overrunning the drier parts of the fen.

The delta is noted for its bird life, particularly ducks. It is one of the few places in inland Essex still haunted by snipe, those evocative birds of the wild fenland. It has reed-, sedge- and grasshopper-warblers and reed-buntings.[271]

The vegetation is very varied, with a long list of species. The lake has a tall fringe of bulrush *Typha latifolia*, bur-reed *Sparganium neglectum* (a rare Essex plant), gipsywort, fleabane and willow-herb. Further back are huge beds of the handsome sedge *Carex pseudocyperus*; I have never seen so much of it. There is a small reedbed. Along the main channel of the brook is a bed of bulrushes and the umbellifer *Berula erecta*. Away from the lake the vegetation becomes less dense, with the willowherb *Epilobium palustre* (rare and decreasing in Essex) and the horsetails *Equisetum palustre* and *E. fluviatile*; here the sodden ground is carpeted with mosses, notably *Calliergon cuspidatum* and *Mnium elatum* (*seligeri*), very rare in Essex.

The central part of the delta has been fenced off from cattle for many years. Outside the fence, around the edges, the ground is hummocky, with boggy hollows fed by springs alternating with drier ridges; it is difficult to distinguish natural landforms from gravel-diggings. In this zone are two of the Forest's rarities: the little sedge *Blysmus compressus*, at its last Essex locality, and *Triglochin palustre*.

The delta is famous for marsh orchids. There are three species, *Dactylorhiza fuchsii* (with small pale spotted inflorescences, also in woodland), *incarnata* (with massive salmon-pink spikes) and *praetermissa* (with purplish pyramids of flowers), and the three possible hybrids. These can be seen in flower in June in the shorter vegetation. Here they have somewhat decreased in recent years.

From this habitat are recorded a number of rare and local insects, such as the moth *Phalonidia manniana*, whose caterpillar feeds inside the stems of mint and gipsywort,[272] and the fly *Phaonia atriceps*, which breeds in the leaf-sheaths of bulrush.[273] The rare sedge-feeding leaf-beetle *Donacina thalassina* was found in 1949.[274]

The fen is alkaline, with pH around 7.8. *Blysmus* grows in a peaty hollow with pH 6.8. It is amazing to find an old record of cotton-grass *Eriophorum angustifolium*, an unmistakable plant of acid moorland; this has not been seen since 1860, and is now known in Essex only from bogs in Epping Forest.

233

The Shermore Brook fens   The Brook once had beautiful meanders and was lined with fens, but these vanished when it was canalized into 'Public Drain No. 1' under the Enclosure Act. The banks are mostly bushed-over, and there is little opportunity for aquatic plant life. However, there is a second fen around Old Woman's Weaver, the silted-up pond by Dowsett's Coppice. All along the course of the Brook springs break out in little hollows, doubtless from pockets of gravel, and each of these makes another pocket of fen.

These fens also are full of sedges and other aquatic plants, and the three orchids and their hybrids now flourish better than in the delta (Plate 22). Moderate cattle-grazing probably encourages them by keeping down their competitors.

Woodside Green   The green is grazed (under common-rights) separately from the Forest. Alas, it bears the marks of severe 'improvement', and has little but coarse grasses and a few thistles.

The Scrubs

Scrub is young woodland. Land, unless cultivated or grazed, turns into scrub in a few years and into woodland in a few years more. The scrubs in the Forest result from a *temporary* lack of grazing.

Every year tree seeds are brought, mainly by birds, into the plains, and some of them germinate. For instance in 1981, when there were no cattle on the Forest, oaklings sprang up all over the plains, but all were eaten when cattle returned in 1982. There have evidently been many periods when grazing has been insufficient to consume all the young trees. If trees escape for five years or so, they will survive and grow into scrub even if grazing returns. Areas that are less grazed than others turn into scrub first. The Forest thus has scrubs of different ages.

Even the oldest scrubs differ from woodland in having no defined boundaries and in never having been coppiced. Their trees are different. We have seen that oak is at an advantage in wood-pasture. So is hawthorn, although it is very edible until the spines harden. Hawthorn and oak are the two pioneer trees which begin the scrubs. Other trees come in later, but even the oldest scrubs seldom have hornbeam.

Soils under the older scrubs are acidified nearly as much as under woodland (pH 3.7 to 5.9).

Younger scrubs   The 1940 air photographs show that much of the present scrub did not then exist. Most of the increase has been through infilling of gaps in older scrubs and expansion at their edges; for example, the two giant pollard oaks between Emblem's and Collin's Coppices, now surrounded by scrub, were open to the plain on their east sides in 1940. The increase happened soon after and was at an end by 1960; air photographs taken then show the scrubs with sharp edges, held in check by cattle.[270]

Two earlier ages can be distinguished in the 1940 photographs: one of hawthorns then just visible, the other of smallish bushes. None of these are indicated on the 1915 Ordnance Survey. I infer that in the National Trust period there have been three phases of scrub formation, around the years 1925, 1935 and 1945, but none since. Together these nearly doubled the previous area of scrub.

A typical young scrub is on the northern half of the site of Doodle-Oak Coppice. The Ordnance Survey up to 1915 shows this area as a plain, but many timber trees survived from the former coppice. By 1940 the trees had gone – presumably felled in 1924 – and their places were taken by two generations of scrub. Half a century on, this is a dense dark hawthorn-wood, with a few young oaks towering above it and almost nothing growing beneath. The hawthorns of *c*.1925 are spreading trees, with those of *c*.1935 crowded into gaps between them. The oaks, by now quite big trees, are presumably of *c*.1925. (The south of the site of the coppice, with few trees in 1915, is still grassland.)

Older scrubs   The scrub south of the Doodle Oak is about 200 years old; it is shown on the 1804 Ordnance Survey. There has been much later infilling, and the trees are of various ages. Hawthorn and oak are no longer predominant. Trees of the later succession have appeared, with areas of maple, hazel and wild cherry and some elm invasion. Embedded in the scrub are pollard maples and the occasional pollard hawthorn and crab; these were once free-standing in the plain. Great briars climb into the canopy. Old as this scrub is, it has no sign of having been coppiced, except for a few big maple stools which may have grown from the bases of collapsed pollards. It is less dark than the young scrub; it is beginning to acquire woodland herbs, and there is even a patch of dog's-mercury.

Old scrubs in the south of the Forest, of similar age, have much ash and elm; although palatable, these have grown up in the protection of the thorns. Hornbeam is still rare, although there are many pollard hornbeams among others embedded in the scrub. These scrubs are not quite continuous, and in their glades is some of the best old grassland in the Forest; cattle still find their way to it.

Meaning of the scrubs Writers often despise scrub as if it were useless, but it is an essential part of a wooded Forest. Woods of thorns were once an important asset. In a Forest on calcareous soils hawthorn shelters the next generation of trees (timber or pollard) growing up in the plains. Holly does the same in the New Forest and other Forests on acid soils. An Act of Parliament in 1768 whipped and imprisoned him who should maliciously damage holly or thorn.

Although the earliest explicit mention of scrubs is in 1639 (p. 93), they undoubtedly existed long before. All the old trees on the plains (except former coppices) must have grown up in the protection of scrubs that are no longer there. I infer that there has been a slow cycle of scrubs forming in one place and disappearing from another.

How scrubs disappear is not known. The National Trust has grubbed out small areas, and the Houblons may have grubbed others. In earlier times, 'bushes' were commonly cut in the Forest, and grazing after felling may have turned scrub into grassland. Even-aged hawthorns may possibly fall to pieces of themselves as they get old.

Scrubs are an important habitat for birds and insects, and a refuge for shy animals. They deserve to be perpetuated in a way which respects the essential nature of scrub. New areas of scrub need to be formed from time to time – new *areas* of scrub, not expansion at the edges of existing ones, which does disproportionate damage to the grassland. Existing scrubs should occasionally be returned to grassland, preserving any pollards and *old* thorns within them.

Planted Trees on Plains

Planted trees are more prominent on plains than in woods. As we have seen, records go back to the 1750s.

Of planted trees shown on the 1757 map, only the south avenue lived long. It is still shown as an avenue on the 1915 Ordnance Survey, but had disappeared by 1941; the elms were carried off either by the 1924 felling or by Elm Disease soon after. One original elm, and many suckers, were still alive in 1987. This was an avenue of East Anglian elms, an unusual kind of elm for planting at that time. (The row of magnificent East Anglian elms which used to stand outside Round Coppice, dated by annual rings to 1795, may also have been planted.)

On the dam of the western arm of the lake are some giant Scots pines and three magnificent yews, which must date from the extension of the dam in 1757 or soon after. One of the yews had a girth of 14 ft 7 in. in 1987; it cannot be more than 230 years old, and should be remembered by anyone who supposes that big yews must always be of fabulous age.

In the unenclosed Forest, there were legal difficulties about planting in the plains. Most of the horsechestnuts and other planted trees appear to date from soon after this restraint was removed in 1857. Those on the Warren, though I have no tree-ring date, are shown as big trees on a photograph published in 1907;[140] but they can hardly be more than 130 years old, for horsechestnut is a short-lived tree. They are now of awesome size and are beginning to fall to pieces. John VII Archer Houblon was excessively fond of horsechestnuts, but planted some beeches, occasional Turkey-oak, and a few more interesting trees. These include two black walnuts on the Warren (one fell in the 1987 storm) – one of the few eastern North American trees to be grown successfully in England. By the west end of the lake is an Oriental plane: a fine specimen of a tree, at home in a Cretan village square, but incongruous in an English Forest.

In the 1930s a grove of oaks was planted in the eastern plain, and in the 1960s small plantations of horsechestnut, oak, beech, sweet-chestnut and Scots pine elsewhere. These were no doubt well meant, but the species and situations seem to be chosen at random: of what possible beauty or use is a *thicket* of horsechestnuts? Such plantations made holes in the fabric of the Forest, including places where there would have been gravelly grassland.

Grazing and its Effects

In 1987 Hatfield Forest was inhabited by an estimated 170 fallow deer, including 40 bucks which take a summer holiday. There were 290 head of cattle on the Forest from May to October (plus 70 on Woodside Green). How does the impact of these animals compare with that in the New Forest, studied in detail by C.R.Tubbs and R.J.Putman (*NF*; *GTE*)?

Hatfield Forest comprises about 490 acres of coppices and 420 acres of plains (including scrubs); to which we should add Wall and Monk Woods (110 acres). Assuming, roughly, that deer derive their sustenance from all over the Forest, but cattle only from the plains, this works out at one deer to 5.9 acres and one beast to 1.4 acres.

The New Forest comprises 9600 acres of (undemarcated) woods, 39,000 acres of plains, and 21,000 acres of plantations. The plains include large areas of heath and bog and small areas of improved grassland. In 1985 the Forest was grazed by about 1300 cattle (mostly in summer) and 2400 ponies (all the year). Fallow deer are variously estimated at 1000 or 2000, and there are also small numbers of red, roe and sika deer. These figures work out at one beast to 30 acres of plain, one pony to 16 acres of plain, and roughly one deer to 45 acres of total area.

To equate the feeding of the different animals is not easy, but by any standard of comparison Hatfield is grazed at least five times as hard as the New Forest. This is most surprising, considering that the New Forest has a much more bitten-down appearance. Putman describes the impact of grazing there as 'colossal', and mentions the turf in the plains, cropped to a few millimetres high, and the absence of saplings or ground vegetation in the woods. Tubbs, while pointing out that not all effects of over-grazing are ecologically bad, shows that young trees have arisen in the past only when the stocking has fallen below about half of what it is now. In the New Forest most of the vegetation is less productive than the Hatfield grassland, and cattle and ponies congregate on the relatively small areas of improved grassland, but this can hardly account for so great a difference.

In the past, both Forests have been grazed more than at present. In the New Forest, in the last three centuries, there have been up to 5500 cattle, 2900 ponies, and supposedly at least 8000 deer, but not all at once; by Tubbs's reckoning the total amount of grazing has never been more than half as great again as it is now. In Hatfield there are said to have been up to 800 deer (fed, however, in winter) and some hundreds of sheep, as well as donkeys etc., in addition to what can hardly have been less than the present number of cattle, in a slightly bigger Forest. Probably the total grazing has, at times, been at least three times what it is now, but not continuously: there is evidence of a big expansion of scrub and of new trees in the plains in the late eighteenth century.

Grazing is an essential part of the Forest's working. It is particularly necessary for the small fens and the gravel-pit area, since it saves the smaller and less competitive herbs from being squeezed out by their stronger neighbours. The present stocking, which is probably not far above the minimum necessary to prevent trees from invading the plains, seems to be about right. However, there is much to be said for grazing the Forest harder in some years, as has happened in the past. It would be excellent if sheep could be brought back, at least to the drier parts of the plains. Tethered goats are now being tried in the gravel-pit.

11 Pollards and Ancient Trees

If the lord wishes to cut down in the forest any ancient oak which men call 'stock-oak' (*anciene chesne qe hom apelle Stokok*) he may leave the stump in length from the ground to the knee of a man, & the said John shall cut it down and its roots and shall take them away.

Customs of Hatfield Forest, thirteenth century[89]

The man of science and of taste ... will ... discover beauties in a tree which the others would condemn for its decay; he will rejoice when he finds two trees whose stems have long grown so near each other that their branches are become interwoven. ... Sometimes he will discover an aged thorn or maple at the foot of a venerable oak; these he will respect, not only for their antiquity, being perhaps coeval with the father of the forest, but knowing that the importance of the oak is comparatively increased by the neighbouring situation of these subordinate objects. ...

H. Repton, Observations on the Theory and Practice
of Landscape Gardening, 1803

Old trees are a rarity in civilized countries. In wildwood, trees in the latter half of their lives were presumably as common as trees in the earlier half. In Europe almost every tree is cut down when 'mature', at about one-third of its natural longevity, rather like a human population with compulsory euthanasia at age thirty. From Boulogne to Athens one rarely sees a tree more than 200 years old.

England (and Greece) are exceptions. With us, old trees, though uncommon, are less rare, and we have a tradition of using and appreciating them. They are to be found especially in Forests and other wood-pastures. We love their beauty and mystery; we paint their portraits and write verses in their honour and invest them with railings and plaques. Young trees look much alike; individuality develops with age. Each landscape of old trees has its own peculiar glamour, the product of its environment, the genetics of the trees, and its special management history. The ancient oaks of Sherwood Forest, of Moccas Park (Herefordshire), of Staverton Park (Suffolk), and of Hatfield Forest are all different.

Myth-makers have been busy here. We read that trees, like ourselves, have an allotted term of years to live out. Old trees are referred to in anthropomorphic terms of disrespect as 'coming to the end of their days' or 'senile', as if they were an anomaly in a well-ordered landscape. It is alleged that the landscape at large is full of trees all dating from the eighteenth century and now all in a 'geriatric' state. Writers repeat this nonsense without investigating how old trees really are or how long they live.

In reality, trees live for different times. A 200-year-old oak is in its early middle age, but a 200-year-old birch is unknown in England. Within a species, individuals perish by competition or catastrophe at very different ages. The October 1987 storm uprooted far more young than old trees; at Hatfield the ancient oaks were seldom much injured, but some oaks of less than a century were shattered. If we must be anthropomorphic, the battlefield is a better analogy than the almshouse.

A landscape without old trees lacks more than half the beauty and meaning of trees. It lacks three-quarters of the value of trees as a habitat. An old tree, especially a pollard, is a world of different habitats each with its special plants and animals: bats roosting in the hollow trunk; hole-nesting birds in smaller cavities; many special beetles and spiders in the red-rotted heartwood of the trunk; peculiar lichens on the ridges and beneath overhangs of old bark. Any old tree should be treasured, for ten thousand young trees do not provide these habitats. As we shall see, *a big dead tree is just as valuable a habitat as a living one*. There is a special importance in a place like Hatfield where there has been a *succession* of old trees.

Hatfield Forest is a special place for ancient trees. There are eight species of pollards: oak, ash, maple, hornbeam, elm, beech, hawthorn and crab. I know of nowhere else that has more than five. Maples and thorns are specially unusual. Pollard thorns have existed since Anglo-Saxon times, as place-names like Copthorne testify, but are now a great rarity. A few ancient thorns are still famous, like the Hethel Thorn in Norfolk, but Savernake Forest (Wiltshire) is the only other place where I have seen many, and Hatfield is probably the only place where a whole landscape of wonderful gnarled pollard thorns survives. Only a handful now remain of the pollards on Woodside Green, but there are still many pollard oaks, the relics of some kind of wood-pasture, on the nearby hillfort of Wallbury.

Old and Famous Trees at Hatfield

The Broad Oak Hatfield has been called Broad-Oak since 1136.[264] Robert the Bruce VII in c. 1295 exchanged a field, next to the manorial mill, which adjoined 'the Road which leads from Hatfield market up to the broad oak (*latam quercum*)'.[275] The mill lay west of the town (p. 67, Fig. 18), and the Broad Oak was therefore on or near Hatfield Heath.

This oak seems not to be recorded again, unless it was 'the great Oke at Hatfield Heath' sold for £5 in 1628.[198] Presumably a third famous oak gave rise to Dr William Allen's claim in the late seventeenth century that:

> Oake dont decai . . . as was proved in Sr Charles Barrington's Hatfield Oak, a great Tree for a landmark & Limet at the Conquest, and lasted until the Civil War and coming in of K. Charles before it was dead.[276]

There are still giant oaks in Hatfield: two immense pollards just outside the Forest on the Little Barrington Hall side, and a dozen in and around the park of the eighteenth-century Barrington Hall, presumably inherited from Hatfield Priory.

The Doodle Oak This, the most famous tree in the Forest and one of the two or three stoutest trees ever measured in England, stood in the plain just south of Doodle-Oak Coppice. Fanciful stories were told: it has been claimed to be the original Broad Oak, or 'mentioned in Domesday Book', or an Oak of Doom whereon offenders against Forest Law were hanged. (It is unreasonable that the parish should have been named after a tree in a remote corner; and to hang a medieval criminal on this, or any living, tree would have been a gross breach of etiquette and of somebody's right of gallows.) It is just possible that this was the lord's best oak in the Hatfield customal of 1328 (p. 77) – that the lord always chose the same tree and let the blacksmith choose any other. The Doodle Oak might have been about the right size in the later middle ages.

242

'Dowdle oke' was already a landmark in *c.* 1630 (p. 114). Salmon in 1740 says that the Doodle Oak

... covered a great deal of ground ... [it] looks as if fresh branches had grown out of the roots, as the others decayed, or were cut.[277]

There are two portraits. One, engraved in 1807, shows the oak with a short, hugely stout, pot-bellied trunk and a remarkably spreading crown (Fig. 34); it could originally have been a coppice stool, as Salmon implies. The figure in Loudon's *Arboretum*, 1838, also emphasizes the spreading habit. Loudon measured it as

42 ft in circumference at the base; in 1813, before a large portion of the trunk fell in, it was upwards of 60 ft.[279]

This girth is much bigger than any oak in England now; in Loudon's time it was exceeded only by Damory's Oak at Blandford (Dorset). Applying this measurement to the 1807 portrait would make the trunk 35–40 feet high. The oak seems not to have been an ordinary pollard, but could have been a 'giraffe-pollard', cut especially high. This is a style of medieval and Tudor pollarding, still visible in the oldest oaks of Windsor and Sherwood Forests and Staverton Park. The mention of 'topmost branches' for browsewood (p. 76) could refer to the practice.

The meaning of the name is uncertain. The Essex Field Club, venerating the relics of the tree in 1889, agreed that it had something to do with the dialect word *dool*, a boundary.[276] This cannot be true: the oak was not on a boundary, and the earliest spellings are of two syllables. Mrs J.Evans suggests to me, more plausibly, that the tree was named because it was shaped like a *doodlesack* or bagpipe. I cannot prove that this word was used in Jacobean Essex, but to judge by the 1807 picture the name would have been apt.

The Doodle Oak last produced green leaves in 1858; I speculate on whether this was connected with the draining of the Forest a few years before. Frederick Locker, a minor poet and relative of the Houblons, dropped tears in verse upon it.[281] The gigantic base, with one bough, stood into this century and was photographed.[140] Later it was apparently sawn down and tidied away.

In 1949 the remains of the stump were excavated by Maynard Greville, who found it to have been 49 feet round at the base. He 'counted 101 rings to 10 inches of timber taken well inside the stump', and calculated that the whole tree would have had about 850 annual rings, or more if it grew slowly in its old age. It would have dated from about AD 950.[282]

We have not seen the last of the Doodle Oak. Scanty remains of the oak could still be found, buried in the ground, in my time. Beside them is a young oak, now about 5 feet in girth, which Greville claimed to be a coppice shoot 'attached to the old root'. This tree is now reproducing the short stature and spreading boughs of its original. One oak thus takes us back to the days of Eric Bloodaxe and King Edmund the Magnificent.

A giant of the nineteenth century

Ap. 20, 1819. The large oak tree on Tukely forest, opposite Basingbourn, was taken down this day. There were upwards of 300 people attending to see its fall. It contained 8 loads at 4 feet cube round measure.[a] It was sold for £120 to Mr. Riddington of Harlow, with the top and bark. The tree was afterwards sold for £200, taken to London, and used for the principal crane-post in St. Catherine's docks.

Note by Mr Archer Houblon[140]

[a] Error for 40 cubic feet to the load.

Fig. 34 The Doodle Oak in *c.* 1807.[278] The caption is erroneous.

We must imagine an oak with a trunk 40 feet long and from 3 to 4 ft in diameter – a gigantic tree, though there are at least four bigger in the Forest today. It would have been on the north edge, by the west end of Takeley Street half-village. This was a time to sell big oaks: the price of oak-trees was higher (in real terms) than ever before or since (*AW*). Mr Houblon made rather a bad bargain. The average price of *ordinary-sized* oak-trees was nearly £10 per load, so he got only 50% extra for this being an exceptional tree. (The biggest oak ever known in Britain, the Golanos Oak in Monmouthshire, was felled in 1810; it produced eight times the timber of the Hatfield oak; it fetched only £405 standing, but its purchaser was the Navy, who were bad payers.[279])

Notable Trees Today

Which is the biggest tree in the Forest? Possibly the magnificent oak north of the Shell House. Its trunk, tapering like a lighthouse, rises smoothly to a height of nearly 25 ft, when it divides into eight limbs each as big as an ordinary oak tree. High on one of these limbs is a gigantic gall – a sphere of solid wood six feet across. The shape of the tree shows that this is one of the few timber trees surviving from Warren Coppice. The tall underwood which once surrounded it, destroyed over a century ago, prevented it from branching in the lower 25 ft but allowed it to form a crown above this height.

To compare it with other trees, we may take the 'girth at breast height', 20 ft 0 in. at 5 ft above the ground (in 1986). This is not specially enormous, but few oaks of this diameter have so long a bole. The volumes of trees are estimated by the seventeenth-century rule publicized by Mr E. Hoppus in 1736 and still widely used: the square of one-quarter the girth, multiplied by the length, gives the volume.[284] The average girth above the taper is 18 ft 7 in., which (subtracting the bark thickness) comes to a volume of nearly 500 cubic feet of timber. The branches amount to over 300 cubic feet; the total volume comes to some 820 cubic feet or 20½ loads. This is bigger than any oak, except possibly the Doodle Oak, that has ever been in Hatfield Forest in historic times. It is over twice as big as the 1819 oak. In the middle ages this oak would have been almost unbelievable; the smith's second-best oak in the Forest is unlikely to have been more than one-tenth its size.

How old is the Shell House oak? A nearby tree was felled many years ago, and its annual rings showed that it started life *c.*1690. The present tree is much bigger, but its huge crown of branches will have encouraged faster growth, and I estimate that it is probably of the same date and now some 300 years old. (I counted 215 rings in a high branch broken in October 1987.) It is now in middle age; it seems not to have suffered from the raising of the water-level in the lake; it should live for some centuries more and will become one of the biggest oaks in England.

In the scrub in the south-east of the Forest is a pollard oak which, though difficult to compare, is probably bigger still. This giant has a girth at 4 ft high of 21 ft 11 in. – it is 7 ft in diameter. It has been pollarded higher than usual, with a bolling 16 ft high and five limbs each the size of a big oak. The calculated volume, for what it is worth, is over 1000 cubic feet. Being a pollard, this oak will have grown very slowly for the first years of each pollarding cycle. It is probably about 500 years old.

Another giant oak, probably not a pollard, stands just outside the eastern end of Beggar's Hall Coppice. It has a girth at breast height of 20 ft 1 in., but its lack of height makes it no more than 430 cubic feet. The pair of huge pollard oaks between Emblem's and Collin's Coppices (Plate 13) are 19 ft 0 in. and 17 ft 1 in. in girth. They have very large crowns and have probably grown rather fast since last pollarded; they may be about 400 years old.

An ash pollard west of London Bridge has a girth of 21 ft 1 in.; it has decayed to a shell now reduced to two separate fragments. A maple in the south of the Forest has a girth of 13 ft 4 in., and is probably the biggest in England. Equally remarkable are an elder near Round Coppice of 4 ft girth, and a clematis stem of 2 ft 3 in. girth in the overgrown plain just outside Dowsett's.

Pollards and Pollarding

Pollard cycles Pollards belonged to the owners of the adjoining coppices: from 1600 onwards, to Barringtons and Morleys and their successors. They formed part of the woodcutting rights, and were used on occasion to provide browsewood for the deer. In Epping Forest much of the pollarding was done by commoners (*EF*), but there were no common-rights of woodcutting at Hatfield.

On the organization of pollarding, the only document that I have is a note in the survey of *c.* 1690:

> The Pollard trees on [Woodside] green of which the lops and tops are felled once in 12 years. . . .   £13.00[138]

The felling cycle for pollards was seldom written down, and was probably not thought of as a *regular* cycle: with pollarding it is possible to cut individual trees here and there, instead of whole areas at once as with coppicing.

A pollard's history is recorded in its annual rings. Each time it is cut, the leafage is suddenly reduced to almost nothing and then gradually recovers. A section of the bolling therefore shows a sequence of sudden drops in ringwidth followed by gradual increases. On this is superimposed the usual, more or less random, pattern of good and bad years which can – if the tree has been long dead – be used to give an exact date to the sequence of rings.

Fig. 35 shows the ringwidths in a great oak which was sawn down, probably in 1924, and has been lying ever since under bushes in the southern scrubs. This tree began life in *c.* 1643 (about 24 rings are missing from the hollow centre) and was made into a pollard at about 30 years of age. It was cut seven times in all, at intervals of from 12 to 36 years. The last pollarding was in 1802, after which the tree gradually developed a full-sized crown and resumed 'normal' growth. Another big oak in the southern scrubs, uprooted in the storm of 1976 and later removed, had begun in 1662; it was first pollarded at 54 years old and thereafter at 11- to 24-year intervals; the sixth and last cutting was in 1803.

The oak pollards, therefore, were normally cut at about the same interval as the coppices, but there is no suggestion of a regular rotation, and sometimes they were left much longer. (The pollards I have examined in Epping Forest indicate a cycle of about 13 years, and in Hainault of 18–25 years.)

The end of pollarding   Pollarding became unfashionable and was partly discontinued by the Houblons. On the evidence of annual

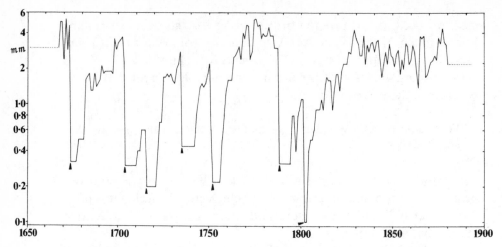

Fig. 35 Widths of annual rings of an oak pollard bolling in the south of the Forest. The tree was pollarded in 1674, 1704, 1716, 1735, 1752, 1788 and 1802; each occasion is marked by a sudden drop in ringwidth followed by gradual recovery. These cycles are superimposed on the normal fluctuations of good and bad years due to weather and caterpillars. The last 40 annual rings, mainly sapwood, have rotted away; it is nevertheless possible to determine the exact dates by recognizing the good and bad years. I am indebted to Dr Gavin Simpson and Dr Martin Bridge for supplying a standard set of ringwidths with which to do this, and to Professor John Birks for help with the measurement.

rings, the oaks west of the Shermore Brook were last cut between 1803 and 1821. East of the Shermore, where the trees were in Barrington hands until the mid-1830s, the oaks (and the few elms) were last cut between 1812 and about 1837. John VII Archer Houblon probably stopped pollarding oaks when he acquired the tree-rights. Lady Alice Archer-Houblon, 75 years later, could deny that there had been pollarding! Evidence for other species is less clear. Lawrence Sisitka finds that the hornbeams on the eastern plains were pollarded up to the 1920s. West of the Shermore I have found a hornbeam last cut c.1855 and a maple c.1845.

Pollards as they are now   Counting pollards is not easy: many are hidden in scrubs, and sometimes (especially with hawthorn) it is difficult to decide whether a particular tree is a pollard. I tried to count the pollards (except hawthorn) in the 1970s, and Mr Harry

Lamb made a more complete count in 1987; together we estimate that there are about 600 pollards in all (Table 5).

Table 5   Pollards in Hatfield Forest

	Original plains	Site of three eastern coppices	Total
Hawthorn	273	3	273
Hornbeam	15 + 9	131 + 2	144 + 12
Maple	48 + 10	19	49 + 12
Oak	17 + 7	58	73 + 7
Ash	25 + 3	1	28
Beech	2 + 1	—	2 + 1
Lineage Elm	1	0 + 2	1 + 2
Crab	2	—	2
TOTAL	**360 + 29**	**212 + 4**	**572 + 33**

The added figures comprise dead pollards and others lost since 1970. The count includes a few pollards excluded from the Forest in 1857 and still alive outside it.

The pollards in the east of the Forest are derived from three coppices lost in the early eighteenth century (Plate 17). Most of them appear to be the originals, now nearly 300 years old; a few are double at the base where they come from the previous coppice stools (Plate 12). Elsewhere many of the bollings are much older than this and some younger; the youngest are probably of c.1800. Most of the huge pollard oaks are probably of the sixteenth century, but some may be medieval. The biggest are not necessarily the oldest; very ancient oaks have a small head of branches in comparison with the diameter of the bolling.

The ex-coppice pollards comprise much more hornbeam, and less ash and maple, than those in the pre-1700 plains. Evidently they grew up in coppices which (like the surviving coppices adjacent) contained much hornbeam. Since hornbeam is slow to invade scrubs (p. 234) it is not surprising to find it scarce among the pollards that are not derived from coppices.

A great curiosity is a giant beech in the southern scrubs (Plate 15). Most beeches in the Forest are clearly Houblon plantings, but this one appears to be a pollard (therefore likely to be indigenous) and is evidently of much greater age: the graffito 'RJ 1801' is still legible, hardly stretched, in its bark. The girth was 13 ft 5 in. in 1987. A bough has bent down to the ground and taken root. There are remains of a few other apparent beech pollards. Beech as we now know it is largely a tree-planters' tree. As a wild tree, before the eighteenth century, it was local and usually in wood-pastures on very acid and infertile soils. In Essex beech is still abundant in Epping Forest, and a few pollards remain in South Weald Park; but there are medieval records in Writtle Forest and on other South Essex hilltops where there is now only planted beech (*AW*). Although the Hatfield clays are not an obvious beech site, the balance of evidence is that these are the last of a third native Essex population of the tree.

Hawthorn pollards are rather inconspicuous; they were not recognized until the 1970s. Each small patch of scrub on the central plain contains an ancient gnarled thorn, usually split and fallen in different directions but very much alive (Plate 16). Careful search reveals that these patriarchal thorns are pollards. They are surrounded by younger thorns and elder-bushes, the result of birds sitting on the boughs of the parent tree. The original thorns have lost the shaggy bark of middle-aged hawthorns and are covered in lichens.

Hawthorn is surprisingly long-lived. The Hethel Thorn has been a famous ancient tree since before 1765.[279] In Heveningham Park (Suffolk) there are thorns like the Hatfield ones, marked as 'Ancient Thorn' on Lancelot Brown's 'improvement' plan of 1781 and still there two centuries later. Pollard hawthorns are present on both the Morley and the Barrington sides of the Forest. Since they are almost absent from former coppices, I infer that nearly all of them are over 300 years old. Historians tempted to rely on documents alone should note that this very distinctive feature of the Forest has no written record whatever.

The Wildlife of Ancient Trees

Ancient trees are themselves wildlife, and display the full range of genetic variation which is less easy to distinguish in younger trees. For example the hornbeams near Bush End, especially those longest uncut, are all different in habit: some grow upright, some horizontally, and others in curves. (The clusters of twigs, 'witches'-brooms', on some hornbeams are attributed to a parasitic fungus, *Exoascus carpini*.)

The study of ancient trees as a habitat for wildlife is relatively recent, and much of it is specialized. A book has been written on special lichens and insects (*PW*). But it will be many years before all kinds of wildlife have been investigated for a place like Hatfield. Ancient trees are easily recognized as a habitat for the three species of woodpecker and for hawfinches. Anyone in the Forest at dusk will appreciate the abundance of bats, but to find out more about them, or even which species there are, is not easy. The old trees are full of fungi, especially brackets such as the brilliant yellow *Laetiporus sulphureus* on oak and the white *Tyromyces lacteus* on hornbeam. The fungi in turn are hosts for many specialized insects. Some live in the fruit-bodies; others depend on the condition known as 'red rot' produced by certain fungi in the heartwood of oak and hawthorn.

Mistletoe   Ancient trees harbour the mistletoe which is a wonder of Hatfield Forest – perhaps the greatest stronghold in Britain of this awesome plant. Sprouting as it does mysteriously out of another tree, mistletoe is sacred all over Europe, even in lands such as Scotland where it does not grow. Here it is abundant on ancient hawthorns and maples in the plains (Plate 19). It is rather inconspicuous, and only in March, when the 'golden bough' of mistletoe stands out from afar, can its profusion be appreciated. According to Lawrence Sisitka, most of the mistletoe in the Forest is male and has no berries.

Mistletoe is not uncommon in south and middle England, but usually on cultivated trees, especially apple, hybrid lime and hybrid poplar, where people have often sown it. Hatfield Forest is exceptional in that mistletoe and its hosts are both wild. I have never seen it elsewhere on maple. It is not entirely confined to ancient trees. It grows occasionally on hybrid poplar and once on a horsechestnut (my only record anywhere for that host), and has been observed on ash. Once I found it on a maple in Beggar's Hall Coppice – the only time I have heard of mistletoe in a *wood* in England. Mistletoe is specially sacred when growing on oak; this has never been recorded at Hatfield, though it once grew on oaks in Epping Forest.[285]

251

Beetles and other invertebrates   Apart from butterflies and moths, Forest insects were little known until 1973, when A.A. Allen began studying the beetles; this was followed by visits by K.N.A. Alexander in 1986 and A.P. Foster in 1987, who have kindly allowed me to make use of their records, notes and conclusions. These visits, and a few other records, are only a beginning, but already it is clear that the Forest is of national importance for the special insects of ancient trees. The only comparable site in Essex is Epping Forest.

For example, in a fallen oak bough was found the black click beetle *Procraerus tibialis*, which lives (adults and larvae) in rotten wood, mainly red-rotted oak. This species is confined to ancient wood-pastures including Sherwood, Savernake and Windsor Forests. The *British Red Data Book* lists it as 'Vulnerable'.[286] A related rare species, *Ischnodes sanguinicollis*, also in Epping Forest, lives here in the mouldering heartwood of a particular ancient maple. The rare *Xyleborus dryographus*, in contrast, lives in freshly-dead timber. Flying around hornbeam pollards at dusk were many adult *Prionocyphon serricornis*, a small brown beetle. Its larvae develop in wet rot-holes in trees and may live on the larvae of various flies. This is another *Red Data Book* insect, confined (or almost so) to ancient wood-pasture. The pollards themselves are bored by the exit-holes of a wood-eating longhorn beetle, *Leptura scutellata*, hitherto found mainly in wood-pasture beech. The ordinary visitor may notice bases of fallen trees riddled with the big holes of the Lesser Stag-beetle, *Dorcus parallelipipedus*, a relatively common insect.

Many of these beetles have even more specialized ways of life: they require, not just a particular kind of tree, but a specific niche among all the crannies and cavities that an old tree provides. Most of these habitats come from decay, and do not occur at all in young or 'mature' trees; they start to appear about halfway through a tree's natural life-span, but earlier in a pollard. For example, the rare beetle *Cicones variegata* lives in dry hornbeam rotted by the fungus *Ustulina vulgaris*. The local *Ctesias serrata* goes with spiders' webs under loose bark, and feeds on the spiders' leavings. *Aulonium trisulcum* specializes in eating the grubs of the elm bark-beetles that transmit Elm Disease. Beetles that eat bracket-fungi include *Litargus connexus* and *Triplax russica*; *Anisotoma humeralis* lives on the fungi hidden behind dead bark.

Dr Paul Harding has listed 185 species of beetle associated, to differing degrees, with places where there has been a continuity of old trees (*PW*). Eighteen have been found at Hatfield (including all those named except *Dorcus*, *Litargus* and *Anisotoma*), and there are doubtless many others to be discovered. According to Dr Alexander, the false-scorpion *Chernes cimicoides*, common under dead bark at Hatfield, is also special to ancient wood-pasture; so is the carnivorous bug *Xylocoris cursitans*. Also in this category is the tree-living ant, *Lasius brunneus*, which nests in hornbeam pollards; it may have yet more specialized insects living in its nests (*PW*).

There are records of two very rare flies, *Paraclusia tigrina* which goes with big trunks in wood-pasture (found by D.K.Clements in 1986) and *Astiosoma rufifrons* which goes with old bonfire sites and sawdust piles (found by D.A.Smith).

Lichens   Lichen experts have been visiting Hatfield Forest for a century. The first list was published by E.M.Holmes in 1890,[287] a second list in 1924,[288] and a third by K.L.Alvin in 1958.[289] Others who have been to the Forest more recently include F.Rose (1969) and J.F.Skinner.[290] To collate the lists is difficult because lichenologists fail to agree about nomenclature.

By my reckoning, 109 species have been found, of which probably 103 were on bark or wood – one of the longest lists for Eastern England. In recent years ancient maples have been the most rewarding trees, followed closely by old ashes and oaks. Ancient hawthorns are quite rich, but mainly in species that grow on other trees too. Lichens occur also on the tall oak stools in Lodge Coppice and on elms and old elders. Hornbeam is rather poor.

There are a number of lichens associated with places where it is thought that there has been a continuity of old *trees*, rather as oxlip and other herbaceous plants are associated with ancient *woodland* (*PW*). In contrast to the many specialized insects, only two of these lichens have been recorded here: *Enterographa crassa* and *Arthonia impolita* (*pruinosa*)[291] – both being not-very-conspicuous grey or whitish crusts on bark. But Hatfield, with its documented continuity of old trees, is not necessarily a counter-example to the theory. Only a fraction of the 600 pollards have been searched; and the Forest has suffered from acid rain.

Mosses and liverworts   In Eastern England, because of the dry climate, trees are not clothed with mosses as they are in the west. Hatfield Forest is relatively rich because of its old elders, sallows and maples, whose bark is less arid than that of other trees. (I doubt whether there are any pollard elders, because they do not live long enough.) On these trees are some of the last remaining Essex occurrences of *Orthotrichum affine* and the liverworts *Frullania tamarisci* and *F. dilatata*. (The best area is the part of Gravel-pit Coppice that was abandoned in the last century.) The next most interesting trees are fallen hornbeam pollards.

Acid rain   It has been known for 25 years that most lichens and a few mosses are sensitive to acid rain. They accumulate acids, especially sulphuric, in their tissues and are poisoned. Abundant lichens on trees mean that the atmosphere is clean and the rain no more acid than it naturally would be. As pollution increases, lichen species disappear in a definite order; a vast amount of research was done in the 1960s on using the absence of particular lichens as a measure of air and rain pollution. As can be seen in the middle of London, most trees appear to be quite unaffected by pollution severe enough to purge them of *all* lichens.

In medieval houses in Suffolk I have found wattle rods, made from underwood, which still have the bark on, encrusted with original lichens; these prove that in the middle ages lichens grew as freely on coppice poles as they still do in the clean rain of Somerset. The present scarcity of lichens in eastern England is thus attributable to acid rain, not to the dry climate (except in that a given amount of acidity does more damage where there is less rain to dilute it).

Acid rain has existed for as long as men have burnt coal: the sulphur in the coal turns to sulphuric acid in the rain. Already by 1620 old St Paul's Cathedral had been dissolved to such an extent that James I launched a public appeal for repairs.[292] Probably this was local, confined to areas down-wind of coal-burning cities like London and Cambridge. Only later, with the rise in population, the coming of the railways which burnt coal themselves and took it to remote places, and the dispersal of coal-burning industry, would acid rain have fallen on the countryside in general.

We have no record of the lichens of Hatfield Forest in its original state, but there are eighteenth-century records from Epping Forest, including the tree lungwort *Lobaria pulmonaria*. If this extremely sensitive species then still grew so near London, it would have grown at Hatfield too; the old trees would have been shaggy with this and other leafy lichens, their bark hardly visible, as trees still are in Devon.

By 1890 *Lobaria* was not recorded, but the shrubby *Ramalina fraxinea*, which is nearly as sensitive, was still common; Hatfield Forest was still only slightly polluted, as Dorset is today.[293] In 1924 a few species of the next lower degree of sensitivity still hung on, such as *Anaptychia ciliaris* and *Parmelia perlata*; but by then the flora was dominated by leafy lichens, especially other *Parmelia* species, which withstand a moderate degree of acid rain. By 1958 many of these had disappeared, and the list comprises more resistant species such as *Lecanora chlarotera* and *Hypogymnia physodes*; Hatfield Forest was getting quite polluted, although nowhere near as badly as Hayley Wood (Cambridgeshire) or south Essex today. The commonest lichen in the Forest is the notoriously resistant *Lecanora conizaeoides*. Lichens linger longest on trees with naturally alkaline bark, especially ash and the old maples which abound at Hatfield.

Why did acid rain come so late to Hatfield Forest? The south-east Midlands were industrialized late, producing a general background of brimstone, augmented by Bishop's Stortford three miles upwind. This had been a country town of about 2000 people, which would have burnt at least some coal since 1766, when it acquired a canal. It grew during the nineteenth century and became more dependent on coal after the railway came in 1842. By 1890 the population was 6600. It then grew much faster as commuters, burning coal (or oil, which is worse), came and lived there; the population reached 9000 by 1924 and doubled again by 1958. Fig. 36 shows that the degree of air pollution, as inferred from the lichen flora, matches very closely the growth of the town.

What has happened since 1958? The town has continued to grow – the population is now at least 23,000 – but the lichen flora is if anything a little better. *Parmelia saxatilis* still exists, and several more sensitive species, such as *Pertusaria albescens*, have been recorded in 1969 or since. Similar recoveries have been noted near other towns.[294] Probably the worst of the acid rain is now over in England; we now burn less coal and very little crude oil. The chief fuel in Bishop's Stortford is gas, which contains hardly any sulphur.

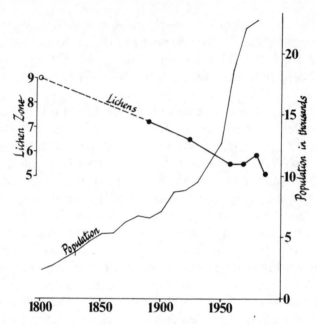

Fig. 36 Growth of the population of Bishop's Stortford and decline of the lichen flora of Hatfield Forest. The lichens are expressed in terms of the zones devised by D. L. Hawksworth and F. Rose,[293] each zone being defined by the more pollution-sensitive species present. Zone 9 implies a clean atmosphere with a mean of less than 30 micrograms per cubic metre of sulphur dioxide. Zones 8, 7, 6 and 5 correspond to 35, 40, 50 and 60 μg m^{-3} of SO$_2$.

Hatfield Forest is among the last refuges in Essex of three mosses, said to be sensitive to pollution: *Cryphaea heteromalla* on old elders, *Tortula laevipila* on old elms and maples, and *Ulota bruchii* on black-thorn and sallow.

Conservation

The 1876 Ordnance Survey, that miracle of cartography, appears to record every tree in the eastern plain, nearly all of which would have been pollards. The next two editions record the changes in these trees in 1896 and 1915, and the story can be taken down to the present with the help of air photographs. (In the other plains the trees are closer together and thus less likely all to have been

256

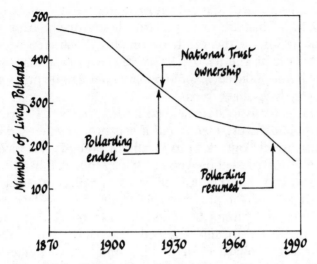

Fig. 37 Numbers of pollards in the east of Hatfield Forest (formed in *c.* 1700 out of Low Street, Middle and Bush-End Coppices). Predominantly hornbeam; the few hawthorn pollards are omitted.

mapped, and it is difficult to distinguish pollards from scrub and planted trees). The result (Fig. 37) indicates a steady loss of uncut pollards, which in the 1960s and 1970s amounted to about 1½% per annum. Most of this seems to have been natural wastage. Few ancient trees were felled in 1924 – probably they were not regarded as timber – and few seem to have succumbed to the great plague of defoliating caterpillars which came in the preceding years (*HW*).

In the early National Trust years the chief peril may have been tidying-up. When I first knew the Forest in 1971 it had less than its share of fallen boughs, and men were busy sawing down and burning the bases of trees broken by storms. Even the dead Doodle Oak seems not to have been spared. Happily, there has been less tidying lately.

In 1977 the National Trust, much to its credit, began to re-pollard the trees on the eastern plain. So far about 95 trees, nearly all hornbeams, have been cut. Of the hornbeams, 69% have grown; complete success was not to be expected with hornbeam after a 50-year interval. These trees had already begun to fall apart, and re-pollarding saved them from massacre by the gales of the 1980s.

257

Whether re-pollarding should be extended is not a simple question. It would be a mistake to re-pollard all the magnificent oaks last cut in the 1830s, or the mistletoe maples. Each tree needs to be considered on its merits, its likely response to pollarding or its longevity if not pollarded. Some pollards need to be protected from overtopping by younger trees.

The next stage is to start new pollards. It is over 150 years since any new pollards were made, and if it is not resumed the tradition will eventually die out. A Forest without pollards will have lost its point as a Forest; it will be well on its way to becoming an ordinary public park. It will also be less effective as a place of ancient trees: maiden trees, even if preserved into old age, are less long-lived than pollards and cannot be relied upon to provide all the special habitats. Some hornbeams, planted near Bush End in the 1960s, are about to be pollarded for the first time. Other pollards should be started among the young oaks, ashes and maples in the scrubs. Except in the eastern plains, there is no shortage of young trees: they need to be set on the way to becoming the ancient trees of the future.

The care and perpetuation of ancient trees is a test of human tenacity of purposes and attention to detail. The idea that pollards and hollow trees are somehow abnormal no longer prevails, but the urge to burn up fallen trees and rotten logs lives on. This can be disastrous for the rare Forest animals and plants: sometimes a species is confined to just one tree or log. Small fallen logs are of less importance, but it diminishes the Forest to remove any log more than a foot thick unless it has a significant timber value. The new management proposals specifically provide for dead wood. A dead bolling or a fallen pollard (which may remain alive) keeps its historic meaning and its value as a habitat for many years. The public, and our successors, must be taught to value the Forest as it is and has been, not to force it to conform to preconceptions of what Forests ought to be.

12 The Future

We consider that above all else it is the Trust's duty to preserve its inalienable properties, so far as possible, in their natural and traditional state, and that there should be no deliberate change in the character and appearance of these properties, even though there may be a public clamour for such change. We think that to give way to such pressure would be against the interests of the nation ... and a breach of faith with donors and others who have given their property ... to the Trust .... This has been the Trust's policy hitherto; we think that it is right and that it should continue to be followed in the future.

Benson Report on the National Trust, 1968

Today the pressures upon its properties ... are immensely greater than could have been imagined over seventy years ago, yet the principle first clearly enunciated by John Bailey (Chairman of the Trust from 1923 to 1931) that preservation is its first task which must always take precedence over public access, still stands. 'Preservation', he said, 'may always permit of access, while without preservation access becomes forever impossible.'

The National Trust, *Conservation and access*, 1980

If the amenity land manager is ever in doubt as to his best course of action, he has merely to think of what a modern farmer or forester would do, and do the opposite.

B. H. Green, 1983[295]

We might expect that the Forest's troubles are now over and its future assured. As we saw in Chapter 6, the mere fact that Hatfield belongs to a conservation body does not guarantee 'sympathetic' management, but the National Trust ought gradually to find out what the Forest's historic features are and how to perpetuate them. The Forest, however, finds itself by a rare chance assaulted from without, through the growth of Stansted Airport out of a redundant wartime airfield. Even if this had not been so, the conservation of a Forest is one of the longest-term of all human activities and has its own problems of philosophy and psychology.

The Immediate Future

Hatfield Forest now seems to prosper. Pollarding and coppicing have been resumed; most coppiced areas are adequately fenced against cattle; the grazing in general is about right for the grassland; and the grassland itself is slowly returning to a natural state. The great increase in the number of visitors has been coped with very well, and the Forest is more peaceful than it was fifteen years ago.

The Forest is better understood than it ever has been, and I have every hope that by the time these words appear there will be a management plan paying due attention to the details of the historic fabric – the product of much thought by the present Warden and his advisers.

The most immediate problem is that of living with deer. It is intended that about 70% of the woodland shall be coppiced on a rotation of about twenty years. Fencing against cattle will be done before felling. It is proposed to hold the numbers of deer down to about 100 head, two-thirds of the present, which will reduce the damage to underwood. Piling unwanted lop-and-top over stools is to be tried in order to give some protection.

In the plains, work will shortly start on removing some of the recently-encroached scrub in order to free the remaining 'unimproved' grassland and some of the ancient trees. A decision will shortly have to be taken on whether, and in what form, the trees of the tree-planting era are to be replaced.

Stansted Mounfitchet Airport

Stansted Airport is an accidental by-product of World War II. It was one of more than a hundred airfields in Eastern England in the middle stage of the war. 'Great Dunmow' airfield lay at Little Easton perilously close to the east, Matching seven miles south, Hunsdon south-west, Nuthampstead north-west, and Debden to the north. No trace of these airfields appears on the German air photographs of 1940. Their building was a heroic task and a transformation of the landscape; it was the main cause of loss of ancient woodland between 1870 and 1945. Presumably they were intended to last only for the duration of the war. By now, apart from some that are still military bases, most have been demolished (more or less) and their sites are again farmland.

The early history of Stansted has been told by M.J.F.Bowyer.[296] It was built by the Americans in only a year (1942–3). At first it was unimportant, an air depot with three runways, the longest a little over a mile. It had six months of glory when the United States 344th Bomb Group was stationed here and fought in Normandy.

After the war Stansted, although still only a minor airfield, was somehow chosen for a civilian airport. It was first so used in December 1946. Two years later it had attracted the attention of the Minister of Civil Aviation himself, who proposed it as one of the chief London airports. The United States Air Force continued to keep an interest, and in 1954–6 lengthened the runway to nearly two miles. This exceptionally long runway was never used as intended, and was abandoned by the military in 1958. But its existence has cast a shadow over the area for thirty years.

In this haphazard way Stansted became an airport. Civilian use gradually increased, and again attracted the notice of the government. In 1963 Stansted was recommended in the report of the 'Interdepartmental Committee on the Third London Airport'.

The prospect of a big airport was unwelcome to most people for thirty miles around, and opposition to it was coordinated by the North-West Essex & East Herts Preservation Association, founded in 1964. The expansion of the airport was the subject of a Public Inquiry in 1965. The case made by the Committee failed to stand up, and the Inquiry found against it. The government, however, had set its heart on Stansted, and announced in 1967 that it would continue to favour the expanding of this airport.

This announcement attracted immense local opposition and was denounced as perverse by much of Parliament. The consequence was that the Roskill Commission was set up to consider possible airport sites. This Commission rejected Stansted at an early stage, and considered four other sites in detail. Its report, in 1969, recommended an entirely new airport on the mudflats of Foulness Island;

a wildly impractical proposition which no government since then has dared to try.

Our airport, however, already existed; 'Stansted Airport' appears on the 1963 edition of the Ordnance Survey. Whatever public inquiries, commissions or governments might say, it grew into London's fourth airport. Airlines did not like it, and it was used chiefly for freight and for repairing planes. Legendary cargoes include the plane-loads of whisky in which Field-Marshal Amin, tyrant of Uganda, was said to indulge, and the crate containing a kidnapped Nigerian intercepted by Customs in 1984.

Presumably as a result of this growth, Stansted still attracted the favour of successive governments, Labour and Conservative. This led to yet another committee reporting, to a planning application by the British Airports Authority, and finally to another Public Inquiry beginning in September 1981. The proposals were to add terminal buildings, a railway and other installations to the 1956 Stansted runway, making it capable of receiving 15 million passengers a year; and to keep open the option of a second runway (parallel to the first and half-a-mile to the east) for a further 10 million passengers. The first stage would make of Stansted a big airport, busier than Gatwick; the second stage would make it one of the busiest in the world.

The Inquiry was the longest there had ever been, ending in July 1983. The Inspector's report came in December 1984. In effect, it recommended the first stage but not the second: the Airports Authority would make the existing runway capable of receiving 15 million passengers a year, but would not keep the option of a possible second runway.

The government found itself in a difficulty. Nobody except the Airports Authority decisively approved of the Inquiry's recommendation; it was opposed by local people, by most of the airlines, and by those who wanted a big airport in northern England or Scotland. Had an Act of Parliament been necessary, it would not have been forthcoming: on the one occasion when the House of Commons debated the matter, not a single Member voted in favour. At the time of writing, the government has compromised: the Airports Authority (as a nationalized body) has been authorized to make Stansted capable of flying 8 million passengers a year. This increase, which would just make it the third of the London airports, can be squeezed through without the consent of Parliament, except for the new railway. Anything further will require an Act of Parliament. The railway and many other works are now in progress.

Direct consequences of the airport Most of what I say is based on evidence submitted to the second Public Inquiry, mainly by the opposition,[297] although the Airports Authority commissioned two learned studies. One, from Warren Spring Laboratory, dealt with air pollution.[298] The other, by the ecologist Mrs P. Anderson, was an admirably thorough ecological survey which revealed unexpectedly many good habitats, especially grassland and hedges, within the area proposed for the airport itself; but it was not much concerned with the area indirectly to be affected, including the Forest.[299]

At the Inquiry the Forest played only a small part among a very wide range of considerations. If I do not denounce the Authority in as strong terms as were used by some of the witnesses, it is not that I approve of the airport; nor am I indifferent to the huge area which may be blighted by it, or to the fate of the inhabitants. My purpose is to arrive at the best prediction of the future of the Forest itself, given the often tenuous and conflicting evidence.

The consequences of the airport can only vaguely be foreseen. Even the number of passengers is a matter of pure speculation. An argument against the expansion was that even the present airport was not fully used: in 1985 it was said to be used by $\frac{1}{2}$ million passengers a year, though it could then have taken 2 million. Although, presumably, more people will come when there is a railway, it is guesswork whether the total could reach 8, 15 or 25 million a year. The 40-year history of the airport shows that neither local nor national government has much control over how much or how little it is used. These matters depend on remote decisions, such as whether the Common Market succeeds in abolishing the price-fixing which keeps air travel artificially expensive in Europe.

The actual destruction of the Forest is not in question. Since the land is the National Trust's, this would take an Act of Parliament, which would not be forthcoming. Even the Airport Authority's most ambitious proposals leave the hapless villages of Takeley and Takeley Street as a buffer zone between the airport and the Forest.

The runway ends half a mile from the north-west corner of the Forest, and aircraft taking off generally turn southwards over the

Hallingburys; the noise and smell can be obtrusive. The second run-way, if it ever were to come, would end half a mile north-east of the Forest, and aircraft would take off or land directly over the Forest.

Noise, sight and smell of aircraft will undoubtedly be very damaging to the amenities of the Forest, though not enough to keep visitors away. I doubt if they will have much effect on the fabric or wildlife. Most birds and other animals are surprisingly indifferent to noises that do not concern them.

Potentially more damaging is pollution. Aircraft and airport vehicles appear to be negligible burners of sulphurous fuel, but like dragons they exhale oxides of nitrogen. The Warren Spring study found that in 1980 the airport produced 0.3 ton of NO_x daily, compared to 1.3 tons coming from Bishop's Stortford. It was estimated that with an increase to 2 million passengers per annum the airport would emit 0.7 ton per day, and with 15 million it would emit 4.2 tons per day. Most of this comes from aircraft taking off; it is unlikely to be reduced by future changes in the design of engines. We can therefore expect that if there are 8 million passengers per annum the airport will emit roughly $2\frac{1}{2}$ tons of oxides of nitrogen each day, which will make it the biggest source in the area. Again relying on Warren Spring figures, this will add something like 50% to the present concentration of NO_x in the atmosphere around the airport. There will be a further contribution, though not quite so great, from the extra vehicles on roads leading to the airport.

We can predict that rain in Hatfield Forest is unlikely to go on getting less acid; in future nitric acid will replace sulphuric. Things may well be worse than this, because (according to the Warren Springs study) the concentration of NO_x fluctuates enormously. The Forest may get soaked with short blasts of nitrous acid whenever planes take off in heavy drizzle. The prospects for lichens and other sensitive plants are not good. The National Trust intends to keep a watch on the lichens of particular trees.

The Shermore Brook rises within the airport. This is not bad in itself, for Stansted, like most airports, consists at present mainly of grass; but the Brook may be contaminated by spillages and those nameless puddles of liquid that one sees around airports. To prevent this from happening the runoff from the airport has already been diverted into a sewage system elsewhere. Whether this diversion will withstand three inches of rain in a day remains to be seen. Unfortunately the remaining catchment may not be enough to sustain the flow of the Brook and the Forest wetlands.

It has been decided to divert the A120 main road (Stane Street) away from Takeley Street village through the southern fringes of the airport. This will greatly benefit both village and Forest.

Indirect consequences At the Inquiry many critics pointed out that a big airport would attract not only extra traffic but more people to live in the area. The airport proposal was vague about how many people were expected to come or where they would live, and was silent on what they were expected to do of a Sunday afternoon. Sir Colin Buchanan predicted that a population of 200,000 would depend on the airport; others guessed up to 300,000. In reality the answer will depend on how thickly manned the airport is, how many passengers and visitors want hotels in the area, how many incomers can afford the local house-prices, etc. – on a host of decisions yet to be considered. New or expanding towns will attract people and industries connected with the airport only at second or third hand, or not connected at all. Even if the airport ever disappears, the towns will remain.

We would be wise to reckon with at least a doubling of the population within the 20-mile radius of the Forest from which most visitors come. At the Inquiry there was a vague idea that this would come about, not through a new city, but through the expansion of Bishop's Stortford, Braintree, Harlow, and other places. If the airport is a success, there is little chance that this can either be prevented or controlled; too many local authorities are involved for there to be much hope of a coherent policy. The new inhabitants will add to the atmospheric pollution, especially from cars, though probably not as much as will come from the airport.

More serious still is the increase of visitors. Hatfield Forest is much the biggest public open space within twelve miles. We can expect greatly increased use of the Forest by new residents, by visitors with business at the airport, and through better roads making it easier to reach the Forest from a distance. Some of the extra visitors will have an interest in the Forest as such or will appreciate its special beauty; others will us it as an ordinary place of recreation, for which any public park would be a substitute. Experience at

Brandon Park, Suffolk, where noise from military aircraft is much worse than any likely to reach the Forest with the present runway, shows that even this does not keep visitors away.

As I have shown in south-east Essex, urbanization is not necessarily a disaster for ancient woodland; the woods there have survived better than they might have done had their surroundings remained rural (*SEE*). A wood-pasture, however, is much less robust than a wood, and grassland and ancient trees are more easily damaged.

Sutton Coldfield Park is a warning of what might happen. This ancient park, in the midst of the Birmingham conurbation, is more than twice the size of Hatfield Forest, but is built-up all round. It is full of cars and car-parks, and has been much eroded by paths, including its prehistoric earthworks. The ancient dammed lakes have installations for various kinds of formal and commercial recreation. Although still recognizable as a medieval compartmented park, it has lost much of its distinctive character and is on the way to becoming an ordinary municipal park.[300]

Hatfield copes quite well with the present number of visitors, though with no great margin of safety. In the past damage has been done to the fabric of the Forest by excessive trampling, motoring and horse-riding. This has now been brought under control, though at the cost of further damage to the Forest by making car-parks and hard roads, and of more work for the Forest wardens.

Any large increase in visitors will result in more intensive use of the present much-visited areas; intensive use may also extend to those parts of the Forest that are now little visited and which, on the whole, are less robust than the parkland round the lake. It may become difficult to continue the grazing. New problems may appear which are not now serious, such as litter, loose dogs, stealing dead wood, and setting fire to hollow trees. Not all these are insuperable, but to deal with them will need more staff and also buildings, car-parks, hard roads and paths and other works which are damaging in themselves and are unlikely to be paid for out of increased revenue. My experience of management committees elsewhere is that they find it hard to resist pressure to carry out works for the benefit of visitors, even though these damage the site. Hatfield examples include the heightening of the dam of the lake, and identifying supposedly 'dangerous' trees and making them 'safe'.

At Hatfield Forest it might, in the end, be necessary for the

National Trust to restrict public access in some way. A precedent would be the Trust's property of Wicken Fen, only a fraction of which is open to the public, and then only on foot. Such a decision would be difficult and painful, and could only be taken after much damage had already been done.

This is a problem that *could* be solved with money. The best way to conserve the antiquities, wildlife and *genius loci* of the Forest would be for adjacent land to be acquired for a Country Park, and for the more intensive kinds of recreation to be taken outside the Forest. (The opportunity might even be taken to restore some of the lands lost to the Forest in 1857.) Such a big operation would have to be financed from outside the National Trust; circumstances will probably not combine in a fortunate enough way, but it is just possible that they might. It would be proper for the Airports Authority, if it causes all this trouble, to be invited to contribute towards putting it right.

There is also the effect on the surroundings of the Forest. To the east, south and west – the site of Hatfield Park and the lands of the Barringtons and Morleys – is still a medieval countryside, much less damaged by modern agriculture than is usual in eastern England. In its way it is nearly as remarkable a survival as the Forest itself. If this setting were to be encroached upon, the Forest would lose much of its meaning. This area has been designated as a Nature Conservation Zone by Essex County Council. No proposals for development have so far been made, but if the airport succeeds they will doubtless come. Let us hope that our successors will always remember to oppose even minor development in the surroundings of the Forest.

A Philosophy for the Next 900 Years

Although the conservation of historic landscapes has much to learn from that of historic buildings, the parallels must not be taken too far. Landscapes have a bigger biological component, which makes them less easily understood by the human mind. Plants and animals need more research to understand their behaviour than stone or lead. Even the objectives of conservation, though we may feel equally strongly about them, are less easy to set down in precise terms. Much of what is done is necessarily experimental.

This last section of the book is concerned with wider issues than Hatfield Forest, and is not specifically addressed to the National Trust. Far be it from me to suggest that the Trust is more or less subject than other conservation bodies to the perils of managing historic landscapes, except that it is responsible for more such landscapes than anyone else. But it is from Hatfield, because it has been in conservationist hands for so long, that we learn about the general problems of conserving complex ecosystems.

In a rational world, the custodians of such a place would gradually find out more about it, would discover its *genius loci*, its special features and meanings and how it differs from other landscapes, and would accumulate knowledge on how to perpetuate them. Some things inherently cannot be perpetuated, but would not be destroyed before their time (as apparently was the Doodle Oak). It would be possible to deal rationally with rare events such as hurricanes, or with new problems such as the arrival of grey squirrels or what to do with too many visitors.

The first obstacle is that people die or are promoted, and often their knowledge dies with them. This is worse in these days of professional officers and wardens than when men learnt from their fathers how to manage estates. A historic landscape should have a management plan, written specifically to ensure that knowledge is handed on. This plan must be flexible, but we must not expect it to be simple. Our successors can use their discretion as to which particular coppice to cut in AD 2038. They need to be told that such-and-such a dead tree is the only habitat in Essex for a particular insect, or that the Gravelpit area needs a particular degree of trampling to maintain its 'Breckland' plants. (But the amount of detail, even in a Forest as complex as Hatfield, is not so very great by the National Trust's standards of attention to detail in historic buildings.)

In a place like Hatfield Forest, it should in theory be possible to ensure that conservation takes precedence over other considerations. The National Trust has stoutly maintained that where conservation conflicts with public access, conservation shall prevail. In practice the conflict is usually a matter of degree: how much 'conservation' is sacrificed by a given amount of public use? As public use increases, at what point is the principle breached? The answer is not cut-and-dried. Management committees elsewhere have not always resisted insidious demands that paths be drained or 'improved' for the benefit of visitors. To pay for making-up a path is easier than to tell visitors that the wet state is normal and they should come in gumboots. It is not only the big conflicts that matter, but gradual erosion by chronic minor damage and minor tidiness.

Conservation has to fight deep habits of human thought which are not always recognized as anti-conservation. Tidy-mindedness, which outside the Forest is the second enemy of conservation (after greed), can penetrate even here. At times Hatfield has been misunderstood, has been confused with a garden or a landscaped park, and has been subjected to standards of tidiness which are a solecism in a Forest. Most of us have been indoctrinated that dead wood and dead trees are somehow unnatural and unsightly, and that our disapproval is a good enough reason for burning them. We need often to remind ourselves, and to teach the public, that rotten logs and dead trees, and the things that grow on and live in them, are part of the meaning and ecology – yes, and the beauty – of a wooded Forest, and that it is the world outside that is unnatural in not having them. The new management proposals explicitly provide for deadwood, for keeping big logs in one piece and for putting them in places where they can rot undisturbed.

Then there are conflicts between one conservation objective and another. Deer and coppicing are both essential parts of Hatfield Forest, and a balance is now having to be struck between them; the traditional method of temporary deer-proof fences seems to be beyond the resources of the twentieth century.

There can be a conflict between conserving different aspects of a place's history. Horsechestnuts and other exotic trees, planted by the Houblons, make it difficult to appreciate the Warren earthworks. In principle the issue is simple: as a wooded Forest Hatfield is unique, but it is merely a fourth-rate nineteenth-century landscape park, and the Forest aspect should prevail. However, it would be entirely improper to banish all trace of the Houblon period. Let us take warning from Athens in the nineteenth century. The Athenians decided to preserve the monuments of their 'best' age – the latter centuries BC – and carefully to destroy most others. One now searches sadly and in vain for material remains of the Athens of Basil the Bulgar-slayer or of Otho de la Roche, the Athens of *A*

Midsummer Night's Dream or of Suleyman the Magnificent, or even of the heroes of Greek Independence. May this kind of thing never happen to Hatfield. Probably the right course is to let the horsechestnuts stand until they blow down but to plant successors nearer the lake where they will not detract from the real character of the Forest.

Places such as Hatfield have suffered from fashions in conservationist thought: the 'do nothing' phase, the 'pollards are unnatural' phase, the thinning phase, the 'plant trees anywhere' phase. We may think that in the enlightened 1980s we know better, but doubtless there will be other fashions in future, probably with no better scientific basis than these. In a rational world each generation would add to its predecessors' knowledge, but in our world unreason often triumphs and knowledge can diminish as well as grow. One of the great ecological themes of the 1920s was succession – the fact that any piece of land, left to itself, turns into a wood – and research was done, and books written, and students examined, on how this happens. In the 1960s succession was all but forgotten. How many recent books on woodland or conservation give it the chapters that it deserves?

Management plans tend not to be read. Conservationists carry out their own ideas and enthusiasms without looking at the ideas of their predecessors. A classic example is Epping Forest. The Epping Forest Act of 1878 requires the Conservators of the Forest to

> protect the timber and other trees, pollards, shrubs, underwood, heather, gorse, turf, and herbage growing on the Forest.

These admirable prescriptions were embedded in the text of an Act of Parliament which nobody seems to have read. The early Conservators pursued their own enthusiasm, which happened to be for timber trees. They disapproved of pollards and would not let them be cut, disapproved of hornbeams and bogs, and did nothing to prevent trees from overrunning the heather, gorse and shrubs. The Forest has by now lost much of its unique meaning and interest and is on its way to becoming just an ordinary beechwood. The changes were controversial, but both parties regarded the management of Epping as a matter of taste; it did not occur to their opponents to quote the Act against the Conservators.

The immediate future of Hatfield Forest seems brighter than for many years. Over the middle term there hangs the cloud of Stansted Airport, which will call for much skill and judgement in averting some of the consequences. For the long term I may sound pessimistic, but that is because others are usually over-optimistic. Landscape conservation is seen in terms of technical solutions – coppicing here, tree-planting there, scrub-clearing elsewhere – which are thought to be predictable, like repairs to a building. The real problems are psychological and have yet to be addressed. An American forester once made the wise remark to me that American forestry is not really about trees but about people.

We cannot guarantee that our successors will be men of goodwill or of steadfast purpose, but we can tell them what we propose and why. (If we often are baffled by what conservationists did even 25 years ago, this is because they assumed that we would know why and did not tell us.) This is what a management plan is for. It needs to be descriptive: not to be just a bald list of biological or archaeological features, but to mention everything that is special or wonderful or beautiful, and above all to set out the *meaning* of a place.

A management plan should give some protection against changes of conservationist fashion. Over the years it will be revised, but let us hope that most of the revision will be additions: new discoveries, new insights, experiments that did not work, and new meanings that we had not known. Management will doubtless be revised over the years, but if there is a good management plan changes are likely to be made only for good scientific reasons or because of genuine changes of circumstance. For example, a coppicing programme, once set up, may be altered because the effects are not what was expected, or because somebody invents an easy way of keeping deer out of an area; let us hope that it will become sufficiently entrenched not to be abandoned merely if coppicing again becomes unfashionable.

The chief objective of a management plan is that it should be read. Many modern management plans are useless because unreadable. They are often written to a prescribed form, are platitudinous ('increase populations of rare and notable species'), or written in officialese ('minimize negative nature conservation effects of obligations'), or loaded with conservationists' claptrap about diversity, monitoring or shrub layer. To our successors a generation hence they will sound like a foreign language. The style and presentation of a management plan deserve as much care as those of a book

271

or a popular article. To be effective it has to be eagerly read by each new warden and committee member.

Usually a management plan (or a version of it) should be a public document. It is to the good of conservation in general that the public should be encouraged to take a detailed interest in managing historic landscapes. This often leads to imitation elsewhere. It is also to the good of the particular place. A management plan cannot be quietly forgotten (or lost or burnt) if everyone interested has a copy. If only the National Trust of the 1930s and 1950s had written down and published its plans for Hatfield Forest! Our successors may be fallible, but they are less likely to persevere with mistakes if passers-by point out that what they are doing is not just vaguely disliked but diminishes the *genius loci* in some specific way.

'Those who cannot remember the past are condemned to repeat it'
Fashions in land-use extend into the world of conservation; even people whose business is to uphold continuity are not immune from them. How do we ensure that the wisdom of one human generation is remembered by the next? There is an insidious tendency to put successes on record but to forget about failures. Failures are treated as something to be lived down, rather than as experiments with a definite outcome from which future generations may learn. People thus repeat their grandfathers' mistakes.

The Georgian replanting of Warren Coppice should have been treated as a precedent not to be followed. Instead it was repeated in other coppices in Victorian times, with a similar lack of success. By the 1950s this outcome had been forgotten and the same treatment was again attempted, with less success still. Each time something was lost from the historic fabric of the Forest. I am disconcerted to find that the 1955 controversy has, in its turn, already been forgotten in the Forest. I hope that in the year 2027 people will not for a fourth time be trying to make ancient woods into plantations, nor will they still be thinking it necessary to do something about the damage done by the 1987 storm. Human nature does not encourage me to be optimistic.

Bibliography and References

Bibliography

AW	Rackham, O. 1980. *Ancient woodland: its history, vegetation and uses in England*, Edward Arnold, London
EF	Rackham, O. 1978. 'Archaeology and land-use history,' *Epping Forest – the natural aspect?* ed. D.Corke, *Essex Naturalist* **NS 2** 16–75
FD	Chapman, N. and D. 1975. *Fallow deer: their history, distribution and ecology*, Lavenham
HC	Rackham, O. 1986. *The history of the countryside*, Dent, London
HW	Rackham, O. 1975. *Hayley Wood: its history and ecology*, Cambs & Isle of Ely Naturalists' Trust
NF	Tubbs, C.R. 1986. *The New Forest*, Collins, London
GTE	Putman, R.J. 1986. *Grazing in temperate ecosystems: large herbivores and the ecology of the New Forest*, Croom Helm, London
PW	Harding, P.T. & Rose, F. 1986. *Pasture-woodlands in lowland Britain*, Monks Wood
RFME	Young, C.R. 1979. *The royal Forests of medieval England*, Leicester
SC	Shorrocks, D. 1955. 'Hatfield Forest 1547–1857: a story of conflict', *Essex Review* **64** 54–66
SEE	Rackham, O. 1986. *The ancient woodland of England: the woods of South-East Essex*, Rochford District Council
TW	Rackham, O. 1976. *Trees and woodland in the British landscape*, Dent, London

References

AE	*Archaeology in Essex to AD 1500*, ed. D.G. Buckley, CBA Research Report **34** (1980)
BARIS	*British Archaeological Reports International Series*
BSDNHS	Bishop's Stortford & District Natural History Society
CBA	Council for British Archaeology

Bibliography and References

CL   Country Life
CPR   Calendar of Patent Rolls
EN   Essex Naturalist
ERO   Essex Record Office
JE   Journal of Ecology
QS   Quaderni Storici
PRO   Public Record Office
SPI   Documents submitted to Stansted Public Inquiry
TEAS   Transactions of Essex Archaeological Society
VCH   Victoria County History
W   Houblon family papers at Welford Park, Berks, referred to by
            their box labels

1   Brown, E.H. and Hopkins, S.V. 'Seven centuries of the prices of consum-
    ables, compared with builders' wage-rates', Economica 23 (1956) 296–313
2   HC p. 131
3   ERO: T/M 347
4   PRO: C135/48(2)
5   AW p. 141
6   Gonville & Caius Coll. (Cambridge) MS 489/485
7   W: 'Rent Rolls Essex 1803–11'
8   F.W. Galpin in Reaney, P.H. Place-names of Essex, Cambridge 1935
9   English Dialect Dictionary
10 Austad, I. 1985. Vegetasjon i kulturlandskapet: lauvingstrær, Sogn og
    Fjordane distriktshøgskule, Norway
    Hæggström, C.-A. 1983. 'Vegetation and soil of the wooded meadows
    in Nåtö, Åland', Acta botanica Fennica 120 1–66
11 Moreno, D. 1982. 'Querce come olivi. Sulla rovericoltura in Liguria tra
    XVIII e XIX secolo', QS NS 49 108–136
12 Troup, R.S. 1928. Silvicultural systems, Clarendon, Oxford
13 Peters, B.C. 1978. 'Michigan's Oak Openings: pioneer perceptions of
    a vegetative landscape', Journal of Forest History Jan. 1978 19–23
    Lindsay, M.M. and Bratton, S.P. 1979. 'Grassy balds of the Great Smoky
    Mountains: their history and flora in relation to potential management',
    Environmental Management 3 417–30
14 Rackham, O. 1988. 'Trees and woodland in a crowded landscape: the
    cultural landscape of the British Isles', The cultural landscape: past,
    present and future, ed. H.J.B. Birks, Cambridge
15 Birks, H.J.B., Deacon, J. and Peglar, S. 1975. 'Pollen maps for the
    British Isles 5,000 [radiocarbon] years ago', Proceedings of the Royal
    Society of London B189 87–105
    HC p. 70
16 Rackham, O. 1986. 'The ancient woods of Norfolk', Transactions of Nor-
    folk & Norwich Naturalists Society 27 161–77
17 Godwin, H. 1975. History of the British flora, 2nd ed. Cambridge
    Pott, R. 1985. 'Vegetationsgeschichtliche und pflanzensoziologische

Untersuchungen zur Niederwaldwirtschaft in Westfalen', *Abhandlungen aus dem Westfälischen Museum für Naturkunde* **47**(4)

18 Wymer, J.J. 1980. 'The Palaeolithic of Essex', *AE* 8–11
19 Jacobi, R.M. 1980. 'The Mesolithic of Essex', *AE* 14–25
20 Kindly told me by Deborah Riddy of Essex Archaeological Unit
21 Hedges, J.D. 1980. 'The Neolithic in Essex', *AE* 26–39
22 Rackham, O. 1977. 'Neolithic woodland management in the Somerset Levels: Garvin's, Walton Heath, and Rowland's Tracks', *Somerset Levels Papers* **3** 65–71
23 Couchman, C.R. 1980. 'The Bronze Age in Essex', *AE* 40–6
24 Brooks, H. 1987. *Relics and runways*, preliminary report on the Stansted Airport investigations
25 *VCH*, Essex **1** 272
26 Peglar, S.M., Fritz, S.C. and Birks, H.J.B. 1988. 'Vegetation and land-use history at Diss, Norfolk, England' (in press)
27 Drury, P.J. 'The early and middle phases of the Iron Age in Essex', *AE* 47–54
28 Williamson, T. 1986. 'The development of settlement in north west Essex: the results of a recent field survey', *Essex Archaeology & History* **17** 120–33
29 Drury, P.J. and Rodwell, W. 'Settlement in the later Iron Age and Roman periods', *AE* 59–75
   Bassett, S.R. 1982. *Saffron Walden: excavations and research 1972–80*, CBA Research Report **45**
30 *Transactions of Essex Archaeological Society*, 1858, **1** 198
31 Information kindly given by Mr Mark Dodd
32 Armitage, P., West, B. and Steedman, K. 'New evidence of the black rat in Roman London', *London Archaeology* **4** (1983) 375–83
33 Warwick, R. and Warwick, K. 1977. *Historic churches: a wasting asset*, CBA Research Report **19**
34 Gelling, M. 1973–6. *The place-names of Berkshire*, English Place-name Soc., Cambridge
35 Kemble, J.M. 1839–48. *Codex diplomaticus aevi Saxonici*, no. 711. London
36 *AW* p. 241–2
37 *HC* p. 141–4
38 *AW* p. 119–23
39 Moore, S.A. (ed.) 1897. *Cartularium monasterii Sancti Johannis Baptiste de Colecestria*, Chiswick, London
40 Documented especially in the muniments of New College, Oxford
41 Brodribb, A.C.C., Hands, A.R. and Walker, D.R. 1968–73. *Excavations at Shakenoak*
42 Steane, J.M. 1974. *The Northamptonshire landscape*, Hodder & Stoughton, London
43 Chapman, D.I. 'Deer of Essex', *EN* NS **1** (1977) 3–50
44 Grimm, J. and W. *Deutsches Wörterbuch*, Band IV.i.1, Leipzig 1878

45   *HC* chapter 17
46   Birrell, J. 1987. 'Common rights in the medieval forest: disputes and conflicts in the thirteenth century', *Past & Present* **117** 22–49
47   Round, J.H. 1897. 'The Forest of Essex', *Journal of the British Archaeological Association* NS **3** 36–42
48   Whitelock, D. 1930. *Anglo-Saxon wills*, Cambridge
49   Cantor, L. 1983. *The medieval parks of England : a gazetteer*, Loughborough Munby, L.M. 1977. *The Hertfordshire landscape*, Hodder & Stoughton, London
50   *HC* p. 123–4
51   *TW* p. 143
52   *HC* p. 47
53   *Oxford English Dictionary*
54   Carpenter, R. 1966. 'The deer of Hatfield Forest', *EN* **31** 354–7
55   Kindly told me by Capt. C.G.E. Barclay
56   ERO: D/DB T15/9
57   *CPR*, 1374–7, p. 85–6
58   Liebermann, F. 1906. *Die Gesetze der Angelsachsen*, vol. 2 Halle
59   Leland, J. 1542. *Itinerary* (ed. L.T. Smith, London 1907)
60   *Rotuli Litterarum Clausarum*
61   *Calendar of Close Rolls*
62   ERO: D/DB L1/3/40
63   Baillie-Grohman, W.A. and F. (eds), *The Master of Game, by Edward, second Duke of York*, Ballantyne, Hanson 1904
64   La Curme de Saint-Palaye, 1875–82. *Dictionnaire historique de l'ancienne langage françois*, Niort
65   Lowndes, G.A. 1878, 1884. 'The history of the Barrington family', *TEAS* NS **1** 251–73, **2** 3–54
66   Fisher, W.R. *The Forest of Essex*, Butterworth, London 1897
67   ERO: D/DB L1/5/8
68   Turner, G.J. 1901. *Select Pleas of the Forest*, Selden Society
70   ERO D/DB T16/6; T15/8
71   Eland, G. 1949. *At the courts of Great Canfield*, Oxford
72   ERO: D/D Ba M 1, 10, 11, 27
73   ERO: D/D Ba M3
74   ERO: D/DK M1
75   Lowndes, G.A. 1884. 'History of the priory at Hatfield Regis alias Hatfield Broad Oak', *TEAS* NS **2** 117–152
76   Parsons, M. 1983. 'Hatfield Broad-Oak', *VCH, Essex* **8** 158–86
77   ERO: T/M 347
78   W: '1 Drawer 5'
79   Pollard, E., Hooper, M.D. and Moore, N.W. 1974. *Hedges*, Collins, London
80   Lowndes, G.A. 1878. 'The history of Hatfield Broad Oak', *TEAS* NS **1** 65–8
81   Kirk, R.E.G. 1899–1910. *Feet of Fines for Essex*, p. 120

82   ERO: D/DB L1/5/10
83   Barrow, G.W.S. 1976. *Robert the Bruce and the community of the realm of Scotland*, 2nd ed. Edinburgh
84   Alexander, J. and Binski, P. (eds) 1987. *Age of Chivalry: art in Plantagenet England 1200–1400*, Royal Academy, London
85   *CPR*
86   ERO: D/DB T16/5
87   Rackham, O., Blair, W.J. and Munby, J.T. 1978. 'The thirteenth-century roofs and floor of the Blackfriars monastery at Gloucester', *Medieval Archaeology* **22** 105–22
88   Hart, C.E. 1966. *Royal Forest: a history of Dean's woods as producers of timber*, Clarendon, Oxford 1966
89   ERO: D/D Ba T2/10
90   ERO: D/DB L1/3/52
91   ERO: D/DB L1/3/56
92   ERO: D/DQ 18
93   ERO: D/DB L1/3/46
94   ERO: D/DP M200-1, 210, 1422
95   ERO: D/DB L1/10/27
96   Rogers, J.E.T. 1866. *A history of agriculture and prices in England. Vols I, II: 1259–1400*. Clarendon, Oxford
97   ERO: D/DB L1/5/9, 10
98   ERO: D/DB L1/5/6
99   Lewthwaite, J.G. 'Acorns for the ancestors: the prehistoric exploitation of woodland in the west Mediterranean', *Archaeological aspects of woodland ecology*, ed. M. Bell and S. Limbrey, *BARIS* **146** (1982) 217–30
100 ERO: D/DBa M2
101 ERO: D/DP M200
102 Galpin, F.W. 1926. 'Pigs and pannage. A short chapter on medieval stock-rearing illustrated by some Essex Manorial Records', *Transactions of Essex Archaeological Society* **17** 1–9
103 Cherry, J. 1981. 'Medieval rings', *The ring*, ed. A. Ward and others, Thames & Hudson, London, p. 64. [The ring is in the British Museum, catalogue 1980, 12–2,1. I am indebted to Dr Cherry for helpful correspondence]
104 Parker, R. 1975. *The common stream*, Collins, London
105 Macfarlane, A. *The origins of English individualism*, Blackwell, Oxford 1978
106 Taylor, C.C. 1972. 'Medieval moats in Cambridgeshire', *Archaeology and the landscape*, ed P.J.Fowler, John Baker, London, 237–49
     Aberg, F.A. 1978. *Medieval moated sites*, CBA Resarch Report **17** *HC* p. 360–4
107 *AW* p. 17–18
108 Morris, C.A. 1982. 'Aspects of Anglo-Saxon and Anglo-Scandinavian lathe-turning', *Woodworking techniques before A.D. 1500*, ed. S. McGrail, *BARIS* **129** 245–62

109 *Statutes of the Realm* **1** 97
110 Text derived mainly from Lord Morley's copy, ERO: L1/6/3; some amendments from draft, PRO: E/178/5297, and a later copy, ERO: L1/6/10
111 Emmison, F.G. 1970. *Elizabethan life [in Essex]: disorder*, Essex County Council
    Emmison, F.G. 1976. *Elizabethan life: home, work & land*, Essex County Council
112 Harris, B.J. 1986. *Edward Stafford, third Duke of Buckingham*, Stanford University Press
113 ERO: D/DB T15/3
114 Smith, G. 1967. *The Barrington family and Hatfield Forest in the late sixteenth and seventeenth centuries*, M.Sc. thesis, Unversity of York (ERO: T/Z 75/1)
115 Morant, P. 1768. *The history and antiquities of the county of Essex*, London, **1** 26
116 ERO: D/DB L1/10/29
117 ERO: D/DB 16/2
118 ERO: D/DB T 15/12, 26, 27
119 ERO: D/DBa F9/3
120 *Acts of the Privy Council* 14 June 1627
121 ERO: D/DB L1/2/1
122 ERO: D/DB L1/9/1
123 ERO: D/DB 1/3/8
124 ERO: D/DHt M 49
125 ERO: D/DB L1/5/2
126 ERO: D/DB L1/7/29
127 Sixsmith, R.A. 1958. *Staple Fitzpaine and the Forest of Neroche*, Staple Fitzpaine
128 ERO: D/DB L1/6/12
129 'History of Hatfield Forest', *TEAS* **NS 2** 259–65
130 ERO: D/DB L1/6/13
131 ERO: D/DB L1/2/16
132 ERO: D/DB L1/7/30; T15/25
133 ERO: D/DKw E1/4
134 ERO: D/DB L1/5/5
135 W: 'Box 10 Drawer 3'
136 ERO: D/DB L1/3/52
137 ERO: D/DKw E1 [*sic*]
138 ERO: D/DKw E1/8
139 Kindly told me by Mrs Puxley, a descendant
140 Houblon, A.A. 1907. *The Houblon family: its life and times*, Constable, London
141 Hunter, J.M. 1985. *Land into landscape*, Godwin, London
142 Hyams, E. 1971. *Capability Brown & Humphry Repton*, Dent, London

143 Thompson, E.P. 1975. *Whigs and Hunters: the origin of the Black Act*, Penguin, London
144 W: 'Accounts Essex about 1810'
145 ERO: L1/3/61
146 W: 'John Archer₇ Houblon died 1891'
147 *Home, work & land* (ref. 111)
148 ERO: D/DQ 14/191
149 Morant (ref. 115)
150 ERO: D/DBa E8
151 ERO: D/DB P37
152 ERO: D/DQ 14/38
153 Chapman, J. and André P. 1777. *A map of the county of Essex*, London
154 British Library Map Room: O.S. Drawing no. 140, Part 1
155 ERO: D/CT 166
156 ERO: D/DB T15/25
157 ERO: D/DB T15/11
158 ERO: D/DB L1/1/7
159 ERO: D/DB L1/3/15
160 ERO: D/DB L1/3/30
161 Morant (ref. 115) **2** 501
162 ERO: D/DB L1/3/48
163 ERO: D/DKw E1/7
164 ERO: D/DB L1/3/20
165 ERO: D/DB L1/11/2
166 *AW* p. 168
167 ERO: D/DB T15/30
168 ERO: D/DB L1/8/13
169 ERO: D/DB L1/2/4
170 W: 'Rent Rolls Essex 1812–19'
171 ERO: D/DB L1/9/4
172 ERO: D/DB T 16/4
173 Welford: '8 Drawer Charles Cotton receivership 1783'
174 ERO: D/DH L14
175 ERO: D/DB L1/10/26
176 Galpin, F.W. 1945. 'The household expenses of Sir John Barrington (1645–1667).' *TEAS* **NS 23** 280–97
177 ERO: D/DB L1/5/3
178 ERO: D/DB L1/2/11
179 ERO: D/DB L1/2/24
180 ERO: D/DB L1/8/2
181 ERO: D/DB L1/10/36
182 ERO: D/DB L1/3/17
183 ERO: D/DB L1/6/10
184 ERO: D/DB L1/10/38
185 ERO: D/DB T15/53
186 ERO: D/DB L1/2/5, 6

187   ERO: D/DB L1/8/9
188   ERO: D/DB L1/2/8
189   ERO: D/DB L1/2/16, L1/3/61
190   ERO: D/DB L1/3/59
191   ERO: D/DB L1/7/27
192   ERO: D/DB L1/7/5
193   ERO: D/DB L1/12/2
194   ERO: D/DB L1/12/4
195   ERO: D/DB L1/2/18
196   I have been shown a copy by a local resident. The original is probably at Welford
197   ERO: D/DKw M2
198   Galpin, F.W. 1912. 'The household expenses of Sir Thomas Barrington.' *TEAS* **NS 12** 203–24
199   ERO: D/DB L1/9/15
200   ERO: D/DB M30
201   ERO: D/DKw M7
202   ERO: D/DB L1/8/8
203   ERO: D/DC 21/9/16
204   ERO: D/DB L1/2/3
205   Berry, M.F. 1950. *A history of the Puckeridge Hunt*, Country Life, London
206   Ball, R.F. and Gilbey, T. 1896. *The Essex Foxhounds*, Vinton, London
207   ERO: D/DBa F9/1
208   ERO: D/DB L1/3/31
209   ERO: D/DKw E6
210   'Dedication of Hatfield Forest', 1927 *EN* **21** 24–6
211   ERO: Q/R Um 2/138
212   Information from Capt. C.G.E. Barclay
213   W: diaries of H.L. Archer Houblon
214   *Kelly's Directory*
215   'Hallingbury Place, Essex, the residence of Mr Lockett Agnew' 1914 *CL* **36** 390–6
216   Strong, R., Binney, M. and Harris, J. 1974. *The destruction of the country house 1875–1975*, Thames & Hudson
217   Buxton, G. 1927. 'The late Mr E.N. Buxton and the preservation of three Essex Forests', *EN* **21** 12–4
      Buxton, E.N. 1884. *Epping Forest*, Stanford, London
218   Dymond, T.S. 1909. 'The re-afforestation of Hainhault (part of the old Forest of Waltham)' *EN* **16** 1–25
219   *The Times*, 19.1.24, 12.5.24
      Buxton, A. *Hatfield Forest [guide]*, National Trust [*c.* 1964]
220   Fedden, R. 1968. *The continuing purpose: a history of the National Trust, its aims and work*, Longmans, London
221   Reports and correspondence kindly made available to me by R. Jarman, of the National Trust

222 United States National Archives, Group 373: GX 10019 SD no. 175; GX 10450 no. 066

223 *The Times*, 20.7.55, 22.7.55, 26.7.55, 30.7.55, 5.8.55, 10.8.55, 24.9.55, 23.10.55. I am indebted to R. Jarman for bringing these to my attention.

224 Harris, S. 1974. 'The ecology and distribution of squirrels in Essex', *EN* **33** 64–7

225 Chatters, C. and Minter, R. 1986. 'Nature conservation and the National Trust,' *ECOS* [journal so called] **7** 25–32

226 Muniments of New College, Oxford *passim*

227 ERO: D/DHf M19

228 Wilkinson, P. 'Portingbury Hills or Rings', Huggins, P.J. 'Pappus and Portingbury' 1978, *Essex Archaeol. Hist.* **10** 222–6

229 Sheail, J. 1971. *Rabbits and their history*, Newton Abbot

230 Williamson, T. and Loveday, R. 1988. 'Rabbits or ritual?: artificial warrens and the Neolithic long mound tradition' *Archaeological Journal* (in press)

231 O'Brien, C.A.E. 1976. *An integrated astronomical complex of earthworks at Wandlebury and Hatfield Forest from the third millennium B.C.*, Thaxted
Hoppit D. 'The Wandlebury enigma solved?' *Telegraph Sunday Magazine* 19 Mar. 1978

232 Devereux, P. and Thomson, I. 1979. *The ley hunter's companion*, Thames & Hudson, London

233 Williamson, T. and Bellamy, L. 1983. *Ley lines in question*, World's Work, Kingswood, Surrey

234 Thom, A. 1967. *Megalithic sites in Britain*, Oxford

235 Hogg, A.H.A 1975. *Hill-Forts of Britain*, Hart-Davis, London

236 Cummings, A.L. 1979. *The framed houses of Massachusetts Bay, 1625–1725*, Belknap, Harvard

237 Kneale, K.J. 1965. *Queen Elizabeth's Hunting Lodge, Chingford*, Chingford Historical Society Bulletin **3**
Hewett, C.A. 1980. *English historic carpentry*, Chichester

238 Shirley, E.P. 1867. *Some account of English deer parks*, Murray, London

239 Rackham, O. 1927. 'Grundle House: on the quantities of timber in certain East Anglian buildings in relation to local supplies', *Vernacular Architecture* **22** 105–22

240 Department of the Environment 1981–3. *List of buildings of special architectural or historic interest: District of Uttlesford, Essex*

241 *EN* **21** (1927) 189

242 Peterken, G.F. 1974, 'A method for assessing woodland flora for conservation using indicator species', *Biological Conservation* **6** 239–45

243 Christy, R.M. 1884. 'On the species of the genus Primula in Essex ...' *Transactions of Essex Field Club* **3** 148–211

244 Martin, M.H. 1968. 'Conditions affecting the distribution of *Mercurialis perennis* L. in certain Cambridgeshire woodlands', *JE* **56** 777–93

245 Darwin, C. 1881. *The formation of vegetable mould through the action of worms*, Murray, London

246 Pigott, C.D. and Taylor, K. 1964. 'The distribution of some woodland herbs in relation to the supply of nitrogen and phosphorus in the soil', *JE* **52 suppl.** 175–86

247 Sturdy, R.G. 1971. *Soils in Essex I: sheet TQ 59 (Harold Hill)*, Soil Survey, Harpenden

248 Piussi, P. and Stiavelli, S. 1986. 'Dal documento al terreno:archeologia del Bosco delle Pianora (Colline delle Cerbaie, Pisa)', *QS* **NS 62** 445–66

249 Richens, R.H. 1983. *Elm*, Cambridge

250 Richens, R.H. 1967. 'Studies on *Ulmus*. VII. Essex elms', *Forestry* **40** 184–206

251 *AW* pp. 68, 69, 273

252 Peace, T.R. 1960. *The status and development of elm disease*, Forestry Commission Bulletin **33**

253 Kindly told me by J. Fielding

254 Brown, A.H.F. and Oosterhuis, L. 1977. *Management effects in coppice woodlands: the buried seed flora of overgrown coppicewoods*, Institute of Terrestrial Ecology, Merlewood

255 Records by BSDNHS including Emmet and Firmin; these and other records kindly sent me by K.N.A.Alexander

256 Records by BSDNHS

257 Records by BSDNHS and G. Sell

258 Records by Emmet, 1985

259 Records by R. Crossley

260 A. Buxton (ref. 219)

261 Peterken, G.F. 1976. 'Long-term changes in the woodlands of Rockingham Forest and other areas', *JE* **64** (1976) 123–46

262 Baker, C.A., Moxey, P.A. and Oxford, P.M. 1978. 'Woodland continuity and change in Epping Forest,' *Field Studies* **4** 645–69

263 Bennett, K.D. 1983. Devensian Late-glacial and Flandrian vegetational history at Hockham Mere, Norfolk, England', *New Phytologist* **95** 457–87

264 Reaney (ref. 8)

265 John Phibbs kindly drew my attention to this passage

266 Babington, C.C. 1860. *Flora of Cambridgeshire*, London

267 Wells, D.A. 1977. 'Neutral grasslands', *A nature conservation review*, ed. D.Ratcliffe, Cambridge, 183–94

268 Records by K.N.A.Alexander

269 Watt, A.S. 1940. 'Studies in the ecology of Breckland, II', *JE* **28** 42–69

270 Hunting Aerial Survey photograph: ESSEX/60/11, 18 June 1960

271 BSDNHS 1984. *The birds of Hatfield Forest*, National Trust

272 Record by Emmet, 1981

273 Record by D.A.Smith

274 Record by R.D.Weal

275 ERO: D/DBa T1/4

276 *EN* **3** (1889) 225–232

277 Salmon, N. 1740. *The history and antiquities of Essex*

278 Young, A. 1807. *General view of the agriculture of the county of Essex* **2**, Plate 45

279 Loudon, J.C. *Arboretum et fruticetum britannicum*, Longmans, London

281 Lampson, F. 1878. *London lyrics*, Kegan Paul, London

282 Greville, M. 'Trees of a Royal Forest', *CL* 3 June 1949, 1317–8
Greville M. 'Oaks of a Royal Forest', *CL* 2 June 1950, 1630–1

284 Hoppus, E. 1736. *Practical Measuring Made Easy to the Meanest Capacity*, London

285 Jermyn, S.T. 1974. *Flora of Essex*, Essex Naturalists' Trust

286 Shirt, D.B. (ed.) 1987. *British Red Data Books 2: Insects (1)*

287 *EN* **4** (1890) 219–25

288 *EN* **21** (1927) 87–9

289 Alvin, K.L. 1950. 'Lichens of Hatfield Forest', *EN* **30** 166–9

290 This includes records kindly sent me by Mr J.F. Skinner and Dr. F. Rose

291 Seaward, M.R.D. and Hitch, C.J.B. 1982. *Atlas of the lichens of the British Isles, vol 1*. Institute of Terrestrial Ecology

292 Dugdale, W.D. 1658. *The history of S'Paul's Cathedral...*, Warren, London

293 Hawksworth, D.L. and Rose, F. 1976. *Lichens as pollution monitors*, Edward Arnold, London

294 Hawksworth, D.L. 1987. 'Lichen impoverishment without air pollution', *British Lichen Society Bulletin* **61** 1–2
'Lichens return to central London' 1986. *ibid.* **58** 28–9

295 Green, B.H. 1986. 'Controlling ecosytems for amenity', *Ecology and design in landscape*, ed. A.D. Bradshaw and others, Blackwell, Oxford, 195–210

296 Bowyer, M.J.F. 1979. *Action stations 1: Wartime military airfields of East Anglia 1939–1945*, Stephens, Cambridge

297 Coleman, D.E. 1981. [*Evidence on behalf of the Countryside Commission*] SPI: CC 3
Fielding, J.L. 1981. [*Evidence on behalf of Essex Naturalists' Trust with accompanying report.*] SPI
Rackham, O. 1982. [*Evidence concerning Hatfield Forest*] SPI: NWEEHPA 45
Ranson, C.E. 1982. *Proof of Evidence of the Nature Conservancy Council* with accompanying papers SPI: NCC 1

298 Williams, M.L. and others 1981. *Air pollution of Stansted airport – a monitoring/modelling study in connection with airport developments proposed by the BAA*, SPI: BAA 106

299 Anderson, P. 1981. *The development of Stansted Airport ecological study*, SPI: BAA 223, 223a

300 Visits by C.E. Ranson and the author; Nature Conservancy Council evidence to Stansted Inquiry

301 Hunting Aerial Survey: ESSEX/70/1081, run 53, no. 4337. Reproduced by permission of Aerofilms Library and the Nature Conservancy Council

Index and Glossary

Words here given a definition are printed in **_bold italic_**. Further explanations are to be found on pages numbered in **_bold italic_**. Page-numbers in **bold** are main references.

Br	Berkshire	Ht	Hertfordshire
Ca	Cambridgeshire	Hu	Huntingdonshire
Do	Dorset	Nf	Norfolk
Dv	Devon	Nh	Northamptonshire
Ex	Essex	Sf	Suffolk
Ha	Hampshire	So	Somerset
HBO	Hatfield Broad-Oak parish	Wi	Wiltshire
HF	Hatfield Forest		

284

Index and Glossary